W. K. Kellogg Foundation Grant

14.50

D1257937

ENVIRONMENTAL GEOLOGY

HARPER'S GEOSCIENCE SERIES

Carey Croneis, Editor

ENVIRONMENTAL GEOLOGY

CONSERVATION, LAND-USE PLANNING, AND RESOURCE MANAGEMENT

PETER T. FLAWN
Bureau of Economic Geology
The University of Texas at Austin

HARPER & ROW, *Publishers*   *New York, Evanston, and London*

CONTENTS

Editor's Introduction   xiii

Preface   xvii

1. Introduction   1
    Man and the earth, 1   The stuff of the land: rocks and
    soils, 3   The composition and structure of the upper part of
    the earth's crust, 6   The significance of landforms, 11
    Geologic units, geologic maps, and their use by planners, 13
    The jargon of geology, 16   Sources of geologic maps and infor-
    mation, 16

2. Earth Processes   18
    The kinds of earth processes that affect man and his works, 18
    MOVEMENTS OF THE SURFACE CAUSED BY INTERNAL CRUSTAL
    PROCESSES, 21

Tectonic movements, 21   Measuring earthquakes, 23   Effects of earthquakes, 25   Prediction, prevention, and protection, 28   Long-term changes in level, 29   Movements resulting from volcanism, 31   Isostatic movements, 32
MOVEMENTS OF THE SURFACE CAUSED BY SURFICIAL PROCESSES, 33
Mass movements on slopes: landslides, mudflows, and creep, 33   Slides, 34   Creep and mudflows, 37   Collapse and subsidence, 39   Solution and collapse in limestone terranes, 39   Subsidence due to withdrawal of fluids, 42   Subsidence over mine workings, 46   Movements due to volume changes in surficial materials, 49   Permafrost, 50   Movement of surficial earth materials in water-, ice-, and wind-transport systems, 52   Rivers and coastlines, 52   Air-transported sediment, 58   Ice-transported sediment, 59   Conclusion, 59

3. Engineering Properties of Rocks and Soils   63
General statement, 63   Classification of soils, 65   Plasticity, Atterberg limits, shrink-swell potential, and other parameters, 70   Conclusion, 77

4. Earth Resources   81
GENERAL STATEMENT ON RESOURCES AND LAND USE, 81
HIGH-VALUE EARTH RESOURCES, 93
LOW-VALUE EARTH RESOURCES: WATER AND CONSTRUCTION
     MATERIALS, 104
Regional water plans: California, Texas, and the North American Water and Power Alliance, 108   Construction materials, 111

5. Man As a Geological Agent: The Geological Consequences
    of Industrialization   117
Introduction, 117
ENVIRONMENTAL ALTERATIONS, 119
The highway, 119   Cities, 121   Wastes, 126   Gaseous wastes—the new atmosphere, 127   Liquid wastes, 141   Subsurface disposal of liquid wastes, 145   Solid wastes, 148   Urban debris, 154   Metalliferous wastes, 155   Animal wastes, 156   Special municipal and industrial wastes, 157   Radioactive wastes, 159   Mines, quarries, and well fields, 162   Water resource projects, 167   Coastal installations, 177   Agriculture, 178   Summary, 180

6. **Conservation and Management**   **186**
   General statement, 186
   MANAGEMENT OF THE ENVIRONMENT, 190
   The physical system, 191   The biological system, 192
   The oceans, 192   The cultural system, 193
   ALTERNATIVES IN MANAGING THE ENVIRONMENT, 196
   Multiple working hypotheses, 200   Benefit-cost analysis, 206
   The role of the environmental geologist in conservation, 214

7. **Application of Environmental Geologic Data**   **218**
   General statement, 218
   MECHANISMS FOR ACTION, 221
   Codes and ordinances, 221   Direct public action, 225

8. **Austin, Texas—An Example**   **227**
   General statement, 227   The geology of Austin, Texas, 228
   RESOURCE, ENGINEERING, AND PLANNING SIGNIFICANCE OF THE
   GEOLOGIC MAP, 235
   General remarks, 235   Resources, 238   Engineering
   properties, 242   Solid waste disposal, 248   The Atomic
   Energy Commission accelerator competition of 1965, 249

Appendixes   **253**
   I.   INTERNATIONAL CONFERENCE OF BUILDING OFFICIALS: UNIFORM
        BUILDING CODE OF 1964, CHAPTER 70, "EXCAVATION AND
        GRADING," 255
   II. CLASSIFICATION OF ROCKS, 270
   III. GLOSSARY OF TERMS COMMON IN ENVIRONMENTAL GEOLOGY, 275

Index   **299**

6. Conservation and Management

ILLUSTRATIONS

1. Soil profiles on Sierra Nevada Granodiorite and Kentucky Limestone   4
2. Section of bedrock formations through Portland, Oregon   8
3. Section northeast-southwest through San Francisco   9
4. Uplift in Scandinavia due to removal of the glacial ice   31
5. An ideal landslide and its salient features   35
6. Development of a man-made bedrock landslide   37
7. Landslide: Palos Verdes Hills, Los Angeles County, California   38
8. Collapse of a cavern near Leeds, Alabama, resulting in damage   41
9. Subsidence contours and water-level decline, Houston-Galveston area, Texas   43
10. Subsidence caused by withdrawals of ground water, Houston, Texas   44
11. Faults and subsidence in the Houston, Texas, area   45

12. Land subsidence in California from withdrawal of ground water   46
13. Subsidence at Long Beach, California, 1928–1968   47
14. What a swelling clay can do to a concrete slab   51
15. Relationship between various uses of the term *soil*   64
16. Comparison of engineering soil groups in bearing values   68
17. Comparison of common soil classifications by particle size   69
18. Relationship between liquid limit, plasticity index, and soil composition   71
19. Increase in number of mineral commodities in commercial use   83
20. A sound-proofed drilling rig in the Los Angeles urban area   97
21. Rates of growth for sand, gravel, and stone production   125
22. What it costs to cut the sulfur content of fuel oils   134
23. Complex reactions in photochemical air pollution   135
24. Surface waste disposal and ground-water contamination   152
25. Aggregate water transfers between major river basins   175
26. Environmental elements that must be considered in management   191
27. Simplified geologic map of Austin, Texas   229
28. A junior high school in an abandoned quarry   241
29. Collapse of a reenforced concrete retaining wall   244
30. Slope adjustment after removal of the toe of a natural stable slope   245
31. Photographs of the slope shown diagrammatically in Figure 30   246
32. Uniform Building Code required setbacks   265

Color Map Insert: Geologic map of the Austin West Quadrangle, Texas

TABLES

1. Movements of the land surface   20
2. Modified Mercalli Scale   24
3. Observed displacement related to earthquakes   27
4. Engineering data of soils commonly measured   74
5. Allowable bearing capacities of earth materials   75
6. The planner's choice   87
7. Concentration of industrial mineral production in urban areas   124
8. State regulations on sulfur limits in fuel   133
9. Percentages of materials leached from refuse and ash   151
10. Waste produced by processing minerals and fuels in 1965   157
11. Relation of soils to geologic formations in the Austin, Texas,
    area   236

EDITOR'S INTRODUCTION

Environmental Geology by Peter T. Flawn, director of the Texas Bureau of Economic Geology, is a new volume in Harper's Geoscience Series. Its general subject—long one of prime importance to geologists, ecologists, and conservationists—recently has become a major concern of the man in the street, a viable issue cherished by politicians and would-be office holders, and a growing preoccupation of architects, sociologists, reformers, urban designers, and national planners. Editorial and headline writers also have had a field day with the problems generated by the accelerating decay of the earth's environmental assets correctly considered essential to the welfare of mankind. "Pollution could be death of man" is typical of the bolder newspaper headlines on the subject. "Life on a dying lake" is the appropriate title of a recent magazine article in which it is stated that Lake "Erie could, without warning, turn into a huge swamp."

On reflection then, it is not surprising that John F. O'Leary, director of the U. S. Bureau of Mines, in late summer 1969 pronounced the following commandments: "Thou shalt not tear up the land. Thou shalt not contaminate the water. Thou shalt not pollute the air." The author of *Environmental Geology*, however, recently added that there is another commandment: "Thou shalt provide society with the mineral resources it needs." O'Leary's three commandments come from the god of conservation; Flawn's comes from the powerful competing god of industrial society. According to Flawn, ". . . a natural resource company is an economic enterprise. It must compete. It must show a profit. . . . It cannot undertake costly social projects—land reclamation, for example—without raising the price of its product. It cannot raise the price of its product unless its competitors also raise their price—in this case, unless its competitors also undertake similar social projects. But any industry-wide price increase receives close government scrutiny. . . ."

The consequences of urbanization itself have also been realistically, but disturbingly, expressed by Flawn when, in 1965, he observed that "the city has a gargantuan appetite for resources of all kinds. Mineral stuffs and food stuffs flow from the land into the city. There is a return flow of contamination from the city to the land. The city is the nucleus of the contamination, and the nuclei themselves are spreading."

"Science discerns the laws of nature—industry utilizes them for the good of mankind" is an aphorism which, some three decades ago, was inscribed around the base of the great dome of Chicago's Museum of Science and Industry. Today, however, many contend that although science may indeed discern the laws of nature, neither science nor business, nor indeed industry or government, utilizes them for the good of mankind. On the contrary, the growing belief now is that as man's expectations rise, the more sophisticated secrets of nature concurrently discovered tend not only to negate those expectations but also to be "utilized" in the development of human woes.

Dr. Peter T. Flawn, the current president of the Association of American State Geologists, has long believed, and taught, and, indeed, pointed out to all who would listen, that such pessimistic views can and must be overcome. Although he has had very considerable influence for good in this connection, he now extends that influence through *Environmental Geology*. This text and reference book comprises eight rather long chapters which are divided into numerous subsections. This arrangement should facilitate the use of the book in the many new courses in environmental geology wherein student enrollment is burgeoning. It also should become a well-thumbed volume on the desks of urban planners, mayors and city managers, engineers, architects, metal miners, those who extract energy resources from the earth, and earth scientists generally.

CAREY CRONEIS

Rice University

PREFACE

Environmental geology is a branch of ecology in that it deals with relationships between man and his geological habitat; it is concerned with the problems that people have in using the earth—and the reaction of the earth to that use. Emphasis is placed on earth processes, earth resources, and engineering properties of rocks and surficial deposits insofar as these are important to or in some way affect human activities. Environmental geology includes the traditional fields of engineering geology and economic geology, or at least that part of the latter which pertains to mineral resources.

A little reflection makes clear why the term *urban geology* is commonly used interchangeably with environmental geology. In urban areas the use of the earth is most intense and society has the most urgent earth problems. Complex engineering systems must be protected against potentially destructive earth processes and lives and vast sums of money can be saved if systems are designed with full geological knowledge. The pressure for land is the greatest in urban areas, and planners must be geologically informed if their land-use recommendations are to be sound. Supplies of earth resources—water and construction materials—must flow without interruption; outflows of wastes must be disposed of without poisoning the earth.

In 1964 William P. Kimball, former dean of Thayer School of Engineering of Dartmouth College, said in an address to the American Society of Civil Engineers:

I learned in my tennis-playing days that the surest way to lose a match was to play the other fellow's game. I think we civil engineers have in too many cases lost sight of that fact. In these days of the atom and electronics and automation and space exploration, we have been tempted to say, "Yes, we too are important in those fields." We should play our own game, not the other fellow's. Without in any way meaning to underestimate the effects of these developments on society, I believe even more people will be directly and vitally affected in the foreseeable future by developments in the traditional civil engineering domains of water resources and environmental health, transportation, land use, housing, and urban and regional planning. It is in these areas, rather than in the glamorous areas of the infinite and the infinitesimal, that I believe civil engineers will make their most significant contributions.*

This wise counsel applies to geologists as well as engineers. In this field of environmental geology there is a great opportunity for geology and for geologists to make their science more vital by broader and more direct involvement with human needs. Geologists can establish a broader professional base through application of the science to the problems that beset planners, social scientists, conservationists, and lawmakers.

Planning is an intellectual process wherein (1) data are analyzed and (2) a program is formulated to bring about a desired result. It is a process by which change is initiated, promoted, and controlled in an orderly manner or, more realistically in today's context, by which some degree of order is brought to inevitable change. Many plans are in part theories—the distinction between plans and theories involves the objective. The program of actions is the plan; that the program will bring about the desired result is the theory. For example, the so-called master

* William P. Kimball, "Men with ideas," *International Science and Technology*, no. 28, 1964, pp. 97–98.

plan of a growing city is properly named a plan in the sense that it controls construction through zoning and schedules a magnitude of public-works projects according to a predetermined timetable or formula. But insofar as the master plan is designed to provide a satisfactory future environment for an anticipated future population, it is very much a "master theory."

Inasmuch as geology is the science of the earth—concerned with the configuration of the surface of the earth, the geometry of the crust, earth materials, earth processes, and earth history—it would seem a truism that any planning which involves the land should consider geologic information. Put another way, land-use planning that does not consider geologic data has diminished chances of success because not all of the pertinent data have been analyzed.

Why, then, has geology only rarely been included in the training of planners? The fault lies partly in the difficulty in American higher-education systems to break down the walls of traditional departments and develop curricula adequate to prepare the man who desires to build a career "outside the walls." Planning is, of course, a classic example of a profession that must draw upon many of the traditional disciplines— on physical and social sciences, on engineering, and on the humanities. Geologists, during the last two decades when the need for professional planners has grown so rapidly, have been in a frenzy to quantify the classical descriptive natural science of geology. As geologists find more advantageous ways to use physics, chemistry, and mathematics, they must not neglect their responsibilities in the areas of resources and environmental problems.

PETER T. FLAWN

Austin, Texas

ENVIRONMENTAL GEOLOGY

INTRODUCTION $\qquad$ I

Man and the earth. At this point in the history of man and earth, man, an organism, finds himself rather suddenly possessed of an enormous capacity to change inanimate as well as animate things—things that heretofore had been considered as permanent or unchangeable as, for example, "the everlasting hills." This capacity has come through the creative intellectual abilities developed largely in Western culture in the areas of science and engineering, commonly called technology. Man is now able to apply efficiently large amounts of energy at relatively low cost to almost any kind of engineering project anywhere on the globe. Breaking and moving rock presents no real problem, nor does changing the regimen of streams, rivers, and ocean (littoral) currents. Extraction of large quantities of mineral matter for materials, fuels, and crop nutrients is accomplished at rates of billions of tons and barrels per year. The "doing" or "changing" is not a problem. The problem lies in (1) foreseeing the second- and third-order effects of the action over both the short and long term, or, put another way, in understanding the dynamic nature of the earth and the interaction of physical and biological systems so that there can be a *quantitative* prediction of the effects of change once initiated, and (2) controlling change—that is, controlling the initiation of actions as well as guiding their courses.

This latter problem is grave. The implications of change induced in and on the earth by Western society—the industrial culture with its teeming population; voracious appetite for natural resources; abundant, cheap energy and machines to apply it—are shocking to anyone who thinks in terms beyond his own lifetime and serious enough for those whose interest in the future is limited to a few decades (Chapter 5). The initiation of change is not *voluntary*. Of course, man can exercise control over this or that project. He can decide, for example, *not* to build a particular dam, or *not* to excavate a particular tunnel or canal, or *not* to build a particular jetty, or *not* to develop a particular tract of woodland for residential housing. By political processes or by administrative management decision he can exercise a certain selectivity. But his industrial culture does commit him, or, more strongly, it forces him to build dams, excavate tunnels and canals, build jetties, and develop residential tracts somewhere. He has no option. As long as the industrial culture is to grow, the earth must be prepared for it. Habitability must increase. If the population is allowed to increase, if the population aspires to the Western "high standard of living," then society is committed to intensive use of the earth—and to changing it through use. To support an ever larger population man is committed (1) to digging pits and shafts for minerals; (2) to drilling thousands of wells for mineral fluids, including water; (3) to redistributing this earth stuff (rock, metals, water) and concentrating it in certain areas with the result that the composition of that part of the crust and atmosphere changes; (4) to developing and maintaining highly organized agriculture requiring massive applications of fertilizers (part of the redistribution mentioned above) and control of "pests" so the simple crop ecosystem will flourish; (5) to recontouring the land surface and rerouting drainage for construction of buildings and transportation systems; (6) to changing the natural wind and water systems of erosion-transportation-deposition, particularly around harbors and river mouths; and (7) to providing for the disposal of enormous amounts of solid, liquid, and gaseous wastes, wastes which can be changed in form through gasification, liquification, or solidification, but which ultimately must be dealt with by man, either now or in subsequent generations. The industrial culture also seems to be committed to changing the composition of the atmosphere through combustion. The consequences of combustion and a possible alternative are considered in Chapter 5. Apart from the pollutants, however harmful to plant and animal life, that have only a short term in the atmosphere before they settle out—pollutants that would "go away" if we stopped spewing them into the atmosphere—there is the consequence, through combustion of coal and petroleum, of releasing to the atmosphere in a short span of two centuries the carbon dioxide that was fixed in deposits of fossil fuels over some 600 million years. There are compelling reasons to believe that through burning large quantities of fossil fuels man will raise the CO_2 content of the atmosphere and significantly change the heat regimen of the earth—possibly to the extent of melting the ice caps and flooding the coastal plains where such a large part of the population and the food-production capacity of the world is located.

The question is, Can the industrial culture gain a measure of control over the basic factor that makes change such a mindless juggernaut—the uncontrolled growth of population? That question cannot be answered in this largely geological discussion. The text that follows is an attempt to examine and explain the relationship between man and natural earth processes, to explore some of the consequences of actions taken without knowledge about the earth, to look at the second- and third-order effects of irreversible environmental reactions, and to suggest how society might improve its earth-management skills.

The stuff of the land: rocks and soils. It is in a sense strange that two simple, common English words like "rock" and "soil" need to be defined; and yet they do. (See Figure 15.) The reason is that geologists, soil scientists, and civil engineers have gone their separate ways and evolved their own definitions. To a geologist *rock* is a mineral aggregate, coherent, but not necessarily hard. The degree of coherence is a matter for some debate, but geologists consider a relatively soft mineral aggregate, such as sandy clay which is easily crumbled in the hand, as rock. Rock in this broad sense includes water-, wind-, and ice-deposited sediments such as alluvium, loess, and glacial drift. To the geologist, *soil* is what rock becomes through exposure to the atmosphere and weathering. It is a mantle of earth material lying on bedrock and, as a result of chemical, physical, and biological processes, distinct from rock, although it may be derived from it and grade into it. It may be in place as a residual soil or transported by natural processes from the place in which it formed. It is generally unconsolidated or very weakly coherent material, but locally it may be hard due to precipitation of a salt such as calcium carbonate within the soil body. The geologist has been able to recognize ancient soils within rock sequences.

To the soil scientist a soil is a naturally formed body at the earth's surface containing living matter and capable of supporting plant life. Its lower boundary is the lower limit of the common rooting of native perennial plants (Soil Survey Staff, Soil Conservation Service, 1960). Byers and others (1938, p. 948) defined soils as follows: "Soils are natural media for the growth of plants. They are mixtures of fragmented and partly or wholly weathered rocks and minerals, organic matter, water, and air, in greatly varying proportions, and have more or less distinct layers or horizons developed under the influence of climate and living organisms." The various layers or zones of altered rock material between the surface and the fresh bedrock are together called the *soil profile* (Figure 1). Most soil profiles have two or three well-defined layers or zones which commonly are labeled, from the surface downward, as the *A-horizon, B-horizon,* and *C-horizon*. The use of horizon, which to most people connotes a line or plane, is unfortunate but well entrenched through usage. In very general terms, the A *zone* or *topsoil,*

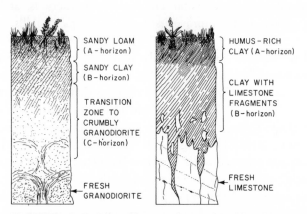

FIGURE 1. Soil profiles on Sierra Nevada Granodiorite and Kentucky Limestone. (After Gilluly, Waters, and Woodford, 1959, Fig. 4-3.)

is leached of soluble constituents and clay and enriched in organic materials. Soil chemists commonly use the term *eluviation* to refer to movement of soil material from place to place within the soil as, eluvial horizons have lost material or illuvial horizons have gained material. Eluviation includes movements of material as colloids whereas the term *leaching* is restricted to movement in solution. The B *zone*, or *subsoil*, is commonly the layer in which clays washed out of the upper zone are deposited; in some soils calcium carbonate or iron oxide is deposited in the B zone. The C *zone* is a transition zone between the B zone and fresh, unaltered rock; it is not everywhere present. Where soils have formed on unconsolidated sediments such as alluvial deposits, the underlying sediment is the parent material and there is no fresh rock in the conventional sense.

The civil engineer concerned with the mechanics of soils generally regards all of the loose or unconsolidated material which lies on hard rock as "soil."

Thus the geological definition is a genetic definition based on recognition of the product of physical, chemical, and biological processes; the soil science definition is a descriptive biological definition; and the engineering definition is a descriptive physical definition.

The nomenclature problem is of practical as well as academic interest to the planner because of his need to communicate with all three groups and to use data developed by all three disciplines. For example, there might be within an urban planning area a body of silt, sand, and gravel deposited by a river in its previous history—a stratified accumulation of unconsolidated sediment ranging from a few feet to more than 100 ft in thickness. It might be the foundation of large buildings; it might contain pipelines; it might contain supplies of ground water; it might contain deposits of sand and gravel. Because of its unconsolidated nature, engineering reports consider the entire body as "soil," report measurements of its thickness, and classify it according to the sizes of the material and its engineering properties. A soil survey of the area describes the upper few feet in terms of a soil individual and a soil series lying on a parent material composed of sandy gravel; detailed information is presented on the composition and perhaps on the engineering properties of the soil individual and series. A geological report refers to the material as a fluviatile terrace deposit of Pleistocene age composed of gravel, sand, and silt, and describes the stratigraphy, mineral deposits, and engineering properties. The planner is faced with the job of coordinating the information and of making beneficial use of it. Therefore, he must know what these various kinds of reports are talking about.

The composition and structure of the upper part of the earth's crust.
The worst sin of the land-use planner is two-dimensional thinking—there are few uses of the land which are two dimensional. Animal husbandry on unimproved range, certain recreational uses such as hiking, hunting, camping, and bird-watching are for practical purposes concerned only with the surface of the land; but for other beneficial and productive uses, man penetrates into the earth. In agricultural uses the penetration is mostly limited to the upper few feet: that part cut by the plow and harrow, that part excavated for small surface water reservoirs (ponds and tanks), or the few hundred feet penetrated by a water well. There are some large farms in dry areas that have drilled water wells several thousand feet deep, but these are the exceptions. Civil engineers penetrate the surface to greater depths than farmers. Excavations for pipelines, foundations, and tunnels are commonly tens of feet below the surface and in some places more than 100 ft below the surface. The deepest penetrations are effected by mineral engineers. The world's record for the deepest well is 25,340 ft, currently held by Phillips Petroleum Company's No. 1-EE University in West Texas; the deepest mines are the gold mines of South Africa's Witwatersrand, some in excess of 10,000 ft deep; the biggest and deepest open pits are the great copper mines of the western United States, and the biggest man-made hole in the earth is Utah Copper's pit in Bingham Canyon, Utah, where about 1 billion cubic yards of ore and waste have been extracted from a pit which is now about 2200 ft deep.

But civil engineers will in the future be increasing their underground activities in depth and volume of excavation. In his remarks to the Northwest Mining Association at Spokane, Washington, on December 2, 1967, Walter R. Hibbard, Jr., director of the U. S. Bureau of Mines, pointed out that the mining industry is not alone in needing markedly improved technology for underground excavation. Of some $20 to $50 billion that will be spent for underground excavation by 1990, a very substantial part will be spent by public agencies for underground urban facilities and for water resource projects. San Francisco is building a 75-mi mass transit system that will include 16 mi of subway and 4 mi of tunnel under the bay. Montreal recently completed a 15-mi subway system. In Toronto there is a four-level subsurface shopping center and garage. Chicago is considering temporary containment of sewer overflows in deep tunnels. The California Aqueduct includes 300 mi of tunnels and pipelines.

The *Kansas City Star* of December 1, 1968, reported on a plan for construction of an underground freeway to solve the traffic problems in the Kansas City area. The plan calls for utilizing a sequence of limestone and shale underlying Kansas City. The *Star* quoted "engineering opinion that due to favorable 'geology' an underground transportation system could be built at less cost than a surface system if the cost of acquiring and destroying many square miles of residential neighborhoods was included."

The earth's crust, even the few tens of feet or hundreds of feet of immediate concern to the planner, is rarely homogeneous. Therefore, in planning for the maximum beneficial use, or for multiple uses, it is necessary to know what the earth materials are, how they react to loads and other stresses, whether they are permeable or impermeable, whether they contain materials of value such as water or construction materials, and whether they can support agricultural, animal, or forest industries. The planner also needs to know what earth processes are active in the planning area: How stable is the land? Are there active faults or slides in the area? What are the rates of erosion and deposition? He needs information on the regimen of streams: What are the flood cycles and where are the areas subject to flooding?

The interior of the earth as interpreted from geological and geophysical data consists of a relatively dense *core* (radius 3400 km) surrounded by a less dense *mantle* (thickness 3000 km) and covered by a still less dense *crust*. The crust ranges from 10 to 12 km thick under the ocean basins to 30 to 40 km thick under the continents. The oceans are floored with *basaltic rocks* (rather dense rocks rich in iron and magnesium). The *continental crust*, at least in its upper part, is composed of rocks with a high content of silica, alumina, and the alkali elements sodium and potassium. In a *very* general way, the upper continental crust is composed of *granitic rocks* (granites and granite gneisses) with masses of metamorphosed volcanic and sedimentary rocks. On top of these crystalline rocks, the crystalline *basement*, of the crust are *sedimentary basins* of different depths, sizes, and shapes, containing as much as 50,000 ft of sediments or sedimentary and volcanic rocks, including (1) clay, silt, sand, and their rock equivalents, shale and sandstone; (2) limestone and

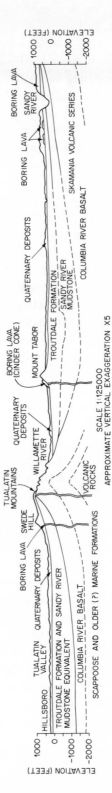

FIGURE 2. Diagrammatic section showing stratigraphic relations of Tertiary bedrock formations, drawn generally east–west across the Portland area through the city of Portland, Oregon. Length of section 37 mi. (After Trimble, 1963, Plate 2.)

8

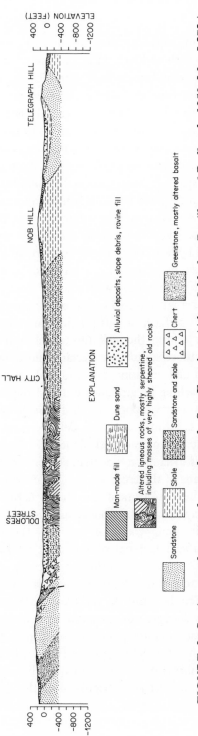

FIGURE 3. Section northeast-southwest through San Francisco. (After Schlocker, Bonilla, and Radbruch, 1958, Map I-272.)

EXPLANATION

Man-made fill

Dune sand

Alluvial deposits, slope debris, ravine fill

Altered igneous rocks, mostly serpentine, including masses of very highly sheared old rocks

Sandstone and shale

Chert

Sandstone

Shale

Greenstone, mostly altered basalt

9

dolomite; (3) gypsum, anhydrite, and salt; and (4) volcanic accumulations such as volcanic ash and lava. In some basins the sedimentary and volcanic rocks have been broken and deformed by compressive and tensional stresses after their deposition; in other basins their attitudes have been little changed since deposition and lithification.

The geometry of the rock masses that make up the crystalline crust and the overlying sedimentary sequences is not simple—the earth's crust is not like an onion skin made up of successive congruent layers (Figures 2 and 3). Through spans of time measured in hundreds of millions of years earlier-formed rocks have been deformed and altered, intruded by younger igneous rocks, and covered by younger sedimentary and volcanic rocks. In some areas, all of these rocks have been depressed in deep crustal folds, altered by heat and pressure to a crystalline rock complex, deformed and broken by powerful stresses, and then elevated again, eroded, covered with sedimentary and volcanic rock, and perhaps intruded by even younger igneous rocks. And each time that a rock mass is exposed at the earth's surface, various physical and chemical weathering processes set to work to bring the rock into equilibrium with the surficial environment. These processes include freezing and thawing, wedging by plant roots, abrasion and corrasion by wind and running water, hydration, solution and leaching by ground water and organic and inorganic acids. In some areas where topography and climate permit, the result is a soil; in other areas disintegrated rock debris lies on the rock surface or accumulates at the base of bare rock slopes.

The earth's crust is dynamic rather than static. Because of the earth's internal processes, parts of the crust are rising while other parts are sinking. In some areas the displacements are in the nature of broad *warps* or *flexures* without any rupture. In other areas crustal blocks are displaced vertically or laterally along zones of fracture—these are *faults* and *fault zones*. The surficial material of the crust is also in movement. Weathered rock products are transported by water, by wind, and by mass movements such as creep and slides. Rock material from the continental highlands is everywhere in transit to the great sea basins, or to interior basins for temporary storage. For the most part, in terms of the years that human beings use to measure time, these changes are imperceptible or very slow. Only when the natural processes act with unusual violence —as in sudden land displacements accompanied by earth tremors or in landslides, mudflows, or damaging floods—does the dynamic nature of the crust become all too apparent. But even without the violent reminders, a man who has been familiar with a particular terrain for half a century can see abundant signs of change—changes in the course of a stream or the contour of a hill, the disappearance of a sand bar or beach. The works of man, of course, cause far more drastic modifications of the land. Sherlock (1922, p. 327) compared the effects of man on the land to those of a glacier, which gouges out holes and piles up mounds of debris.

It is rare that the planner deals with an area underlain by only one kind of rock or is concerned with an area free of potentially destructive earth processes. Most cities grew up in areas where there was a surface water supply, a lake or river. Thus the city must live with and control the normal fluvial and lacustrine processes of erosion, deposition, and flooding. Cities located at the confluence of rivers because the rivers were transportation and trade routes must likewise live with the rivers that gave reason for their birth. Many of the large urban areas were nourished by a port and therefore must engage in engineering control of marine coastal processes of erosion and deposition, processes which during times of storm are capable of moving enormous volumes of sediment. Some cities were originally, knowingly or *unknowingly*, located for geologic reasons. Perhaps a waterfall or rapids provided hydroenergy for a mill; the waterfall could well be due to streams passing from hard rock to soft rock, as along the famous Fall Line of the eastern Piedmont. Perhaps a settlement was made at the site of a large flowing spring; the spring could well mark a fault zone where water issues in large quantity along the fault, as it does in the Balcones fault zone of central Texas. Perhaps a valuable mineral deposit attracted the people; coal, iron, copper, oil, and gas have nourished many cities (Pittsburgh, Cleveland, Butte, and Beaumont) and they commonly occur in areas of anomalous rock type and structure.

Thus within a planning area there may be crystalline rocks, sedimentary rocks, and alluvium—all with different engineering properties; movements of the land may occur; there may be fluvial systems or marine erosion-deposition systems; there may be valuable earth resources to consider.

The significance of landforms. The surface of the earth has been sculptured by the natural forces which act upon it and, increasingly, by man.

The kinds of natural landforms which characterize a region, the shapes of the hills and valleys for example, are determined by a combination of geologic factors acting in concert, including (1) climate; (2) the composition, structure, and attitude of the rocks; and (3) elevation above the base level of erosion. The active working forces are water, ice, wind, and gravity. The landscape is dynamic and changing, with material being removed from one place and deposited in another. The rates of denudation and deposition change in short cycles from season to season and in long cycles from one geologic epoch to another. The branch of geology which deals with the origin and nature of landforms is *geomorphology*; the description of landforms is commonly referred to as *physiography*. It is important that the civil engineer and planner understand that in sculpturing the land the natural forces of erosion have worked toward establishment of slopes and gradients that are relatively stable. When the work of man changes a hill slope and destroys its equilibrium, the natural forces immediately set about restoring a stable slope. Natural restoration involves mass movements through soil creep, slumping, or even landslides. Where, for example, the lower part of a slope is excavated (unloaded) to locate a highway at the base of a hill, natural processes work to reduce the oversteepened slope; the result might range from a slow creeping encroachment of soil on the highway to sudden falls of large masses of rock and soil. In this example, proper design of the highway would include stabilization of the hill slope, and the necessity for stabilizing the slope should come from advance study and experience and not as an unpleasant and costly surprise after construction.

From geologic maps, topographic maps, and aerial photos the grain or texture of the land, the characteristic landforms, and the drainage patterns are immediately apparent, and many conclusions about earth processes and earth materials of value to the engineer and planner can be drawn without ever setting foot on the ground. In fact, such terrain analyses have been made for many years by military geologists, who commonly must provide data on construction sites for airfields and other buildings, sources of construction materials, water supply, and transportation routes before the terrain has been occupied. These data on land use are the same as those needed by the planner who goes about his task with less urgency and therefore with opportunity for more thoroughness than his military counterpart.

Geologic units, geologic maps, and their use by planners. Geologists deal generally with three kinds of units: time units, time-rock units, and rock units. Only the latter, the *rock units*, are of direct interest to the planner. The kinds of rock units differ according to the scale of the geological investigation, ranging from gross units such as Groups down through Formations and Members, to very small individual beds, laminae, or other minute bodies. Of course, any recognizable body of earth material or any data with spatial relationships can be represented by a map or model. An areal geologic map is really a model. It commonly shows the distribution of rock formations which crop out at the surface of the earth, and by a series of conventions also indicates the attitudes of the units, thus permitting interpretations in the third dimension. These commonly are included with the map as one or more cross sections or structure sections.

Geologic maps are on many scales for many purposes. For mapping of geologically hazardous areas in subdivision planning the scale might be 50 ft to the inch or larger; for urban mapping in problem areas in Los Angeles, for example, maps at 400 ft to the inch have been prepared; for regional planning 2000 ft to the inch is a common scale.

The Color Map (inside back cover) is a typical geologic map. In the explanation a column of units is described and arranged in order of age, with the oldest at the bottom. All of the rocks shown are sedimentary rocks. Because the strata are more or less flat-lying and fault displacements are simple, in terms of the scale of the map, a cross section is not included. In other areas intrusive igneous rocks are common. These rocks, emplaced in a molten state following the deposition of the sedimentary rocks, are younger than the rocks they intrude. On maps of such areas the convention is to show the kinds of igneous rocks in a separate column with the oldest on the bottom.

A *geologic formation* is a genetic unit. It includes earth materials that were deposited or formed by the same processes at more or less the same time; it is also a mappable unit. This is not to say that a geologic formation has the same composition or structures throughout. A formation can be composed primarily of sand in part of its extent and primarily of silt and clay in another part, yet nevertheless be a genetic and mappable unit. Two or three units of different composition resulting from natural processes operating in a natural rhythm or cycle might be grouped together as one formation. Subsequent to deposition, parts of the formation might have been altered by solutions, heat, pressure, or deformation so that the rocks are very different from what they were originally. However, the map explanation makes clear these variations in composition from place to place.

Thus, a geologic formation will probably not everywhere have the same engineering properties, but most units will have a range of properties that permit engineering evaluations. Sites within these formations must be tested further. The Austin Chalk, for example, is a formation which outcrops extensively in Texas and supports parts of four major cities. It is composed of fine-grained calcium carbonate and clay in varying proportions, ranging from fine-grained limestone or chalk to marl to marly clay. It weathers to a dark calcareous clay or clayey loam soil which is thin in most places. The Austin Chalk in general has excellent foundation properties, but the soil derived from it has poor foundation properties. Load-bearing strength of the chalk ranges from 25 to 150 tons per sq ft. In good engineering practice the thin soil is removed from construction sites, or foundations are put through the soil into the underlying chalk. In some places the Austin is soft enough to be excavated by ripping so that blasting is not required. Estimates of rippability can be made from measurements of the seismic velocity of the formation, but these estimates must be confirmed on the site. Excavation costs are, of course, substantially less where rocks can be ripped instead of blasted. Thus the geologic map that shows the outcrops of the Austin Chalk and other formations enables the educated planner, with geological assistance, to make a rapid preliminary evaluation of land-use potential. It does not take the place of site investigations of engineering properties nor does it eliminate the need for detailed studies of mineral deposits, but it can answer such questions as:

1. What part of the planning area is suitable for large, high-rise structures?
2. What part of the planning area has productive agricultural soils for greenbelts?
3. Where in the planning area are there deposits of construction materials?
4. Where in the planning area are excavation costs high? Where are they low?
5. Where in the planning area are there highly corrosive earth materials?

6. Where in the planning area is the water table high? Where is it low?

Most geologic maps do not present engineering data. The map user must correlate existing engineering data with the geologic formations mapped in the area. However, the U. S. Geological Survey has in recent years published a number of "engineering geology maps." These are derivitive maps from the basic geologic maps. For the most part, these maps describe (1) distribution and thickness of units; (2) terrain, natural slope, and slope stability; (3) drainage, permeability, and water table; (4) frost susceptibility; (5) suitability for foundations; (6) earthquake stability; (7) excavation characteristics; and (8) suitability for subgrade, fill or borrow, and compaction characteristics. The above properties or characteristics are generally described qualitatively in terms of good-fair-poor or high-low. Commonly numerical values are given for size classification, Atterberg limits, plasticity index, and density. Geologic map units are not generally homogeneous and, therefore, they include a range of engineering properties.

Hackett (1968) has described geologic factors in community development at Naperville, Illinois. He considered slope and topographic relief, drainage and streamflow, and the nature and physical characteristics of earth materials at the surface and in the subsurface as they pertain to floods, water supply, water quality, excavation, construction, and use of open space. In his conclusions he emphasized (p. 15) that:

In terms of over-all community development, the physical environment can also provide specific benefits. In the northern part of the community, along the valley of the West Branch DuPage River, extensive deposits of sand and gravel suitable for use as construction materials occur, and studies of the subsurface indicate that these deposits extend below the normal river level. In that area certain multiple-use benefits might be realized. Properly controlled excavation of the gravels for commercial use might be followed by development of public recreational lakes or of private lakes for residential estates or industrial parks. The excavations also could be used as storage basins for flood flows or as ground-water recharge pits.

The valley of Spring Brook in the southwestern part of the Naperville area is unusually well suited to development of a surface water reservoir. The Spring Brook site was recognized in a study of forest preserves in DuPage County by the Northeastern Illinois Planning Commission. In that study . . . it was determined a reservoir with a water depth of about 30 feet could be developed to provide a recreational lake in a region where water-based recreational facilities are at a premium.

The jargon of geology. Geology, like other sciences, has built a terminology that stands as a barrier between the geologic literature and its nongeologist would-be user. The student of any discipline must as a first task learn the language. The easiest way is to enroll in a beginning geology course at a college or university. Failing such an opportunity, a good physical geology textbook, a glossary, and a dictionary will explain basic geological terms. To understand areal geological reports and to read geologic maps it is necessary to understand the geologic time scale, basic stratigraphic nomenclature, elementary classifications of rocks, and the names of common structures such as folds and faults (see Appendixes II and III). In areas characterized by glacial deposits, aeolian deposits, and volcanic deposits a more specialized nomenclature must be acquired. However, with about 50 basic terms and a few simple concepts, the planner or engineer will have access to a wealth of useful data about the earth that will return his investment in study many times over.

Sources of geologic maps and information. Many federal, state, and private agencies are actively developing geologic data and carrying on geologic mapping programs. Federal agencies include the Geological Survey, Bureau of Mines, Bureau of Reclamation, Corps of Engineers, Soil Conservation Service, and International Boundary Commission. Of these, only the Geological Survey has a program of systematic geologic quadrangle mapping. Within the last five years the U. S. Geological Survey has carried out programs of geologic study of urban areas which have been variously published as *Bulletins, Miscellaneous Geologic Investigations, Geologic Quadrangle Maps,* and *Hydrologic Investigations.* These data are presented in a manner so that they can be readily used by planners. Other agencies compile geologic maps for special projects. Nearly every state has a State Geological Survey, although it may be called a Bureau or Division of Geology, Natural Resources, or Conservation; under whatever name, it is a research and service agency concerned with geologic studies, mapping, and resource investigations. Some have active geologic mapping programs while others do little mapping. In many states the geologic activies of water-resource agencies are growing and geologic maps are compiled for reservoir-site studies and ground-water investigations. Also in the public realm, but not published, are theses and dissertations on file at various colleges and universities; many of these contain geologic maps. Finding out what is available for a certain area requires a library research effort or at least a letter of inquiry to an information agency such as a geological survey. The U. S. Geological Survey publishes a *Bibliography of North American Geology*. Other federal and state agencies have published bibliographies or at least lists of publications. Indexes to theses and dissertations in United States colleges and universities are also available. For the planner or engineer who does not have a good library, the best approach is a letter to the State Geological Survey or to the U. S. Geological Survey. Pearl (1951) and Kaplan (1965) have written guides to geological literature.

REFERENCES

BYERS, H. G.; KELLOGG, C. E.; ANDERSON, M. S.; AND THORP, JAMES (1938) "Formation of soil" in *Soils and men: U. S. Department of Agriculture yearbook*, pp. 948–978.

GILLULY, JAMES; WATERS, A. C.; AND WOODFORD, A. O. (1959) *Principles of geology*, 2nd ed., copyright 1959: W. H. Freeman and Co., San Francisco, 534 pp.

HACKETT, JAMES E. (1968) *Geologic factors in community development at Naperville, Illinois*: Illinois Geological Survey environmental geology notes, no. 22, June 1968, 16 pp.

KAPLAN, S. R., ed. (1965) *Guides to information sources in science and technology*, Vol. 2, *Mining, minerals and geosciences*: Interscience Division, John Wiley and Sons, New York, 599 pp.

PEARL, RICHARD M. (1951) *Guide to geologic literature*: McGraw-Hill Book Co., New York, 239 pp.

SCHLOCKER, J.; BONILLA, M. G.; AND RADBRUCH, D. H. (1958) *Geology of the San Francisco North Quadrangle, California*: U. S. Geological Survey Miscellaneous Geologic Investigations, Map I-272.

SHERLOCK, R. L.(1922) *Man as a geological agent*: H. F. & G. Withersby, London, 372 pp.

SOIL SURVEY STAFF (1960) *Soil classification: a comprehensive system— 7th approximation*: Soil Conservation Service, U. S. Department of Agriculture, 265 pp.

TRIMBLE, D. E. (1963) *Geology of Portland, Oregon, and adjacent areas*: U. S. Geologic Survey bulletin 1119, 119 pp.

EARTH PROCESSES

2

The kinds of earth processes that affect man and his works. The earth is a dynamic, changing body of mineral matter. Changes are brought about by (1) physical and chemical processes generated in the earth's interior, on the surface, and in the atmosphere; and (2) biological processes operating at or near the earth's surface—these are the physical and chemical changes in earth materials caused by plants and animals, including man. Man, a most powerful geological agent, works directly and purposefully to change the earth in ways beneficial to his culture, but he also brings about second- and third-order changes that are not planned and which may or may not be beneficial. For example, where man has destroyed turf or forest cover one result has been increased erosion, increased sediment load, and changes in stream regimen; where man has dug coal from the earth, a beneficial activity in terms of man's need for energy resources, a secondary result has been the exposure to weather of iron-sulfide-rich materials which oxidize to produce acids which in turn adversely affect the quality of water in streams of the region.

There are natural earth processes that operate irrespective of and in spite of man's activities, and there are natural processes that are set in motion, stopped, or modified as a consequence of man's activities. For example, earthquakes and volcanic eruptions are the result of deep-seated earth processes and as yet, except for minor earth tremors, cannot be started or stopped by human efforts; indeed, they cannot even be predicted with any confidence. Subsidence of the surface comes about naturally through ground-water solution of supporting rocks, but it can also be the direct result of man's withdrawal of subsurface support through mining of rock or pumping of fluids. Man can purposefully or inadvertently start a landslide; he can also stop mass movements of the surface that would occur under natural conditions. Various types of land-surface movements are cited in Table 1.

Movements of the land surface caused by internal crustal movements range from sharp, jarring, and commonly destructive movements known as *earthquakes* or *temblors* (*tectonic movements*) usually accompanied by sudden and marked changes in level, to very slow, imperceptible but measurable changes in level (*isostatic movements*). Isostatic movements, however minute in the span of a year or decade, amount to as much as several feet per century and in the course of two or three generations are sufficient to cause significant changes in mean water levels along sea and lake shores, changing the depths of harbors and channels, inundating or elevating shoreline improvements, and creating or draining swamps and lagoons. Such changes, unlike the violent dislocations accompanying earthquakes, can be predicted on the basis of past records and thus can be considered in planning.

Movements of the land surface not necessarily related to internal crustal movements are called *mass movements*. These movements, powered by the force of gravity, range from sudden and potentially destructive slides involving hundreds of millions of cubic yards of earth materials to very slow downslope movements of soil and unconsolidated rock materials called creep. Mass movements require topographic relief, a slope or declivity. They are commonly initiated by heavy rains or sudden thaws which saturate the rock and soil mass with water, reducing the internal friction to the point where gravity is sufficient to cause movement, or they may be triggered by an earthquake shock sufficient to overcome the inertia of the mass.

Small-scale land movements occur on level surfaces composed of materials, such as clay, which change volume as they absorb or lose moisture, or which contain water and are subject to freezing and thawing. Some regions are subject to sudden local collapse of the surface where supporting rocks are dissolved away by ground water; sinkholes formed by collapse of caverns are common in limestone terranes. Man induces subsidence by withdrawing subsurface support. Of course, in a sense, the land is moving in the form of sediment load in streams, rivers, and their frozen counterparts, glaciers; in waves and currents along the coasts; and, as any resident of the Southwest can testify, on the wind as dust. However, these are movements of earth materials

TABLE 1. **Movements of the Land Surface**

I. Movements of the surface caused by internal crustal processes
   A. Tectonic movements
      Sudden changes of level accompanied by earthquakes and resulting from rapid displacements along faults
      Gradual changes in level due to slow but persistent creep along faults
   B. Movements resulting from volcanism
      Changes in the land surface due to volcanic explosions and eruptions, but excluding changes in configuration of the surface due to accumulation of lava and volcanic ejecta
   C. Isostatic movements
      Gradual changes of level due to loading or unloading of segments of the crust
II. Movements of the surface caused by surficial processes
   A. Mass movements on slopes
      Rockfalls, landslides, mudflows, and soil creep
   B. Collapse or subsidence of the surface
      Collapse of the surface where underlying rocks have been removed by solution, common in limestone terranes, or where supporting subsurface materials have been withdrawn through man's activities
   C. Movements due to volume changes in surficial materials
      Changes in moisture content; freezing and thawing
   D. Movement of surficial earth materials in water, ice, and wind transportation systems
      Sediments carried by streams or moved by wave and current action; sediments moved by glaciers; fine sediments carried by wind

---

in, or in response to, weathering-erosion-transport-deposition systems rather than movements of the land surface. The earth can be set in motion by human activities—blasting, movement of trains and other heavy vehicles, and industrial processes which produce heavy impacts or rhythmic vibrations—commonly grouped together as "industrial vibrations." Even these minor vibrations are harmful to some activities involving delicate instruments. Therefore, in order to seek out quiet, vibration-free sites, the engineer must be able to measure and map areas with varying densities of industrial vibration.

MOVEMENTS OF THE SURFACE CAUSED BY INTERNAL CRUSTAL PROCESSES

Tectonic movements. Tectonic movements are those caused by crustal stresses which tend to deform the earth's crust and change its structure. With regard to earthquakes, the term is used to distinguish shocks resulting from crustal deformation from those caused by volcanic action, landslides, or the collapse of caverns. Tectonic displacements of the earth's surface include movements along faults (sudden or creeping) and changes of level due to warping or folding of rock strata (slow folding at depth is commonly accompanied by faulting of surficial rocks). *Active faults* are faults along which there has been movement in historic or Recent geologic time, or along which recurrence of movement is predicted or is likely to occur; *dead faults* are those along which there is no indication of movement in historic or Recent geologic time and no reason to predict a recurrence of movement. These are, of course, very subjective distinctions. Studies that demonstrate accumulation of strain in rocks in an area would justify reclassification of a dead fault to the active category. Faults in seismic areas, even without a history of movement, are more likely to slip than faults in regions without a history of seismic activity.

Earthquake shocks accompanying sudden movements along faults are the most spectacular announcements that the earth is a dynamic body. Submarine tectonic adjustments which generate great seismic sea waves or tsunamis are equally striking testimony that the crust is stable only to a degree. Large segments of the population are settled in tectonically unstable regions, most noteworthy of which is the so-called circum-Pacific earthquake belt. In the large cities in this region, for example in Los Angeles and San Francisco, pressure for land has resulted in construction on potentially unstable slopes and within known fault zones. Presently, research is in progress to permit prediction of tectonic movements by analysis of changes in stress patterns in rocks, but the work is just beginning and there is little prospect for success in the next several decades. A 10-yr, $137-million-earthquake research program pointed toward earthquake prediction was proposed in 1965 by a panel of earthquake specialists convened by the president's Office of Science and Technology. The chairman, Dr. Frank Press, predicted that earthquake deaths could be reduced 80 percent in 10 years by warning instruments in earthquake areas, careful zoning, and use of special design and construction materials (*Mining Engineering*, 1966, p. 10). Between April 1962 and November 1965, Denver, Colorado, not previously considered an "earthquake area," experienced more than 700 minor seismic movements, none of which was more than 4.3 on the Richter scale (Evans, 1966, p. 11). David M. Evans, a consulting geologist in Denver, astutely correlated the shocks with operation of a 12,000-ft-deep waste disposal well used by the Rocky Mountain Arsenal. Further investigation strongly indicated that injection of a large volume of fluids into a fractured granite gneiss set up fluid pressures, reduced friction along fracture planes, and induced movements along faults below the well (p. 146). Evans (1966, p. 17) concluded that the injection of fluids at pressures as much as 2000 lb greater than reservoir pressure upset previously established equilibrium and resulted in seismic disturbances. Evans also suggested that perhaps stresses along fault zones in urban areas might be released in a controlled fashion by fluid injection and thereby reduce the possibilities of damaging earthquakes. Earth phenomena that might provide warning of the imminence of a large earthquake include (1) a rise in the number of small seismic movements, (2) tilts and strains in the area of the epicenter, and (3) changes in physical properties of rocks along faults as a result of strain build-up (Press and Brace, 1966, p. 1578). Planners should be informed on the frequency of seismic movements in the area of interest, the kinds of stresses that can be anticipated, where they are likely to be concentrated, and, considering the terrain and geology of the unstable region, what kinds of construction and land-use are most secure and beneficial.

Measuring earthquakes. Measurement of seismic activity and research on earthquakes is carried on by the U. S. Coast and Geodetic Survey, Geological Survey, and many university research groups. The branch of science concerned with earthquakes and the elastic properties of the earth is called *seismology*. Early attempts to describe individual earthquakes posed the problem of comparing, measuring, and classifying them. Planners working in unstable regions need to understand basic earthquake terminology and how it developed.

Prior to the invention and distribution of sophisticated instruments to measure seismic activity, earthquake intensities were described in terms of the effect of the shock or shocks on the terrain and on the structures built by man. Numerical scales were proposed with the intensities related to the degree of damage sustained by buildings. These scales are analogous to the early meteorological attempts to measure wind velocities by the Beaufort scale, in which various degree of "breeze," "gale," etc., were related to intensity of movement or disturbance of common objects such as trees, flags, and umbrellas. Several of these earthquake scales are still in use—probably the most common one in the United States is the *Modified Mercalli Scale* (Table 2). Study of the Modified Mercalli Scale will make it plain that the criteria of measurement are so subjective and so influenced by factors other than the amount of shock energy transmitted, that the scale is of little value for comparative purposes. Using Mercalli intensities, it would be impossible, for example, to compare in any meaningful way an earthquake in San Francisco, California, with one in Chilpancingo, Mexico, because of the different kinds of construction and differences in the nature of surficial deposits in the two regions. Nevertheless, such comparisons have been made. The shortcomings of scales based on personal observations of surficial effects of earthquakes became very evident in the early decades of the twentieth century as a network of seismograph stations grew around the world. There was commonly poor correlation between the reported intensities and seismograph records; earthquakes in sparsely settled regions had a tendency to be underrated while earthquakes in or near metropolitan areas were overrated (Tocher, 1964, p. 15).

In 1935 a new scale to measure earthquake magnitude was proposed by Richter (1935) and has subsequently been widely adopted. The *Richter Magnitude Scale* measures earthquakes by relating the magni-

TABLE 2. **Modified Mercalli Scale of Earthquake Intensity**

I. Not felt except by a very few under especially favorable circumstances.

II. Felt only by a few persons at rest, especially on upper floors of buildings. Delicately suspended objects may swing.

III. Felt quite noticeably indoors, especially on upper floors, but many people do not recognize it as an earthquake. Standing motor cars may rock slightly. Vibration like passing truck. Duration estimated.

IV. During the day felt indoors by many, outdoors by few. At night some awakened. Dishes, windows, doors disturbed; walls make creaking sound. Sensation like heavy truck striking building. Standing motor cars rocked noticeably.

V. Felt by nearly everyone; many awakened. Some dishes, windows, etc., broken; a few instances of cracked plaster; unstable objects overturned. Disturbances of trees, poles, and other tall objects sometimes noticed. Pendulum clocks may stop.

VI. Felt by all; many frightened and run outdoors. Some heavy furniture moved; a few instances of fallen plaster or damaged chimneys. Damage slight.

VII. Everybody runs outdoors. Damage negligible in buildings of good design and construction; slight to moderate in well-built ordinary structures; considerable in poorly built or badly designed structures; some chimneys broken. Noticed by persons driving motor cars.

VIII. Damage slight in specially designed structures; considerable in ordinary substantial buildings, with partial collapse; great in poorly built structures. Panel walls thrown out of frame structures. Fall of chimneys, factory stacks, columns, monuments, walls. Heavy furniture overturned. Sand and mud ejected in small amounts. Changes in wellwater levels. Disturbs persons driving motor cars.

IX. Damage considerable in specially designed structures; well-designed frame structures thrown out of plumb; great in substantial buildings, with partial collapse. Buildings shifted off foundations. Ground cracked conspicuously. Underground pipes broken.

X. Some well-built wooden structures destroyed; most masonry and frame structures destroyed with foundations; ground badly cracked. Rails bent. Landslides considerable from river banks and steep slopes. Shifted sand and mud. Water splashed over banks.

XI. Few, if any, masonry, structures remain standing. Bridges destroyed. Broad fissures in ground. Underground pipelines completely out of service. Earth slumps and land slips in soft ground. Rails bent greatly.

XII. Damage total. Waves seen on ground surfaces. Lines of sight and level distorted. Objects thrown upward into the air.

tude of movements indicated on the seismograph to (1) the distance of the measuring station from the epicenter or point of origin of the disturbance, (2) the focal depth of the disturbance, (3) the way in which the energy is disseminated by the several kinds of elastic waves, (4) the mechanism by which the energy is released, and (5) the kinds of crustal material along the path between the epicenter and the recording station. The magnitude rating given to the earthquake is a measure of the total energy released in the form of elastic earth waves, while the intensity is a measure of the effects of this release of energy at any one locality. Thus an earthquake has one magnitude but many intensities. The Richter Magnitude Scale is nonlinear; for example, a rating of 8.9, representing a very large release of energy, is 10 times larger energy-wise than a rating of 7.9, and 103 times larger than a rating of 5.9 (Tocher, 1964, p. 18). The big San Francisco earthquake of 1906 had a magnitude of 8.3, while the sporadic small tremors that are rather common in the same area have magnitudes of 2.0 to 2.3.

Effects of earthquakes. Historical information on earthquakes was summed up in a U. S. Geological Survey news release dated November 24, 1968. Very little information is available prior to the eighteenth century. The first earthquake for which there is descriptive information in any detail occurred on November 1, 1755, near Lisbon, Portugal. Approximately 30 thousand people were killed. The shock was felt in many parts of the world. The earthquakes that occurred in 1811–1812 near New Madrid, Missouri, were felt over approximately 2 million square miles from Canada to the Gulf of Mexico; however, population was sparse so damage was slight. About 700 people were killed in the San Francisco earthquake of 1906. The Alaska earthquake of 1964 released about twice as much energy and was felt over an area of 500 thousand square miles with the loss of 114 lives.

No one who has experienced a moderately severe earthquake will ever forget it. There is literally "no place to hide." In addition to movement, which may be of several kinds—shaking, oscillation, rolling, jarring—depending on the nature of the earthquake and the surface materials, there is noise. In a city, there is a frightful creaking and groaning as structures are subjected to unusual stresses. Electric transmission lines whip about, break, and spark. Broken glass and fragments of building façades crash to the ground. In wooded areas the trees creak, groan, and thrash their branches furiously. Landslides make terrifying noises. Strong winds are raised. Standing water dashes against containing walls. Some observers have reported great roaring noises associated with the movement itself. After the shock, and after the debris is cleaned up and damages are repaired, however, the permanent and lasting effects are recorded in the land itself. Some areas are elevated and some are depressed. There may be open fissures. If the shock triggered landslides, the contour of the hills may be significantly changed and large masses of earth may have come to rest in new locations. Earthquakes may generate large and damaging waves in the oceans or large lakes. Earthquake-induced ocean waves are called *tsunamis*. The largest known was more than 200 ft high; in deep water these waves travel at speeds up to 400 to 500 mph.

The great Alaska earthquake of March 27, 1964, the so-called Good Friday earthquake, is now the best documented and most thoroughly studied earthquake in history. At the time of this writing, an eight-volume treatise on all aspects of the event was in preparation under the auspices of the National Academy of Science. The earthquake was the first to have affected water levels in wells, aquifers, and rivers all over the world (News Report, National Academy of Sciences-National Research Council, 1969). Fluctuations in water levels were recorded in over 700 wells in Africa, Asia, Australia, Europe, and North America. Oscillations of water levels in lakes and streams were recorded in more than 850 gauging stations in Australia and North America and were particularly noted along the Gulf Coast of the United States. The quake triggered some 51 rock avalanches, the largest involving 13 million cubic yards of rock. The largest known surface movements of land in recorded history resulted from this earthquake. The land level was altered in an area of about 70,000 sq mi in south-central Alaska. Between 23,000 and 35,000 sq mi were elevated as much as 33 ft. The subsea extent of land movement is not precisely known, but elevations of as much as 49 ft have been measured. The movements have been described in detail by Plafker (1965).

Albee and Smith (1966) have summed up earthquake-related land displacements in California, Nevada, and Baja California (Table 3). In California a number of vertical movements of the land caused by tectonic activity have been documented: The Owens Valley earthquake of 1872 produced a 23-ft change of elevation (Townley and Allen, 1939, p. 67); following the Long Beach earthquake of 1933, remeasurement of a network of U. S. Coast and Geodetic Survey leveling stations demon-

TABLE 3. Length and Amount of Observed Displacement Related to Earthquakes in California, Nevada, and Baja California

				Observed displacement			
DATE	LOCATION	MAGNITUDE	LENGTH (MILES)	MAX. VERT. COMPONENT	MAX. HORIZ. COMPONENT	MAX. TOTAL ACROSS ZONE	DISPLACEMENT BY RESURVEYING
1857	Fort Tejon, Calif.	7.75	40–250	?	Large		
1868	Hayward, Calif.	7	?	?	Some		
1872	Owens Valley, Calif.	7.75	ca. 50	13'	18'		
1899	San Jacinto, Calif.	ca. 6.75	ca. 2	?	?		
1906	San Francisco, Calif.	8.3	190 or 270	3'	21'a	16'	
1915	Pleasant Valley, Nev.	7.6	24	15'	—	15'	
1932	Cedar Mtns., Nev.	7.3	38	24"	34"	35"	
1934	Excelsior Mtns., Nev.	6.5	0.85	5"	—	5"	
1934	Colorado River delta, Baja Calif.	7.1	?	?	?	?	
1940	Imperial Valley, Calif.	7.1	40	—	19'	19'	ca. 9' Horiz.
1947	Manix, Calif.	6.2	1	—	3"	3"	
1950	Fort Sage Mtns., Calif.	5.6	5.5	5"–8"	—	8"	
1951	Superstition Hills, Calif.	5.6	1.9	—	Slight	Slight	
1952	Kern County, Calif.	7.7	40	4'	2'–3'	3.6'	1–2' Horiz. / 1–2' Vert.
1954	Rainbow Mtns., Nev.	6.6	11	12"	—	12"	
1954	Fallon, Nev.	6.8	14	30"	—	30"	
1954	Fairview Peak, Nev.	7.2	35	14'	12'	18.5'	ca. 8' Horiz. / ca. 4' Vert.
1954	Dixie Valley, Nev.	6.9	31	7'	7'	7'	ca. 7' Vert.
1956	San Miguel, Baja Calif.	6.8	12	36"	31"	36"	
1966	Parkfield, Calif.	5.6	ca. 25	—	4"	4"b	

SOURCE: Albee and Smith, 1966, Table 1, p. 12.
a The commonly cited 21' is partially attributable to lurching.
b Displacement is continuing in association with individual aftershocks.

strated uplifts and subsidence ranging from $+0.61$ to -0.41 ft (Parkin, 1948, p. 22).

Prediction, prevention, and protection. Earthquakes cannot be prevented by any means we now know. Perhaps in the future in some areas accumulated stresses can be released gradually through controlled subsurface explosions or injection of fluids under high pressure. But before earthquakes can be controlled we shall have to know a great deal more about the earth. Earthquake prediction will be possible long before earthquake control is a reality. Right now, damage and loss of life resulting from earthquakes can be minimized by informed planners and engineers backed up by sound land ordinances and building codes. The principal cause of damage in Anchorage, Alaska, was earthquake-triggered landslides caused by slumping of an unstable clay formation known as the Bootlegger Cove Clay. The undesirable foundation properties of this formation had in fact been described prior to the earthquake in a publication of the U. S. Geological Survey (Miller and Dobrovolny, 1959). It should be abundantly clear to those concerned with the future development of Anchorage that areas underlain by the Bootlegger Cove Clay demand special consideration in planning and that recommendations by geologists and engineers must be enforced by a strong zoning ordinance. In Valdez, Alaska, about 125 mi east of Anchorage and 45 mi east of the epicenter, principal cause of damage was a huge submarine slide. About 100 million cubic yards of material slid seaward into Prince William Sound, destroying the harbor installations and generating waves that damaged the downtown area. A remarkable system of fissures opened up and destroyed sewage and water systems (Coulter and Migliaccio, 1966).

The possibility of a major earthquake in the populous areas of the west coast of the United States is a matter of increasing concern because pressure for land has resulted in construction in areas susceptible to earthquake damage. This is particularly true in the San Francisco and Los Angeles areas, where there has been construction on potentially unstable hill slopes, on reclaimed bay land, and on other loosely packed artificial fills. The San Andreas fault is a major zone of potential dislocation. Slow creeping movements are occurring along the Hayward fault zone just east of San Francisco.

The big cities in the seismic region of the west coast are not unmindful of the dangers but it is difficult to enforce strict ordinances without a disaster of sufficient magnitude to arouse the citizenry. San Francisco, strangely enough, did not adopt a building code with earthquake provisions until about 1950 and was one of the last cities in California to take such action. A newspaper article (*Wall Street Journal,* December 23, 1964) quoted a structural engineer for the Pacific Fire Rating Bureau to the effect that in San Francisco's apartment districts, constructed largely in the 1920s, structures are not designed to withstand earthquake stresses. There has been more action in the Los Angeles area. For the last 10 years, under prodding from the Building and Safety departments, Los Angeles and Pasadena have been removing building cornices and other exterior ornamentation likely to be shaken loose in a quake. About 10,000 buildings have been thus "cleaned up." The Field Act passed by the California legislature after an earthquake in 1933 leveled schools in Long Beach, California (fortunately at a time they were empty), set construction standards for schools built thereafter, but many older schools are still in use. As a direct result of landslides caused by earthquakes, landslides caused by heavy rains, and landslides caused by destruction of natural slope equilibria by man through poor engineering practice, the city and county of Los Angeles moved to minimize the dangers of hillside construction by establishing a geological section in the Office of the County Engineer and requiring geologic reports on construction sites in areas of potential geologic hazard. Building codes were revised to include new provisions on excavation and grading. The code drafted by the International Conference of Building Officials in 1964 is reproduced in Appendix I. Geologists, working closely with soils engineers and civil engineers, do not condemn areas but rather make the builder aware of special geologic conditions which require special engineering design to make the site safe for construction. A large-scale geologic map is fundamental to an analysis of the site. Leeds (1966, p. 47) suggested that the first step in engineering design in seismic areas is to set up a model earthquake—a design earthquake—which is that earthquake to which the site is most likely to be exposed. This is simply an estimate of the kind and amount of motion that a structure is liable to experience. If the "design earthquake" is reasonably accurate, the engineer can plan his structure so as to avoid resonance with the ground motion.

Long-term changes in level. Gradual changes in level caused by tectonism but not associated with earthquakes are, of course, not catastrophically dangerous as are sudden movements. For the most part, slow creep of tectonic origin along faults is more of a nuisance, requiring perennial repair of pavements and pipelines. However, in planning for the long term, knowledge about such zones of slow creep is important. Structures and facilities should be routed so as to avoid the zone, not only because of the high costs of repair and maintenance but because of the danger of sudden large-scale movements in the same zone. Buildings should never, of course, be constructed across zones of tectonic creep. Monitoring of some 9000 stations in the Los Angeles area shows continuing basin subsidence (0.045 ft per yr in the center of the San Fernando Valley) and mountain elevation (0.013 ft per yr, San Jose Hills, 0.02 ft per yr south San Gabriel Mountains (Stone, 1961). Very slow elevation or depression of large crustal blocks due to internal tectonic processes, such as folding or warping, is difficult to detect but evidence of such changes of level probably caused by tectonic processes is in the archeological and geological record (Gilluly, Waters, and Woodford, 1959, pp. 112–114). One problem is the difficulty of separating tectonic uplift from elastic rebound or isostatic movements resulting from adjustments to changes in the crustal loading. In the northern Baltic Sea region an uplift of 3 or 4 ft per century is ascribed to rebound following melting of the great Pleistocene glaciers (Figure 4). Farmlands and fresh-water swamps along the Baltic Coast are covered with modern marine shells. The rate of uplift has been measured by monuments constructed a century and a half ago. Near Naples, on the sea coast is an ancient Roman temple (Jupiter Serapis) whose remaining columns show dramatic evidence of submersion of about 18 ft and subsequent elevation. Below a line on the columns, the stone has been holed by rock-boring clams with shells still in the columns—unmistakable evidence of submersion of the structure beneath the sea. Along the coasts of Denmark, campsites and hearths have been found as much as 40 ft below modern sea level. Some harbors in the world are growing deeper, some are getting more shallow. Projection of rates of change determined from tidal gauges over the short term is not conclusive, but clearly shows that some shore installations will be flooded or that the harbor will become too shallow for use within 50 years. There is a great deal of geologic evidence—raised or drowned shorelines, sediment-filled valleys, streams crossing structural axes, lake and swamp deposits—which prove relative changes in land and sea elevations or changes in base level of erosion. It is not possible to ascribe each case directly to tectonic processes. However, *warped*

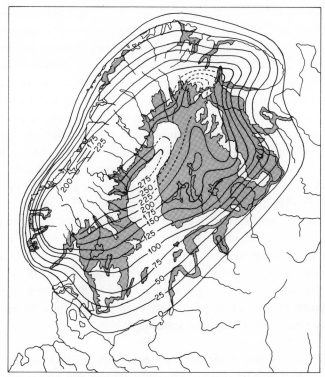

The contours are lines of equal uplift in meters of the highest beach (strand line) left by the sea that inundated the area (shaded) when the ice mass melted. In the center of this area this strand line has been raised 275 m. Scale 1:20,000,000.

FIGURE 4. Uplift in Scandinavia due to removal of the load of glacial ice. (After Daly, 1934, Fig. 28.)

raised shorelines prove differential movements and cannot have resulted from a lowering of sea level. In some areas rising crustal blocks have temporarily dammed up rivers and created chains of lakes. The span of time indicated for such changes is of geologic magnitude, which makes them of little practical interest, except in special circumstances, to planners concerned with man's problems.

Movements resulting from volcanism. Volcanic explosions, like tectonic movements, produce earthquakes and tremors. Explosions in volcanic vents, however, have a relatively shallow focus and the resulting earth movements are likely to be local. The energies of volcanoes released in the form of explosions are derived from gas pressures and are unlike the strain energies released in tectonic earthquakes. Although there are rare cases in recorded history where the birth of a volcano has been observed in an area where there was previously no known volcanism (Paricutín, Mexico, is an example), earth movements caused by volcanism occur around known volcanoes. The cones, craters and associated volcanic deposits attest to previous volcanic activity. The renewal of volcanic activity is commonly marked by seismic disturbances around the volcano and by the emission of gas, ash, lava, and other ejecta. Unlike the sudden tectonic earthquakes, as a rule there is some warning of a volcanic event. Indeed, it is the earth movements, the seismic activity, that give warning of eruptions. Most of the damage done to human populations by volcanoes is from eruption of hot ash and lava rather than from the movements of the land around the cone. Those concerned with land-use in volcanic regions, then, are chiefly concerned with the direct consequences of eruption and only secondarily concerned with land movements resulting from volcanism.

Isostatic movements. Current theories of the earth conceive of the crust as "floating" on a dense, plastic interior; the large-scale surface features such as basins, mountains, and plateaus are not carved out of a rigid crust but are in a sort of flotational equilibrium (see Gilluly, Waters, and Woodford 1959, pp. 156–164, for a discussion of isostasy). Loading or unloading of the crust, therefore, by thick sedimentary accumulations in some areas and deep erosion in others, produces minor adjustments in crustal level. It is difficult, except in theoretical discussions, to differentiate between changes in level caused by isostatic movements from those caused by broad tectonic warping. However, it is well demonstrated that the slow rise in land level observed in areas which were heavily loaded by thick ice accumulations during the Glacial period is the result of an isostatic response to removal of load. These movements, measured in areas of maximum uplift or subsidence in terms of a few feet per century, over the decades may require major engineering projects to maintain coastal installations and protect coastal property; certainly planners working in regions where such movements occur should be aware of them and understand their nature.

MOVEMENTS OF THE SURFACE CAUSED BY
SURFICIAL PROCESSES

One result of the increasing concentration of people in cities is that a large part of the population is shockingly ignorant of the common earth processes with which our forebears lived. Whereas the people that live on the land still must contend in a very personal way with natural processes and their commonly violent extremes, such as floods, the population in well-engineered cities contend mostly with social disturbances due to unstable conditions developed in the human hive itself. The city dweller's reaction to high water over a highway or a road closed by a landslide is one of surprise that such impertinences of nature are allowed to occur. The common saying of his grandfather, "We'll come, God willing and the creeks don't rise," has little meaning for him. Of course, in some cities where there are special conditions citizens have learned the hard way about floods and landslides, mostly because the city authorities themselves were ignorant about the earth out of which their city grew.

Mass movements on slopes: landslides, mudflows, and creep. Included in this category are some of the most destructive and spectacular of surficial movements—rockfalls, landslides, and mudflows,—as well as gentler but nevertheless persistent movements like soil creep. The motive force in each case is gravity. The nature of the movement is controlled by the earth materials involved, friction (internal friction of the moving mass and friction between the moving mass and the stable floor beneath it), and the slope over which the mass is moving. These mass movements, of course, are restricted to lands where there are slopes—topographic relief. They are set off or triggered by an event which upsets previously established equilibrium conditions. Masses of earth at rest do not move without cause. The triggering events commonly include (1) earthquakes directly setting the earth mass in motion, (2) heavy rains or large amounts of melt water that reduce internal friction, (3) unloading or undercutting of stable slopes by natural erosion, and (4), increasingly common, destruction of natural equilibria by works of man.

Landslides are commonly classified as *falls*, in which the earth mass travels for most of the distance through the air in free fall, or bounding and rolling along a surface with fragments separated by air; *slides*, in which the earth mass moves as one or more units, commonly along a slip surface or surfaces; and *flows*, in which the mass moves as a viscous fluid with a great deal of internal movement. There are all gradations between slides and flows; at one end of the spectrum are slides wherein the mass moves along a slip surface with little or no deformation of the sliding mass or movement within it, while at the other end are flowing viscous masses wherein constituent rock fragments are separated by a plastic or liquid mud matrix. Complex slides commonly include several kinds of movement over the course of the transport.

Slides. From an engineering point of view it is convenient to classify landslides as (1) *bedrock slides*, commonly moving along planes of weakness in the rock such as bedding planes, joints, or fractures; and (2) slides (*slumps*) of unconsolidated or weakly consolidated surficial materials, including both natural deposits and man-made fills. The latter type grade into earth flows of various kinds. Figure 5 identifies the features of an "ideal" landslide. Some slides move with speeds clocked in tens or hundreds of feet per second, while others creep along at rates measured in tenths or hundredths of a foot per day.

One of the worst landslides in history was the Vaiont Reservoir disaster in Italy where, on October 9, 1963, a great mass of earth and rock—more than 240 million cubic meters—slid into a reservoir, sent water over the dam, destroyed the dam, and killed some 2117 people in the valley below. The circumstances which led to the slide and subsequent disaster were summed up by Kiersch (1965, p. 11).

1. Rock units adjacent to the reservoir are weak, with low resistance to shear, and dip steeply toward the reservoir. They are mostly limestone filled with solution cavities and clay. They are extensively jointed and fractured. Construction of the reservoir raised the water table. Raising of the level of water in the reservoir further raised the water table.

2. Heavy rains prior to the slide further raised the water table; sinkholes outside the reservoir acted as catchment basins for ground water recharge. Clays in the sequence swelled. The raised water table and swelling clays increased the hydrostatic uplift pressure in the rock mass. The mass, which had been creeping at 1 cm per

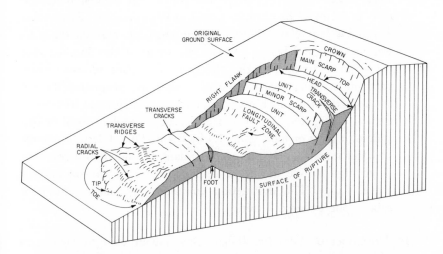

Main Scarp A steep surface on the undisturbed ground around the periphery of the slide, caused by movement of slide material away from the undisturbed ground. The projection of the scarp surface under the disturbed material becomes the surface of rupture.

Minor scarp A steep surface on the disturbed material produced by differential movements within the sliding mass.

Head The upper parts of the slide material along the contact between the disturbed material and the main scarp.

Top The highest point of contact between the disturbed material and the main scarp.

Foot The line of intersection (sometimes buried) between the lower part of the surface of rupture and the original ground surface.

Toe The margin of disturbed material most distant from the main scarp.

Tip The point on the toe most distant from the top of the slide.

Flank The side of the landslide.

Crown The material that is still in place, practically undisturbed, and adjacent to the highest parts of the main scarp.

Original ground surface The slope that existed before the movement which is being considered took place. If this is the surface of an older landslide, that fact should be stated.

Left and right Compass directions are preferable in describing a slide, but if left and right are used they refer to the slide as viewed from the crown.

FIGURE 5. **An ideal landslide and its salient features.** (After Highway Research Board Landslide Committee, 1958, Plate 1.)

week, began to creep at a rate of 1 cm per day in September and early in October the creep increased to 10 cm per day. By October 8, the day before the slide, operating engineers realized the mass was unstable and began to lower the water in the reservoir, but heavy rains diminished the effectiveness of this remedy. Thus, without any triggering earthquake shock, the characteristics and the attitude of the rock mass, the reduction of internal friction by natural events and the man-made structure resulted in a sudden slide of a mass of rock about 1.5 by 2 km. This slide sent a surge of water more than 100 m over the dam; the flood crest was over 70 m high a mile down the canyon where the canyon entered Piave Valley. The destruction continued for miles. The total catastrophe endured 7 min.

In November of 1968 the Italian Government charged eight persons with manslaughter and negligence. The government charged that the dam was built despite knowledge of the geologically unstable nature of the mountain behind it.

Less catastrophic but nevertheless destructive landslides have been plaguing southern California in recent years as urban construction has spread out of the valleys and up steep slopes. Figure 6 illustrates man-made landslide development. One of the worst landslide spots has been the Palos Verdes Hills in southeastern Los Angeles County where slopes have repeatedly failed under the combined influence of inadequate engineering, heavy rains, and hazardous geological conditions in the form of inclined, weakly coherent sedimentary rocks (Figure 7). The Portuguese Bend landslide in this same area caused about $10 million in damages to residential and public structures. The following description is summarized from Merriam (1960).

Rocks involved are tuffaceous shales which dip at angles of 15 to 30° and tend to become plastic when wet. In 1956 a mass of some 300 to 400 acres began to move and over a period of 3 years advanced about 68 ft over a shear plane inclined in general about 6 to 7°, but nearly vertical at the head of the slide; the mass apparently moved plastically with large blocks carried in the earth flow. The head of the slide subsided a maximum of about 12 ft (over 600 days) while the toe rose a maximum of about 4 ft (over 388 days). Merriam (1960, p. 150) believed that the principal cause of the slide was water added to the slide mass through cesspools, lawns, and gardens. About 150 houses

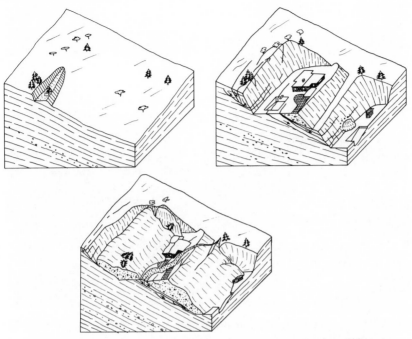

Three stages in the dynamic development of a "dip-slope" hillside. *Left,* a bulldozer cut is made. *Right,* two benches have been completed, and the upper one is already occupied by a house and a pool. Slippage with the bedrock is beginning to occur, and cracks are appearing on the ground surface. Water, leaking from the upper swimming pool, is soaking into the bedrock and promoting further sliding. *Bottom,* sliding has occurred on a large scale as nature tries to reestablish a relatively stable dip slope.

FIGURE 6. **Development of a man-made landslide.** (After Jahns, 1958, p. 20.)

built in the area discharged about 32,000 gal per day into the slide material through cesspools alone. A number of attempts were made to control the slide. A series of concrete caissons set through the moving mass into stable ground to "pin" the slide did not halt the movement. Other plans involved draining and drying out the moving earth mass to increase friction and a scheme to unload the head of the slide by excavation while loading the toe with fill and retaining structures.

Creep and mudflows. *Creep,* as the name implies, is a slow downslope movement of an earth mass. Although not in itself dangerous to life,

FIGURE 7. **Landslide on the north side of the Palos Verdes Hills in southeastern Los Angeles County.** (Courtesy of California Division of Mines and Geology.)

it may indicate development of potentially dangerous slope conditions and it may require engineering control to prevent the earth mass from displacing structures or moving over a road. Tilted telephone poles, fence posts, and gravestones on hill slopes present evidence of and a means of measuring creep. In gullies and road cuts distorted, stretched-out layers of weathered rock demonstrate creep. Fragments of rock moved from upslope outcrops are also evidence of mass movement. Any process which causes a volume change in an earth mass on a slope—for example, wetting and drying, freezing and thawing—results in downslope creep. On expansion, a fragment of material in the mass is moved at right angles to the slope; on contraction, the same particle moves downward under the influence of gravity. Movement of soil by plants and animals also results in downslope movement under gravitational forces.

Mudflows occur where the ingredients of mud—soft, unconsolidated sediments and water—are present on a slope. Commonly a flow results when a mass of unconsolidated sediment is rapidly charged with water so that it becomes saturated and internal friction is reduced. The usual source of the water is heavy rains or sudden thaws which produce water faster than it can drain away. In humid areas of northern United States and Canada soft, unconsolidated masses of clay, silt, and sand that accumulate in valleys may flow down the valley after they have become charged with water from spring thaws. Such flows, moving at rates of 5 or 6 mph or faster, are a danger to life and property. In desert regions, ingredients for mud flows occur in mountain canyons where unconsolidated sediments become saturated with water from heavy rains. Masses of silt, sand, and coarse rock fragments roar down the canyons and flow out onto the alluvial fans which commonly develop where the canyon opens out onto a pediment or valley floor. Curry (1966) described mudflows which occurred in Mayflower Gulch about 60 mi west-southwest of Denver, Colorado, on August 18, 1961, following a 24.5 cm rain in a 24-hr period. According to Curry (1966, p. 771), "The flows occurred as a series of pulses which moved at a maximum velocity of 980 m/min (53 feet/sec) over and through saturated talus on slopes as steep as 41 degrees." In cities such as El Paso, Albuquerque, and Palm Springs where rapid city growth has resulted in construction on alluvial fans along the mountain front, mudflows can be very damaging. City authorities should not permit development of subdivisions or other construction on such alluvial fans unless the risks are fully understood and proper engineering safeguards are adopted. Ingredients for damaging mudflows also exist on the flanks of volcanoes, where deposits of ash and other volcanic ejecta may become saturated with water and move down slope as mudflows.

Collapse and subsidence. *Collapse* or *subsidence* of the surface of the earth occurs when subsurface supporting material is removed. Subsidence is common where man has pumped large volumes of fluids out of weakly consolidated sediments and where he has mined out mineral deposits without leaving sufficient support in the workings to maintain the surface. Collapse and subsidence also occur where soluble subsurface formations have been dissolved or leached away by ground water.

Solution and collapse in limestone terranes. Regions underlain by *limestone*, or *dolomite*, containing solution cavities have a characteristic topography marked by large and small closed depressions, streams that abruptly disappear underground, and large springs. A classic example of such features is the Karst region in the Dinaric Alps of Yugoslavia; the name has been applied generally so that all over the world such regions are known as *karst regions*. In the United States there are karst regions in central Tennessee, Kentucky, southern Indiana, Alabama, northern Florida, and Texas. In areas of high water tables the depressions or sinkholes are commonly filled with water. Communities which utilize such ponds and lakes for water supply must be exceedingly careful because water in the entire subterranean network of connected caverns and passages can easily become polluted from surface streams in the region. Discharge of sewage or other wastes into sinkholes likewise may contaminate the entire system. At Orlando, Florida, in the early 1940s, because of poor local drainage, waste disposal wells were drilled and a variety of liquid wastes including sewage were pumped into the aquifer (Unklesby and Cooper, 1946). A similar situation prevailed in Bellevue, Ohio, where household sewage and drainage were discharged into an aquifer through sinkholes until the practice was stopped in 1946 by the Ohio Water Resources Board and State Health Department (Leggett, 1962, p. 159). Such ignorance of the geologic environment is a menace to public health.

Construction in these karst regions without borings to determine the possible presence of cavernous zones below the site runs the risk of damage by collapse. Robert O. Vernon (personal communication, 1966) listed a number of examples of damage to highways and buildings in the limestone country of Florida through sudden collapse of previously unsuspected limestone caverns. Five houses were damaged in the Pine Hills subdivision of Orlando, Florida, early in 1961 by the collapse of a large sinkhole covering about 40 acres. In May of 1963, a sinkhole 60 ft deep developed at the corner of Baker and Austin Streets in Bartow, Florida, and endangered two residences. In October 1964 part of U. S. Highway 19 and an adjacent building at the northern limits of Chiefland, Florida, were damaged by a sinkhole some 50 ft in diameter. In May of 1965 at Castleberry, Florida, one house was destroyed and three were damaged by development of a sinkhole about 20 ft deep and 80 ft in diameter; cracks extended about 200 ft from the sinkhole. In Lexington, Kentucky, a cement truck dropped 12 ft into a limestone cavern while pouring the foundation for a house; the truck was raised and the cavern filled with stone and concrete (E. R.

Branson, personal communication, 1966). Figure 8 shows a cavern near Leeds, Alabama, that collapsed during construction of a heavy foundation for a cement plant. Recently sinkholes developed in the Inglenook section of Birmingham, Alabama, destroying a number of residences. The area is underlain by the Ketona and Copper Ridge dolomite, soluble formations in which caverns and sinkholes have developed. The city filled the sinks with concrete rubble. Another method used to stabilize limestone riddled with solution cavities is by grouting— pumping concrete slurry into the openings. Such a remedy can be very expensive, particularly if there are large caverns. For the most part,

FIGURE 8. Collapse of a cavern in Ordovician Limestone (Newala and Longview formations) near Leeds, Alabama, resulting in damage to a foundation under construction for a cement plant. Note tilting and subsidence of concrete piers. (Courtesy of Alabama Geological Survey.)

grouting is restricted to sealing permeable formations at dam sites and around mine shafts.

Subsidence due to withdrawal of fluids. Changes in land level commonly result from changes in the water content of sediments, from both subtraction and addition of water. Dewatering of clays and silts removes part of the volume of the mass, causes a decrease in the buoyant pressure, and results in a compaction (decrease in volume) of the mass. Subsidence of the surface generally is gradual. Harris and Harlow (1948, p. 380) reported on settling of 0.45 ft on Terminal Island in Los Angeles County due to dewatering of sediments during construction of dock facilities; changes in level occurred within a 2000-ft radius of the site. Draining of peat lands causes oxidation and decomposition of the organic matter, shrinkage, and subsidence. As much as 12 to 14 ft of subsidence occurred over a 100-yr period beginning in 1850 in the Sacramento-San Joaquin delta area of northern California as the land was drained for cultivation (Weir, 1950). In very dry areas, introduction of water into dry, low-density sediments causes reorientation of sediment particles and collapse of the sedimentary structure. Along the west side of the San Joaquin Valley in central California subsidence of this kind has occurred as a result of irrigation projects. Lofgren (1960, p. 1061) reported as much as 10.5 ft of collapse in a 27-month period in test areas. Damage to structures (roads, pipelines, transmission lines) has been extensive. There have been attempts at stabilizing through precollapsing of sites through injection of water prior to construction.

A city known all over the world for its subsidence problems is Mexico City, whose foundations are in large part the water-saturated clays, sandy clays, and sands of the ancient lake known to the Aztecs as Lake Texcoco. Pumping of water from the lake beds has resulted in slow subsidence or sinking of buildings; in various neighborhoods the older structures have foundered so much that half the first floor is below present ground level. The most famous example is the Palacio de Bellas Artes, a massive stone structure weighing nearly 60,000 tons. Since it was begun in 1904, the building has settled more than 10 ft and is still sinking at a rate of about 1½ in. per yr (Leggett, 1962, p. 476).

Subsidence is also a problem in the modern city of Houston, Texas, where withdrawal of large amounts of water from the poorly consolidated sediments of the Gulf Coast Aquifer has resulted in subsidence

of several feet in some areas, with damage to buildings, pavement
and flood control systems (Figures 9–11). Inasmuch as the area is very
flat, changes in drainage can be highly disruptive. There are active
faults in the same area, one of which has broken pavement on runways
at Houston International Airport. The problems have been described
in detail by Weaver and Sheets (1962) and Van Siclen (1967). Van
Siclen related subsidence in the Houston area to a series of active
faults. Some of the faults show a vertical separation of as much as
1.6 in. per yr with a maximum of 41.1 in. since 1928. He concluded
that the fault movement has been triggered by withdrawal of ground-
water and that the value of the water far exceeds the economic losses
caused by surface subsidence due to withdrawal.

Miller (1966) summarized subsidence effects resulting from with-

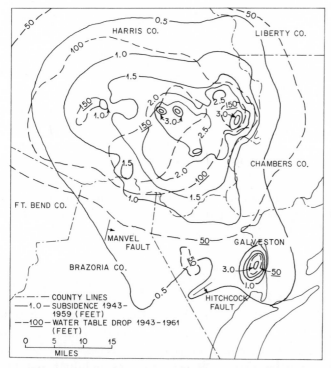

FIGURE 9. Subsidence contours 1943–1959 and water-
level decline in observation wells 1943–1961, Houston–
Galveston area, Texas. (After Weaver and Sheets, 1962,
Fig. 2.)

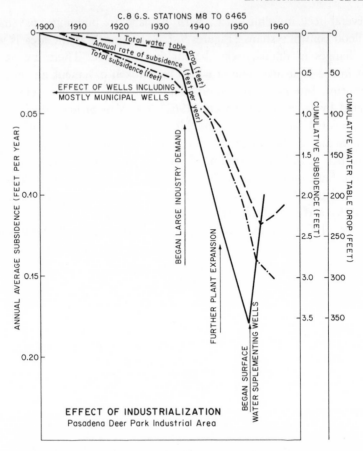

FIGURE 10. Subsidence caused by withdrawals of ground water for industrial purposes in the area of Houston, Texas, 1900–1960. (After Weaver and Sheets, 1962, Fig. 4.)

drawal of water, petroleum, and natural gas in southern California, reporting on the Los Banos-Kettlemen City and Tulare-Wasco areas of the San Joaquin Valley (as much as 1 ft subsidence for each 10 to 25 ft of decline in the water table), and the Antelope Valley, La Verne, and Santa Ana areas (2.8 ft at Lancaster in Antelope Valley between 1926 and 1955, and La Verne 1 ft between 1923 and 1931 and 1.8 ft between 1933 and 1950) as shown in Figure 12. Subsidence at Long-Beach, California, as a result of withdrawals from the Wilmington oil field caused extensive damage. Between 1928 and 1968 a roughly circular

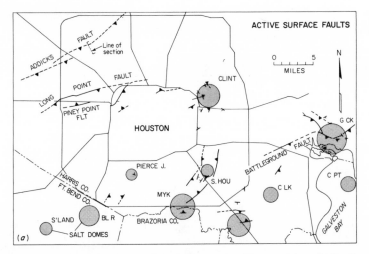

(a) Areal pattern of active surface faults in the Houston area. Light lines show the freeway pattern. The heavy, solid lines indicate known (almost) continuously active faults; the dashed lines show topographic scarps and, rarely, airphoto linears that extend and connect these, but along which definite pavement breaks are rare or absent. The triangles (and little lines on the shortest faults) point toward the downthrown side. The circular patterns show the positions of salt domes, all of which come fairly close to the surface.

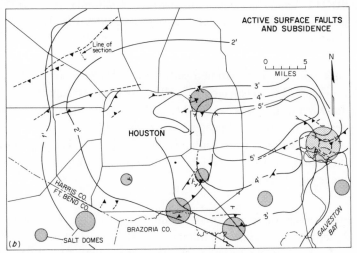

(b) Surface subsidence 1906–1964 compared to areal pattern of active faults in the Houston area. Note the absence of any close similarity.

FIGURE 11. Faults (a) and subsidence (b) in the Houston, Texas, area. (After Van Siclen, 1967, Figs. 4 and 7; subsidence contour through courtesy of McClelland Engineers.)

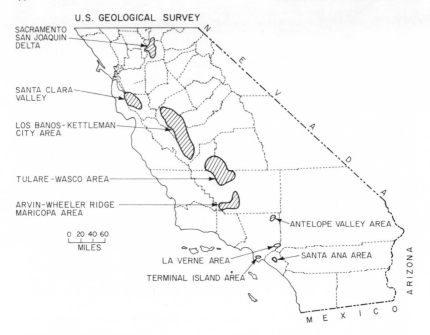

FIGURE 12. **Land sudsidence in southern California resulting mostly from withdrawal of ground water.** (After Miller, 1966, Fig. 1.)

area sank more or less symmetrically with subsidence of 29 ft at the center (Figure 13). Damages to wells, pipelines, transportation facilities, harbor installations, and other industrial facilities are estimated at close to $100 million (Mayuga and Allen, 1966).

Subsidence caused by withdrawal of fluids can be controlled or stopped through injection of fluids and repressurizing of the reservoir to achieve equilibrium.

Subsidence over mine workings. Examples of surface subsidence over abandoned mine workings are numerous in the Appalachian coal mining region. In April of 1963 severe subsidence occurred at Coaldale, Pennsylvania, as a result of collapse of workings over the Primrose coal seam. Some 23 dwellings were damaged or destroyed as a result of the collapse. The damaged property was purchased by the Redevelopment Authority of Schuylkill County and a Federal–State Cooperative Project was set up to stabilize the subsidence area by reenforcing subsurface

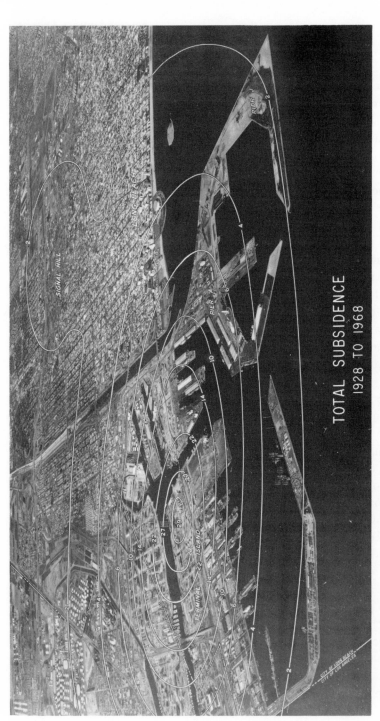

FIGURE 13. **Subsidence at Long Beach, California, 1928–1968.** (Courtesy of D. R. Allen, Department of Oil Properties, City of Long Beach.)

pillars and filling the underground openings with sand, gravel, and spoil-bank fill. The Coaldale project was one of several antisubsidence projects approved by the Department of Interior in the Pennsylvania Anthracite region, according to a Bureau of Mines Press Release dated May 27, 1966. In another release dated April 4, 1966, the Bureau of Mines announced a project to control subsidence of part of northwest Scranton, Pennsylvania, where improvements valued at more than $13 million in a 92-acre area have been damaged. Subsidence first occurred in September of 1964. Plans are to spend more than $1 million in arresting the subsidence by drilling some 600 holes into the underground workings and stabilize them by filling with spoil from mine dumps. Subsidence over old anthracite mines in the area of the Wilkes-Barre, Pennsylvania, Bypass (Route 309) was dramatically illustrated in April 1963. An area some 30 ft in diameter caved in suddenly and dropped an automobile 15 ft; the driver scrambled out of the great hole as his car sank further and disappeared, never to be recovered. A subsidence control project through backfilling of the old workings was approved for the area in March, 1968 (U. S. Bureau of Mines press release, March 28, 1968).

In 1966 the State of Pennsylvania passed a law, *The Bituminous Mine Subsidence and Land Conservation Act of 1966*, to regulate the mining of bituminous coal. Prior to this act, in the Pittsburgh area, where Pittsburgh and Freeport seams have been mined for over a century, the Consolidation Coal Company over the period 1900 to 1957 offered property owners the option of purchasing an agreement to support the workings beneath their property by leaving pillars or ribs of coal in place. The company did not warrant against subsidence during this period. In 1957, the company changed its policy and contracted to insure property against subsidence due to mining for a period of 10 years following extraction of the coal. Vandale (1967, p. 88) pointed out that the new law will force mining companies to leave large amounts of coal in the mines for surface support, coal that they have purchased and paid taxes on for a long period of time. The law reflects a change in social value, with an upgrading of the value of surface real estate as opposed to the subsurface mineral estate.

In this same state, Pennsylvania, an underground fire burning in a coal seam has consumed support for the surface and caused subsidence. In September 1966 the U. S. Bureau of Mines announced a project to control a subsurface fire in Allegheny County which has created a collapse of some 16 acres and is moving toward a residential area.

Movements due to volume changes in surficial materials. In many parts of the United States residents are plagued with sticking windows and doors, unsightly cracks in sheetrock and masonry walls, supporting piers moving out from under frame houses, and even cracks in slab foundations. More often than not, these harassed residents occupy houses built on clay. The correlation is so good between building failure and geologic formation that in Austin, Texas, for example, geologists can map the outcrops of the Taylor Formation by cracked walls and footings of structures built on it. When clays of the Taylor Formation get wet they swell, and when they dry and give up their water, they shrink and develop deep cracks. Where there is a natural slope, the repeated change in volume of the clay sets up a downslope movement or creep (p. 37). As a result of the continuous change in volume of the surface materials, structures whose foundations do not penetrate below the zone of volume change move about, stresses and strains are set up in walls, floors change level, and separations between structure and foundation occur. Concrete slabs that are improperly reinforced fail. Although this change in volume of surficial materials rarely results in any loss of life, damage to structures over a period of years can amount to thousands of dollars and, multiplied by many structures over a wide area of outcrop, the penalty for inadequate engineering is substancial financial loss.

The worst offenders are bentonitic clays. *Bentonite* is a clay material that has the property of swelling markedly on addition of water, a property that makes it valuable as an industrial mineral in many applications. Bentonite's ability to take on a relatively large volume of water is due to the crystal lattice of the clay mineral *montmorillonite*, its principal constituent. Montmorillonite has a weakly-bonded sheet structure which readily admits water. Bentonite is formed by alteration of volcanic ash and is common in those parts of the world which have at one time or another received deposits of ash. In 1962 the Highway Research Board published a number of papers on properties of swelling clays under the title "Moisture, density, swelling and swell pressure relationships." Bentonitic clays of the Eagle Ford Formation caused extensive damage to The University Baptist Church in Austin, Texas.

Although the original design carried concrete footings through about 6 ft of clay to rock, the foundation confined a mass of clay. With increase in moisture, the clay expanded with sufficient pressure to lift the building about 4 in. and break the concrete footing. Other structures in Austin and in other Texas cities along the outcrop of the Eagle Ford Formation have been damaged by swelling bentonitic clays; highways crossing the Eagle Ford have a high maintenance cost. Similar problems exist elsewhere where there are swelling clays. Inasmuch as the kinds and amounts of clay minerals control the amount of swelling and the lateral pressures which develop in clays, it follows that geological information on the mineralogy of clay formations in areas where construction is planned, and particularly in urban areas, is extremely valuable to planners and engineers who know how to interpret it. See Figure 14. Environmental geologic investigations of urban regions now underway in many parts of the country are designed to produce these kinds of data.

In northern regions where there is seasonal freezing of ground, volume changes occur in water-saturated soils and unconsolidated sediments. The result is heaving or swelling as freezing occurs and settling during thaws.

Permafrost. Areas of the earth's surface that are perennially frozen are known as *permafrost areas* and present special engineering problems. In these regions, the ground has remained deeply frozen since the last glacial age; depth of the frozen material ranges from a few inches along the southern margins to as much as 1000 ft (Leggett, 1962, p. 103). In areas where a *soil* is permanently frozen (as distinct from rock), the frozen ground is commonly insulated against surface temperature changes by a mat of fibrous organic material called muskeg. Permafrost areas within the United States are limited to some high mountain regions in counterminous United States and to the state of Alaska; nearly half of Canada is a permafrost region.

If the upper part of the ground surface is composed of rock, or of sand and gravel which can be drained, there are generally no serious engineering problems. However, if the upper part of the ground surface is composed of silt, clay, or peat, and if it is thawed by removal of muskeg, through construction activities, or through transfer of heat from structures built on the frozen ground, the result is a more or less fluid soil mass which cannot drain because the underlying material

FIGURE 14. What swelling clay can do to a concrete slab. Photo taken January 29, 1968, where Loop 111 crosses Boggy Creek, Austin, Texas. The clay is the Taylor Formation.

is frozen and therefore impermeable. The fluid mass is, therefore, subject to flow and creep. Although it may refreeze in the winter seasons, it does not return to its former permanent frozen state. When the thawed material refreezes from the surface downward, water trapped between the top of the permanently frozen subsurface is confined and, under hydrostatic pressure, may break out as springs and form sheets of surface ice. Refreezing of water in the soil mass also causes volume changes, with swelling and heaving of the surface. Remelting causes depressions and results in an uneven surface similar to the "kettled surface" of glacial outwash terranes. Special engineering techniques are required to control the problems presented by surface movements in permafrost regions. Some of these are use of insulation to prevent melting of the frozen ground, drainage of the thawed or active layer, devices to anchor structures to the subjacent frozen ground, and replacement of the fluid mass with a more stable base of sand and gravel (Trefethen, 1949, p. 354). Recent discoveries of major oil fields on the

North Slope of Alaska have brought the problems of building in permafrost areas into the national news.

Movement of surficial earth materials in water-, ice-, and wind-transport systems. Muddy streams are familiar to nearly all citizens of the United States; blowing dust is common in the Southwest and parts of the Great Plains; those few who have seen the terminus of a glacier cannot fail to have noted the rock and earth debris caught up in the ice. All of these phenomena are, of course, proof that earth material is in transit on the earth's surface—coming from somewhere and going somewhere. It would be a reckless and foolish individual indeed who would build a house on the edge of a river bank after seeing the river undercut and chew away a section of that same bank, or who would build immediately downwind of a live sand dune after seeing the dune engulf another structure. It is equally reckless and foolish for a planner or engineer to engage in long-term planning without being aware of the less obvious capabilities of river, wind, and ice erosion—transportation systems, and what happens where established equilibria are changed. If a river is carrying a load of mud, silt, and sand over a bed of a certain grade and in a channel of a certain shape, works of man which change channel shape or grade will increase or decrease the river's capacity to transport and its capacity to erode. The result is either renewed capacity to scour the river bed and cut away the banks, or dumping of sediments that silt up channels.

Rivers and coastlines. Rivers in flood transport many times their normal loads, and where the waters come over the banks of the modern channel they commonly spread a layer of muck and mud over the adjacent flood plain. Although this material must be cleaned from highways and dwellings, it is in general beneficial to agricultural enterprises, for it leaves a layer of new and fertile soil on the fields. The construction of dams and levees and other flood-prevention systems shuts off this natural process of maintaining soil fertility, although most farmers are willing to trade the flood-produced new soil for protection of farm improvements.

Movements of land along coastlines are impressive to anyone who has lived on a coast for a period of years or who has observed the changes wrought by a large storm. Storm waves crashing against a beach, cutting away dune ridges and leaving a broad new wave-cut terrace, or washing over a barrier island to dump sand, fragments of paving, and beach cottages into the bay behind are immensely damaging to coast dwellers. The slow work of *longshore currents* moving sand along the coast—the *littoral drift*—can be equally effective in either nourishing or destroying a beach. Any marine engineering project— dredging of new channels, cutting of passes, construction of jetties— can have far-reaching consequences if they change or modify previously established sediment transport systems. The rapidity of change in coast- lines is due to the fact that the shore is the locus of operation of one of the most powerful natural erosive forces. All of the rivers of the land seek the ocean as ultimate base level and bring their loads of sediments to the shore for disposal; the direct impact of ocean waves on the land adds to this accumulation of shore debris. Along the shore and on the near-shore continental shelf sediments are moved here and there by waves and currents. Storm-produced waves and cur- rents have capabilities of transporting enormous volumes of sediments and changing the configuration of the shore and the offshore slope in hours.

As fishing villages along the coasts of the world became ports, harbor facilities were constructed, and engineers attempted to protect these facilities against the ceaseless attack of the seas. Working empiri- cally, without really understanding marine processes, they constructed jetties and sea walls to keep channels open and protect seaside improve- ments against damage from storm waves. Channels were maintained by dredging. These attempts were not always successful, and history records a number of spectacular failures. Many of these were due to inade- quacies of equipment rather than a lack of knowledge of what had to be done. Modern dredges, draglines, and capabilities to deliver and place jetty stone have made possible coastal engineering projects and continuous maintenance that were beyond the engineers of the last century. Roman engineers fought a battle with the silt brought down by the Tiber to save the port of Ostia, and lost; today the city is 1.5 mi from the sea (Leggett, 1962, p. 697). But some of the failures are clearly geological failures resulting from misunderstanding or under- estimation of natural systems.

In ancient times the Greeks built the city of Ephesus where the River Kayster entered a well-marked recess in the Anatolian Coast (Hunter, 1913, pp. 65–66). Strabo observed that because of the silt load deposited by the river, the coastline advanced about a mile over a

period of seven centuries. By 150 B.C., the accumulation of silt threatened the port city to the extent that the ruling monarch, King Attalus
Philadelphus, employed an engineer to correct the situation. His remedy, a breakwater across the Gulf, was an engineering failure of great
magnitude and ruined the channel. Under the Roman government
engineers struggled at great expense to maintain a canal through the
growing marshes. When Rome fell, the engineering works were abandoned and the once proud port is now 15 mi from the sea. Unfortunately, not all of the failures are ancient history. Modern failures
may not be as geographically spectacular but they are financially
spectacular in terms of the investment needed in remedial work and
yearly maintenance. A modern example of a port city fighting a battle
with silt is Buenos Aires. In the early days shallow-draft vessels had little
difficulty in navigating the La Plata estuary. Larger and deeper-draft
ships could not enter the port, so dredges began to deepen the channel,
and they are now required to work around the clock to keep the port
open to even medium-draft vessels. The task is opposed by a natural
process of sedimentation as the La Plata River deposits its silt load.

Although historically extraordinary efforts were made to maintain
the coastal status quo around ports and harbors, there was prior to
1900 little concern with the rest of the coastline and changes in it
have been the concern of historians rather than engineers. Perhaps
the most interesting record of a changing coast comes from England,
where the island nature of the country, its long recorded history, and
the geologic nature of part of the coast has resulted in a dramatic
record of ancient towns and structures engulfed by the sea or buried
by the sediment it threw back against the land. In 1943, the British
Ministry of Town and Country Planning commissioned a geographer,
J. A. Steers, to make a survey of the coast of England and Wales. The
results of the study, published in 1946 and printed again in 1948, is
the kind of document that should be basic to land-use planning in all
areas. It described the changing face of the land in contact with the
sea in such dimension that it is regarded as a classic. A few quotations
give the flavor of the descriptions and illustrate the kinds of changes
that take place in a span of a few hundred years.

Between Culverhole Point and Humble Point the inland cliffs are of
Chalk and Upper Greensand; the undercliffs are of fallen Cretaceous
material very much disturbed. They slope downwards eventually to rest on

the Lias shore reefs. Dowland's Chasm is the most striking feature: it was formed in 1839. Since June 1838 there had been a very wet period, and also one of strong gales. Fissures and cracks began to appear on the cliff top shortly before Christmas 1839, and on 23 December one of the cottages began to subside, at first in no very alarming manner. But by 5 p.m. the cottage was settling rapidly, and later other cottages were "upheaved and twisted." The great landslip occurred on Christmas night. "During December 26th the land that had been cut off by the fissures in the cliff-top gradually subsided seawards, and by the evening had reached a position of equilibrium in the undercliff. A new inland cliff, 210 feet high in its central portion and sinking to east and west, had thus been exposed, backing a chasm into which some twenty acres of land had subsided. The length of the chasm was about half a mile, while its breadth increased from 200 feet on the west to 400 feet on the east." In all some eight million tons of earth foundered. The movement also caused a ridge of Upper Greensand (Foxmould and Cowstones) to rise in the sea near the beach; it was about three quarters of a mile long, and reached 40 ft above sea level at high water. The beds were much broken, and the mid-part of the ridge was connected to the mainland by shingle. The reef very soon disappeared, but the main chasm of the slip remains much as it was, except that most of the many pinnacles have naturally gone. . . . (p. 266)

On the other hand, Nowell's map of 1576 shows nothing whatever resembling Langney Point. This suggests several possibilities, but the most likely interpretation is either that there was very little shingle at that time, or that the ness had not begun to form. Budgen's map of 1724 shows Langney Point projecting about one and three-eighths' miles, and in 1736 (Desmaretz) this had increased to a mile and a half. The idea has often been put forward that the destruction of Brighton beach between about 1665 and 1705 and the growth of Langney Point may be interconnected. It is doubtful if any positive proof can be found for this view, but it is certainly possible. It is not inconsistent with the later history of Langney: of, only for the sake of argument, we continue to accept as reasonably accurate the cartographical evidence, we may note that in 1778 (Yeakell and Gardner) the ness had shortened to one and a quarter miles, and the Admiralty survey of 1844 shows it as only seven furlongs in length. (p. 313)

One of the most interesting historically documented records of coast erosion has occurred along the east Yorkshire coast between Flamborough Head and the mouth of the Humber River. Current rate of erosion averages about 2 yd per yr, but there are places with much higher rates, and since Roman times it is estimated that a strip 2.5 mi wide, containing at one time or another 29 villages, has been lost.

The area was described in detail by Sheppard (1912) under the title "Lost Towns of the Yorkshire Coast."

In this century, the rapidly expanding population, with improved transportation facilities, leisure time, money, and interest in outdoor recreation, has given rise to a widespread concern for beaches and a giant investment in beach facilities. It is understandable that multi-million-dollar luxury hotels built around beach recreation would view with alarm any deterioration in the quality of their beaches and that chambers of commerce of seaside villages would likewise be prompted to take action upon any undesirable changes in their coastal environment. A small New England resort community learned about natural equilibria some years ago when it looked to bay bottom sediments as a source of fill to create new land. Pumping of the soft sediments from the bay bottom destroyed the established profile of equilibrium and resulted in transport of fine beach sand bayward. What had been a recreational beach was in a few years converted into a coarse sand and pebble shingle. The price of the fill was high indeed. Another case in point is illustrated by the effect of a groin on the movement of sand along the shore. Should a property owner introduce a barrier to the littoral drift along the shore by constructing a groin perpendicular to the shore, he will trap moving sand against the barrier and increase his beach. However, thereby he will unload the long shore current which will pick up sand down current from the groin and erode the neighboring segment of beach. The only defense by the neighbor is to construct a groin of his own. End result is a series of costly structures brought about by ignorance of beach processes. Any structures designed to modify littoral drift must be considered in terms of their effects on a natural beach unit.

According to Slosson (1966a, p. 309) land value of southern California beaches may exceed $50,000 per acre. He said:

Southern California beaches are undergoing constant change; in most cases these beaches are isolated or only infrequently used by man. Thus man, for the most part is unaware of this phenomenon. In areas of year-round use and/or in areas of dense population along the beaches, these changes are very apparent and sometimes very costly. Monthly and annual changes of tide and wave patterns bring about changes in the volume of sand and in beach positions and shapes. Some of the Ventura, Los Angeles, and Orange County beaches are excellent examples of these changes, as seen best by comparison of old and new aerial photographs.

The most significant of changes [occur] during the winter months when the waves and swells become larger and the beaches are cut back or retreat shoreward. During the summer months, the beaches may grow seaward if sufficient sand is available; but in many cases, due to drought and stream reclamation projects, there is insufficient sand for this rebuilding and thus the total volume of beach sand slowly decreases. There are also smaller and more temporary monthly changes that are associated with monthly tidal changes. In general, the beaches are cut back or retreat during the spring (or higher) tides and build outward during the neap (or lower) tides.

Changes related to beach shape and volume of beach sand are of great importance for areas of high recreation and real estate value. Land values for some of the southern California beaches may exceed $50,000 per acre. Thus it is apparent that the knowledge and protection of these beaches has become very important in certain portions of southern California.

The permanent loss of beach sand is generally associated with one of the following processes: (1) it may be transported into deeper water and thus be out of reach of shoreward wave and current action, (2) it may be transported by inshore winds to inland dune areas, or (3) it may be pulverized into particles too small to remain on the beach. The beach sand along this portion of the Ventura coast is generally transported along the shore in a southeasterly direction by the longshore currents. When this sand reaches the intersection of the beach and Hueneme Submarine Canyon, it spills into the canyon and moves seaward into deeper water, there to become a part of a submarine fan and permanently out of reach of wave action.

Slosson (1966b, p. 323) reported on wave erosion damage to the Ventura coastline. His remarks are summarized as follows: Ventura Beach has been losing sand at an average rate of 90,000 cu ft per yr; in 1961 approximately 200,000 cu yd were lost. The loss is ascribed to reduction in sand supply and increased erosion by storm waves. The amount of sand brought to the coast by the Ventura and Santa Clara rivers has been reduced by construction of a dam and diminished flow due to drought. It has been calculated that longshore currents in the area carry 250,000 to 350,000 cu yd of sand per year. If rivers do not supply enough sand to load these currents, they will pick up sand from the beaches. In 1961, the year of very high sand loss, the beach was hit by a major storm. In some areas 8 to 12 ft of sand was removed by high waves. Over a period of 15 years, about 22 acres have been lost from San Buenaventura State Park, a very serious loss considering that the property was valued at $20,000 per acre in 1961 and that the value has subsequently more than doubled. Attempts to halt the erosion and restore the beach have involved construction of groins to disperse the action of waves and currents and transport of large quantities of sand to the beach by truck. Leggett (1962, p. 719) pointed out that the streams and rivers discharging into the Pacific Ocean between Point Conception and the Ventura River supply about 2 million cubic yards of sediment per year and that much of it moves steadily along the coast. He warned (p. 720): "If the supply . . . is interfered with, as can so easily be done by a misplaced engineering structure built on the beach, trouble may soon develop at beaches that have been thus maintained." The interference, however, has come not on the beach but closer to the source of supply—in the river. A dam that destroys $50,000-per-acre real estate can become a very expensive way to control floods and store water.

Air-transported sediment. Live sand dunes moving over highways are persistent nuisances that require men and equipment on duty during the blowing season unless the dunes can be stabilized. Where sand blows due to natural conditions, the inhabitants of the area must deal with it as best they can. Where the potential for blowing sand or dust exists but the potential source area has been naturally stabilized by vegetation, it would be well for planners to take every care to insure that the natural cover is not ruptured due to uninformed acts of man. To restrain such potential source areas, the planners must understand the geologic conditions which permit wind transport of fine sediments. Although the competence of moving air to pick up and carry particles of earth material is much less than that of water, the enormous volume of the transporting medium results in large-scale movement. This is proved by the thickness and extent of old wind-deposited sediments, known as *loess*, and by historical measurements. During the drought-originated "dust bowl" of the 1930s millions of tons of fine earth material was moved in a single storm. For every ton of fine dust that is air-borne about two or three tons of coarser material are moved on the surface and piled up as dunes or drifts. The great storm of May 12, 1934, moved some 300 million tons of soil from the Great Plains states (chiefly Kansas, Oklahoma, Texas, and Colorado) and transported it eastward; deposition in the areas covered by the dense, black dust cloud amounted to 100 tons per square mile. The effects of this single storm deserve classification as a major movement of earth materials (Gilluly, Waters, and Woodford, 1959, pp. 62–63).

Ice-transported sediment. Because areas that nourish modern glaciers are climatically inhospitable, few works of man are affected by the sediment load carried by moving ice. Glaciers that calve into the sea drop their load of sand, gravel, cobbles, and boulders as the ice melts. Glaciers that terminate on land build up terminal moraines. These are generally elongated mounds or ridges of glacial debris which mark the farthest progress of the ice. Moraines left by the great ice sheets in the past are still prominent topographic features in the northern United States. Long Island and Cape Cod are terminal moraines.

Conclusion. Planners and engineers need sufficient knowledge of earth processes operating in their area of responsibility to foresee short-term and long-term consequences of these processes and to plan accordingly. They should know something about the potential geologic hazards produced by these processes and methods and costs of controlling them or living with them. Certainly they should be aware of areas of potentially unstable terrain conducive to landslides and mudflows, solution and collapse, and swelling and heaving. They should also be aware of the geologic hazards created by man in his use of the environment—hazards such as subsidence and collapse due to mining or pumping and mass movement induced by unloading the toes of unstable slopes or increasing the normal moisture content of unstable earth masses.

REFERENCES

ALBEE, A. L., AND SMITH, J. L. (1966) "Earthquake characteristics and fault activity in southern California," in *Engineering geology in southern California*: Association of Engineering Geologists special publication, Los Angeles, pp. 9–33.

COULTER, H. W., AND MIGLIACCIO, R. R. (1966) *Effects of the earthquake of March 27, 1964, at Valdez, Alaska*: U. S. Geological Survey project paper 542-C, 36 pp.

CURRY, K. K. (1966) "Observation of alpine mudflows in the Tenmile Range, central Colorado": *Geological Society of America Bulletin*, Vol. 77, pp. 771–776.

DALY, R. A. (1934) *The changing world of the Ice Age*: Yale University Press, New Haven, 271 pp.

ECKEL, E. B. (1958) *Landslides and engineering practice*: Highway Research Board special report no. 29, National Academy of Science-National Research Council publication 544, 232 pp.

EVANS, D. M. (1966) "Man-made earthquakes in Denver": *GeoTimes*, Vol. 10, no. 9, pp. 11–18.

GILLULY, JAMES; WATERS, A. C.; AND WOODFORD, A. O. (1959) *Principles of geology*, 2nd ed.: W. H. Freeman and Co., San Francisco, 534 pp.

HARRIS, F. R., AND HARLOW, E. H. (1948) "Subsidence of the Terminal Island-Long Beach area, California": *Transactions, American Society of Civil Engineers*, Vol. 133, paper 2338, pp. 375–396.

Highway Research Board (1962) *Moisture, density, swelling, and swell pressure relationships*: National Academy of Sciences-National Research Council publication 958, 91 pp.

Highway Research Board Landslide Committee (1958) *Landslides and engineering practice*: Special Report No. 29, National Academy of Sciences-National Research Council publication 544, 232 pp.

HUNTER, W. H. (1913) *Rivers and estuaries*: Longmans, Green & Co., London, 69 pp.

JAHNS, R. H. (1958) "Residential ills in the Heartbreak Hills of Southern California": *Engineering and Science*, Vol. XXII, pp. 13–20; California Institute of Technology Division of Geological Sciences contribution no. 911, 8 pp.

KIERSCH, G. A. (1965) "Vaiont Reservoir disaster": *GeoTimes*, Vol. 9, no. 9, pp. 9–12.

LEEDS, D. J. (1966) "Engineering seismology in southern California," in *Engineering geology in southern California*: Association of Engineering Geologists special publication, Los Angeles, pp. 35–53.

LEGGETT, R. F. (1962) *Geology and engineering*, 2nd ed.: McGraw-Hill, Inc., New York, 884 pp.

LEIGHTON, F. BEACH (1966) "Landslides and hillside development," in *Engineering geology in southern California*: Association of Engineering Geologists special publication, Los Angeles, pp. 149–193.

LOFGREN, B. E. (1960) "Near-surface land subsidence in western San Joaquin Valley, California": *Journal of Geophysical Research*, Vol. 65, no. 3, pp. 1053–1062.

MAYUGA, M. N., AND ALLEN, D. R. (1966) "Long Beach Subsidence" in *Engineering geology in southern California*: Association of Engineering Geologists special publication, Los Angeles, pp. 280–285.

MERRIMAN, RICHARD (1964) "Portuguese Bend landslide, Palos Verdes Hills, California": *Journal of Geology*, Vol. 68, no. 2, pp. 140–153.

MILLER, R. D., AND DOBROVOLNY, EARNEST (1959) *Surficial geology of Anchorage and vicinity, Alaska:* U. S. Geological Survey bulletin 1093, 128 pp.

MILLER, R. E. (1966) "Land subsidence in southern California," in *Engineering geology in southern California:* Association of Engineering Geologists special publication, Los Angeles, pp. 273–285.

Mining Engineering (1966) "Ten-year earthquake study by Office of Science Technology": "News," *Mining Engineering*, Vol. 18, no. 4, p. 10.

News Report, National Academy of Sciences-National Research Council (1969) "Alaska Earthquake first to show global hydrology effects": *News Report, National Academy of Sciences-National Research Council,* Vol. XIX, no. 1, pp. 1–2, 6–7.

PARKIN, E. J. (1948) "Vertical movement in the Los Angeles region, 1906–1946": *Transactions, American Geophysical Union*, Vol. 29, no. 1, pp. 17–26.

PLAFKER, GEORGE (1965) "Tectonic deformation associated with the 1964 Alaska Earthquake": *Science*, Vol. 148, no. 3678, pp. 1675–1687.

PRESS, FRANK, AND BRACE, W. F. (1966) "Earthquake prediction": *Science*, Vol. 152, no. 3729, pp. 1575–1584.

RICHTER, CHARLES F. (1935) "An instrumental earthquake magnitude scale": *Bulletin, Seismological Society of America*, Vol. 25, pp. 1–32.

SHEPPARD, THOMAS (1912) *The lost towns of the Yorkshire coast:* A. Brown and Sons, London, 328 pp.

SLOSSON, J. E. (1966a) "Engineering geology in the marine environment," in *Engineering geology in southern California:* Association of Engineering Geologists special publication, Los Angeles, pp. 305–318.

SLOSSON, J. E. (1966b) "Wave damage, Ventura coastline," in *Engineering geology in southern California:* Association of Engineering Geologists special publication, Los Angeles, p. 323.

STEERS, J. A. (1948) *The coastline of England and Wales:* Cambridge University Press, London, 644 pp.

STONE, ROBERT (1961) "Geologic and engineering significance of changes in elevation revealed by precise leveling, Los Angeles area": Geological Society of America special paper 59, pp. 57–58.

TOCHER, DON (1964) "Earthquakes and rating scales": *GeoTimes*, Vol. 8, no. 8, pp. 15–18.

TOWNLEY, S. D., AND ALLEN, M. W. (1939) "Descriptive catalog of earthquakes of the Pacific coast of the United States, 1769 to 1928": *Bulletin, Seismological Society of America*, Vol. 29, no. 1, 297 pp.

TREFETHEN, J. M. (1949) *Geology for engineers:* D. Van Nostrand Co., Inc., Princeton, N. J., 620 pp.

UNKLESBY, A. G., AND COOPER, H. H., JR. (1946) "Artificial recharge of artesian limestone at Orlando, Florida": *Economic Geology*, Vol. 41, no. 4, pp. 295–307.

VANDALE, A. E. (1967) "Subsidence—a real or imaginary problem?": *Mining Engineering*, Vol. 19, no. 9, pp. 86–88.

VAN SICLEN, DEWITT C. (1967) "The Houston fault problem," in *Proceedings of the third annual meeting, Texas section, American Institute of Professional Geologists*, pp. 9–29.

WEAVER, PAUL, AND SHEETS, M. M. (1962) "Active faults, subsidence and foundation problems in the Houston, Texas, area," in *Geology of the Gulf Coast and central Texas, Geological Society of America annual meeting, 1962*, edited by E. H. Rainwater and R. P. Zingula, pp. 254–265.

WEIR, W. W. (1950) "Subsidence of peat lands of the Sacramento-San Joaquin Delta, California": *University of California Agricultural Experiment Station, Hilgardia*, Vol. 20, no. 3, pp. 37–56.

ENGINEERING PROPERTIES OF ROCKS AND SOILS

3

General statement. The term "civil engineer" was originally coined for a practicing engineer who was not a member of the military; it serves as a reminder that engineering, at least under that name, was born as a military pursuit. Today, *civil engineer* is generally applied to the man concerned with the design and construction of public works —roads, bridges, dams, tunnels, etc. Thus the civil engineer is intimately concerned with earth materials. *Soils engineering* or *soil mechanics* is the branch of civil engineering concerned with engineering aspects of earth materials, their behavior and properties. Although the soils engineer defines soil very broadly to include all unconsolidated earth materials (p. 5), in practice he works with all earth materials, including rocks (Figure 15). The soils engineer designing a foundation for a structure which passes through soil into rock must, of course, be knowledgable about the engineering properties of the rock as well as the soil. However, more is involved than laboratory measurement of

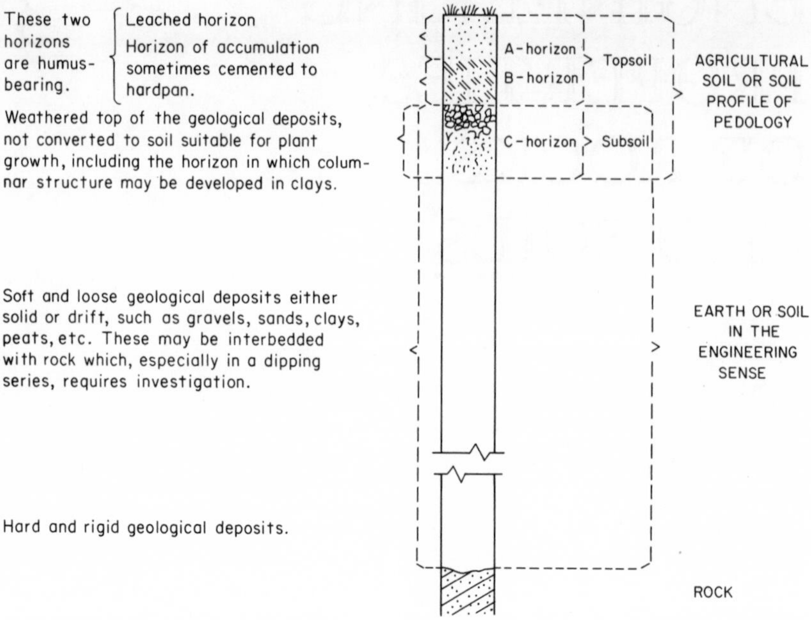

These two ⌈ Leached horizon
horizons │ Horizon of accumulation
are humus- │ sometimes cemented to
bearing. ⌊ hardpan.

Weathered top of the geological deposits,
not converted to soil suitable for plant
growth, including the horizon in which colum-
nar structure may be developed in clays.

Soft and loose geological deposits either
solid or drift, such as gravels, sands, clays,
peats, etc. These may be interbedded
with rock which, especially in a dipping
series, requires investigation.

Hard and rigid geological deposits.

A-horizon ⎫
                     ⎬ Topsoil   AGRICULTURAL
B-horizon ⎭   SOIL OR SOIL
                                                PROFILE OF
C-horizon ⎬ Subsoil   PEDOLOGY

EARTH OR SOIL
IN THE
ENGINEERING
SENSE

ROCK

FIGURE 15. **Relationship between various uses of the term** *soil*. (After *British Standards Code of Practice 2001: 1957 Site Investigations*. Reproduced with permission of British Standards Institution, 2 Park Street, London W. 1.)

certain parameters of soil or rock; the distribution of the properties in terms of geologic units that make up the site or area is equally significant. Moore (1966, p. 328) observed:

With the development of soil mechanics within the past thirty years, impressive advances have been made in the measurement of physical properties and the application of these properties and engineering analysis of foundation performance. Unfortunately, corresponding advances have not been made in the determination of gross structure of foundation materials. Records show that the majority of foundation failures and cases of foundation distress are not due to inaccurate measurement or application of soil properties, but due to the fact that the physical distribution of soil-rock units at the site was not completely known by the engineer, or not properly understood by the geologist. It is in this area, where geologic principles and processes can be applied, that there is the greatest need for advancement.

The purpose of field mapping and measurements and of laboratory testing and analysis is, of course, to produce information about the site which will provide the engineer with facts about the configuration of the terrain, the structure and composition of the earth materials, and the nature of geologic processes in operation. This information guides the design at the minimum cost commensurate with stability and security of a structure that will resist the stresses applied to it. In grading the site and designing the foundation the principal concerns of the engineer are (1) stability of bedrock and fills and (2) costs. All of the data produced by the geologist, the soils engineer, and the laboratory are to make it possible for the project engineer to do his job better.

The first step in understanding the varied and heterogenous aggregate of material that is called soil is to classify, and the engineer classifies on the basis of engineering properties.

Classification of soils. The purpose of a classification is to express relationships between individuals of a group or series in a clear and logical manner. The tests of a classification are consistency, inclusiveness, and usefulness. A classification may include all the members of a group or series, and it may treat them consistently throughout, but if it is not useful it is not a good classification. To be useful, a classification must further the understanding of relationships between members of the series or group. Classifications must be tested by their users, otherwise they may become intellectual crutches or, worse, straight-jackets which prevent thinking about the entities included in the various pigeonholes or boxes. People that derive classifications are generally aware of their shortcomings and weaknesses; people that accept ready-made classifications without critical examination commonly try to extend them further than the originators intended and thereby misuse the classifications. Where items being classified fall into natural groups on the basis of well-defined properties, the job of classification is infinitely more simple than in cases where the classification must deal with a continuum in which there are gradations rather than clear-cut natural boundaries. Soil is, of course, a continuum of materials of varied composition and size; it thus falls into the latter category and is very difficult to classify in a meaningful way because divisions must be drawn arbitrarily. There are, however, some natural limits within the continuum in terms of physical behavior of the aggregate, and these have been emphasized in some engineering classifications (p. 67).

Soil scientists classify soils on the basis of composition and morphology and have proposed an enormously cumbersome classification made more unattractive by an exotic terminology (Soil Survey Staff, U. S. Soil Conservation Service, 1960).

There are a number of engineering soil classifications in common use. They attempt to use the textural character of the soil—the relative amounts of clay, silt, sand, and gravel—as the primary basis for classification because engineering properties of unconsolidated earth materials in large part depend on the size of the constituent particles. However, classification by size is not sufficient to evaluate a soil for engineering purposes because the shape of the grains, mineral composition, the amount of organic material, the amount and composition of contained fluids, and other physical and chemical properties also influence the engineering behavior of the aggregate. For example, size analysis may show a soil to be composed of 25 percent clay, but if the clay is montmorillonite the soil will have a higher swelling potential than if the clay is kaolin (p. 49). Finely divided (silt or clay size) organic material such as peaty mud behaves differently from silt or clay composed of quartz and aluminum silicates. Some physical parameters are measured indirectly; for example, the strength and porosity of the aggregate is commonly measured instead of the shape of the constituent grains. Grain shape influences both strength and porosity.

Determination of moisture content by drying in an oven and classification by size ranges is the first step in evaluation of soils by engineers. Moisture is an important component of soil, and commonly a distinction is made between gravitational water (free to move out of the aggregate under force of gravity), capillary water (held in interstices by capillary forces and free to move out only when capillary forces are overcome), and hydroscopic water (retained as a moisture film on grains after capillary and gravitational water is removed—also known as air-dried moisture content).

The coarse size ranges are separated by a series of standard sieves; the size ranges of fine-grained material are commonly determined through use of a hydrometer, which measures changes in density of a fluid containing the suspended fine sediment as the particles settle out. Settling velocities are commonly calculated by use of a formula derived from Stokes Law (Krumbein and Pettijohn, 1938, pp. 95–110).

It seems as though every agency and association that deals with the earth in any way has its own classification of soil. Some of these include:

1. American Association of State Highway Officials Soil Classification (Bureau of Public Roads Soil Classification)
2. American Society for Testing Materials Soil Classification
3. Federal Aviation Agency Soil Classification
4. Department of Agriculture Soil Classification
5. Unified Soil Classification (Casagrande Classification—Bureau of Reclamation, Corps of Engineers)

Except for the Department of Agriculture classification, these classifications divide soils on the basis of texture (size ranges) and Atterberg limits (p. 70) into groups that reflect their performance as subgrades for roads, airfields, and other structures. A comparison of the soil groups of three commonly used classifications in terms of the bearing values is shown in Figure 16. The differences in terminology for the size ranges of soil particles are very slight and not really significant; perhaps they are beneficial in making clear to the student that the divisions in the classifications are arbitrary. The particle size limits of classifications are compared in Figure 17. Geologists also have textural classifications of sediments; most commonly used are the Udden and Wentworth classifications. The Wentworth classification is included in Figure 17 for comparison.

The usefulness of an engineering classification of soils can be rated on whether or not it provides for uniform and consistent treatment of the member groups, and whether or not soils can be easily classified using standard size-separation equipment. It is also desirable if the size limits of the grade scale are chosen on the basis of a mathematical system that lends itself to statistical analysis. A geometric scale (one that has a fixed ratio between successive elements in the series) is to be preferred over a scale without a fixed geometric interval. Of course, the main purpose of classification is not mathematical convenience but, rather, to distinguish groups of sediments that have related properties. For example, Moore (1966, p. 330) pointed out that behavior of material coarser than 0.02 mm can be analyzed in terms of mechanical forces, whereas behavior of finer material is governed by molecular forces. Here, then, is a natural limit that lends meaning to a size classification. Atterberg attempted to combine mathematical convenience with natural physical properties in his classification of 1905. He ex-

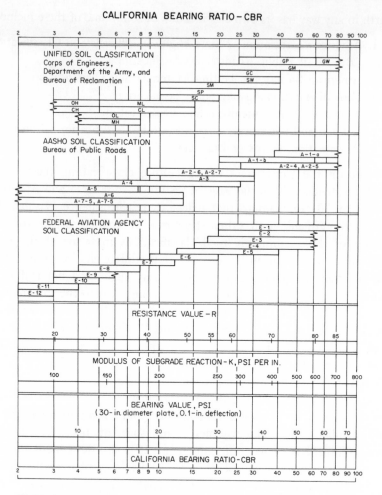

FIGURE 16. Comparison of engineering soil groups in terms of bearing values. (After Portland Cement Association, 1962, Fig. 9.)

pressed limits of particle classes as a unit diameter of 2 mm with a ratio of 10, for example, 0.002, 0.020, 0.200, 2.000, 20.0, and 200.00 mm. He noted that Brownian movement occurs at diameters of less than .002 mm, that 0.02 mm is the limit of discernment of individual grains by the naked eye, and that the coarser limits 0.20 and 2.0 mm reflect changes in the ability of a sand to hold water. The Udden scale of 1898 (the first geometric scale) and the Wentworth scale of 1922 (a modification of Udden's scale) used 2 mm as the basic unit but established classes on a ratio of 2. This resulted in many more classes and, perhaps for this reason, the classification is used more by sedimentary petrologists and less by engineers. It is a particularly satisfactory scale because ASTM sieve diameters are based on the square root of 2 and, therefore, there is a sieve for every Wentworth boundary. Krumbein (1934) modified the Udden classification by converting the size limits to the logarithm base 2 of the diameter of the particle instead of the diameter of the particle; this modification is known as the phi scale.

There are limits to the amount of useful information that can be gained through a mechanical or size analysis of the aggregate alone. Knowledge of the amounts of the various particle sizes in the aggregate make it possible to predict in a general way the amount of compaction that is likely and the permeability of the material. However, for those aggregates containing large amounts of fine-grained material a knowl-

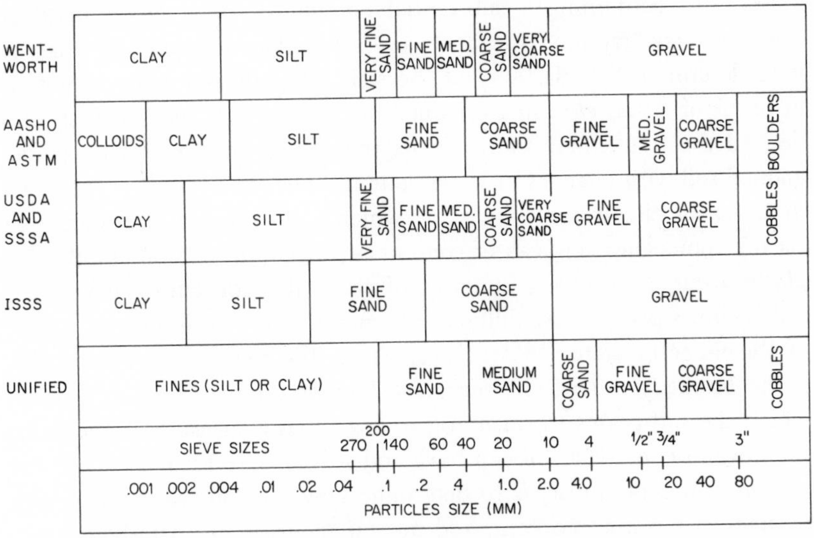

WENTWORTH	CLAY		SILT	VERY FINE SAND	FINE SAND	MED. SAND	COARSE SAND	VERY COARSE SAND	GRAVEL				
AASHO AND ASTM	COLLOIDS	CLAY	SILT		FINE SAND		COARSE SAND	FINE GRAVEL	MED. GRAVEL	COARSE GRAVEL			BOULDERS
USDA AND SSSA	CLAY		SILT	VERY FINE SAND	FINE SAND	MED. SAND	COARSE SAND	VERY COARSE SAND	FINE GRAVEL		COARSE GRAVEL		COBBLES
ISSS	CLAY		SILT		FINE SAND		COARSE SAND		GRAVEL				
UNIFIED	FINES (SILT OR CLAY)				FINE SAND		MEDIUM SAND	COARSE SAND	FINE GRAVEL		COARSE GRAVEL		COBBLES
SIEVE SIZES				200 270 140	60 40	20		10 4	1/2" 3/4"		3"		
PARTICLES SIZE (MM)	.001 .002 .004	.01	.02 .04	.1	.2	4	1.0	2.0 4.0	10	20	40	80	

AASHO   American Association of State Highway Officials
ASTM   American Society for Testing Materials
USDA   U. S. Department of Agriculture
SSSA   Soil Science Society of America
ISSS   International Society of Soil Science

FIGURE 17. **Comparison of common soil classifications by particle size.** (After Legget, 1967, Fig. 2.)

edge of the mineralogy and what happens when the soil gets wet is necessary for engineering evaluation. In certain situations detailed studies of clay mineralogy by X ray are justified, but for most problems it is possible to get the required information by measuring several "limits" called Atterberg limits.

Plasticity, Atterberg limits, shrink-swell potential, and other parameters. Following natural determination of moisture and classification of the soil by particle sizes, the engineer makes a series of additional tests. Procedures followed depend on whether the soils are coarse grained (sand and coarser) or fine grained (silt and clay); some tests are made on soil samples taken to the laboratory, others are made in the field. Methods of testing are described in detail in numerous handbooks and manuals and are not considered in detail herein. (See the American Society for Testing and Materials (1964) *Procedures for testing soils,* 42nd ed: American Society for Testing and Materials, Philadelphia, 540 pp.)

For soils containing a substantial amount of fine-grained material (silt and clay fraction) the next step after moisture and size analysis is to determine the plasticity of the soil. Plasticity is usually expressed in terms of *Atterberg limits*—named after a Swedish soil scientist who derived the test. These limits define the change in strength of a fine-grained soil with changes in water content. The *liquid limit* is expressed in terms of the water content at which soil cohesion (resistance to shear) approaches zero; water content is a maximum at this limit. The *plastic limit* is expressed in terms of the water content at which the soil becomes plastic. The difference between these two limits, a measure of the range of water content over which the soil behaves plastically, is the *plasticity index.* The *shrinkage limit* is the water content below which the soil ceases to shrink on drying—it is a measure of the minimum water content a soil can have and still be saturated. The purpose of these tests, of course, is to determine how the soil will behave with changes in moisture content, and measurement of the Atterberg limits is really measurement of the amounts of water required to induce changes in the physical character of the aggregate. In finely pulverized dry soil the spaces between the solid grains contain air. As water is added (distilled water for testing purposes) the air is displaced. If the aggregate contains a substantial amount of clay it becomes plastic. The coherence of the soil decreases as more water is added. After all the pore space is filled with water, any additional water will convert the aggregate into a liquid and it will begin to flow. The Atterberg limits are the transition points where the solid becomes plastic (plastic limit) and where the plastic becomes liquid (liquid limit). The limits are expressed as the weight of contained water necessary to effect the transition divided by the dry weight of the soil. There appears to be a significant empirical relationship between these limits and soil mineralogy. Casagrande (1948) expressed a relationship as a simple plot of liquid limit against plasticity index (Figure 18); Seed and others (1964) suggested that the ratio of the plasticity index to the amount of clay is a good index of soil mineralogy. This index has been called the *activity index* and is an attempt to express quantitatively the contributions of the clay minerals in an aggregate to such properties as strength of cohesion and plasticity. Another index, the *liquidity index,* is an attempt to express consistency or stiffness of a soil quantitatively. It is calculated by dividing the difference between the natural water

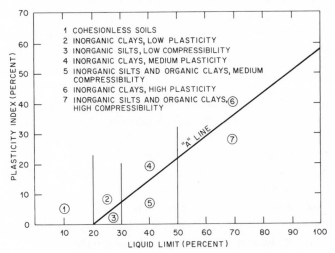

"A" Line An empirical boundary: above the line are typical inorganic clays with low to medium compressibility; below are plastic, compressible soils containing organic clays, inorganic silts, and silty clays.

FIGURE 18. Relationshp between liquid limit, plasticity index, and soil composition. (After Legget, 1967, Fig. 5; modified from Casagrande, 1948, Fig. 4.)

content and the water content at the plastic limit by the plasticity index. Thus a liquidity index of 1 means that the material is at the liquid limit (very soft with no strength) and a liquidity index of 0 means that the material is at the plastic limit (stiff).

Measurement of Atterberg limits and calculation of various ratios derived from them will come into increasing use in the future as scientific tools for rapidly distinguishing differences in mineralogy. From a practical or engineering point of view the Atterberg limits make it possible to predict those changes in physical properties, principally strength, that will occur in earth materials when they get wet. It would seem that the natural water content of solid earth materials must in all cases be less than the liquid limit, otherwise the material would by definition be a flowing mud. However, there are some fine-grained soils that do naturally contain more water than the liquid limit of the pulverized sample. These are mostly found in glacial deposits. This apparently anomalous phenomenon is due to the soil structure, in which the individual particles are arranged in a sort of "honeycomb" that permits the soil to hold large quantities of moisture while remaining in the solid state. One can readily imagine the result if the special structure of these *sensitive clays,* or *quick clays* as they are commonly called, is destroyed by a sudden shock through an earthquake or through detonation of explosives, or if they are set in motion by erosion of the toe of a slope (p. 34). The result is "instant mud" or, if there is a slope, an instant mudflow. Needless to say, indentification of such soils is essential because they do not make safe foundations for engineering structures in their natural state. Testing is simple—working of the soil sample between the fingers will quickly disclose the presence of an excess of pore water. This quick clay should not be confused with the very different quicksand. *Quicksand* is sand held in a very loose or open packing, commonly by a current of water that supports or lifts the grains. Because of this open structure an object will sink into the sand very rapidly, for there is little resistance to penetration.

Fine-grained soils are also tested to determine potential volume changes (*shrink-swell potential*). Tests include measurement of volumetric shrinkage, linear shrinkage, and absorption (swell). *Volumetric shrinkage* (expressed as a percentage of the soil mass when dried) is the decrease in volume as water content is reduced from any given amount to the shrinkage limit (defined above). *Linear shrinkage* is the decrease in one dimension of a soil mass, expressed as a percentage of the original dimension, as water content is reduced to the shrinkage limit. Swell due to absorption (and adsorption), linear and volumetric, can be determined by several techniques where water is added to the sample and volume increase is measured. *Potential vertical rise* is calculated from these data, other soil constants already described, and swell-pressure curves. It is defined as the potential of a soil under specific density moisture and load conditions, when exposed to surface or capillary water, to swell and thereby elevate its upper surface along with structures resting on it.

Soil strength or load-bearing capacity of both coarse and fine-grained soils is measured in different ways. In the field a measure of soil strength can be obtained by penetration tests in which a "dynamic penetration cone" is driven into the soil under controlled conditions. Strength is also expressed in terms of the California Bearing Ratio (*bearing value*)— the ratio *between* the force per unit area required to peneatrate a soil mass with a 3-sq-in. circular piston at a rate of 0.05 in. per min *and* that force required for penetration of a standard soil mass. The most highly regarded laboratory test is the triaxial compression or shear test, where a cylindrical sample of soil in an impervious membrane under confining pressure is axially loaded until it fails. In the unconfined compression test, the unconfined compressive strength is the load per unit area under which failure occurred. From data derived in such tests the capacity of a soil to support a load can be calculated.

Other commonly measured soil parameters include *soil density* (specific gravity) and *soil permeability* (expressed as a coefficient—the rate of discharge of water under laminar flow through a unit cross-sectional area of a porous medium under a unit hydraulic gradient at standard temperature, expressed in centimeters, inches, or feet per second, minute, hour, or day, depending on the rate of flow). This parameter is necessary in assessing the capacity of a soil to drain; evaluation of soils for capacity to drain septic tank effluent is a practical example. Measurement of the acidity or alkalinity (pH) of a soil is useful in evaluating its chemical effects on such buried structures as pipelines. Measurement of the free calcium carbonate in soils generally expresses the degree of alkalinity, but not all alkaline soils are calcareous. Soil resistivity (electrical) has been found to correlate in a very practical way with soil corrosivity.

Corrosion in a general sense is a slow wearing-away or decomposition that proceeds from the surface inward. With regard to metallic objects, corrosion is a chemical or electrochemical process in which the metal atoms making up the surface of the object, through contact with acids or through the action of electric currents, are ionized and thereby rendered mobile or soluble. Eventually the metallic object is "eaten away" or corroded. There are a number of engineering enterprises in which man buries metallic substances in the ground. Pipes and cables come

TABLE 4. **Engineering Data of Soils Commonly Measured**

Classification (unified) (D)
   sieve analysis (s)
   hydrometer analysis (f)
   moisture content (f, s)
Plasticity (Atterberg limits) (D)
   liquid limit (f)
   plastic limit (f)
   plasticity index (f)
Strength (U, D)
   triaxial compression test and/or (U, D, f, s)
   unconfined compression and/or (U, f)
   crushing strength and/or (U, r)
   consolidation-time settlement under load (U, f)
   standard penetration test (U, F)
Volume change (shrink-swell) (U, D)
   volumetric shrinkage and/or (D, f)
   lineal shrinkage and/or (D, f)
   absorption-swell (U, f)
   potential vertical rise (U, f)
Density (dry) (D)
Moisture content (D), (profiles) (F)
Free $CaCO_3$ (D)
pH (D)
Electrical resistivity (F)
Permeability (F)

D: disturbed soils
U: undisturbed soils
F: field test
f: fine-grained soils, silt, clay
s: sand and coarser soils
r: rock

to mind immediately, but many other metallic objects or metal-containing structures are partly or wholly entombed, including fence posts, pilings, caissons, anchors, hydraulic elevator cylinders, drums containing radioactive or chemical wastes, etc. Experience over the years has shown that some of these objects last longer than others, and that identical objects placed in different kinds of geologic formations or soils have lives of significantly different duration. Corrosion rates or corrosivity is much greater in some materials than in others. A corollary is that the shortest pipeline may not be the cheapest if it is located in a highly corrosive environment. The reasons for corrosion are now well known.

Few rocks or soils are completely dry. There is always some moisture in the interstices of the mineral or rock grains that make up the aggregate and, near the surface, the amount of moisture fluctuates widely,

TABLE 5. **Allowable Bearing Capacities of Earth Materials**

Material	Allowable bearing capacity, tons/ft^2
Medium-soft clay	1.5
Medium-stiff clay	2.5
Sand, fine, loose	2
Sand, coarse, loose; compact fine sand; loose sand-gravel mixture	3
Gravel, loose; compact coarse sand	4
Sand-gravel mixture, compact	6
Hardpan and exceptionally compacted or partially cemented gravels or sands	10
Sedimentary rocks, such as hard shales, sandstones, limestones, and siltstones, in sound condition	15
Foliated rocks, such as schist or slate, in sound condition	40
Massive bedrock, such as granite, diorite, gneiss, and trap rock, in sound condition	100

SOURCE: National Building Code of National Board of Fire Underwriters.

depending on precipitation and downward percolation and upward movements of moisture due to capillary forces. The water contains varied amounts of dissolved mineral matter and thus constitutes a very weak electrolyte. Some waters are acid, some are alkaline. Chemical reactions in the earth, such as oxidation, generate weak electrical currents. Bacterial action, particularly the action of sulfate-reducing bacteria, causes chemical reactions in rocks and soils. Some earth materials are naturally highly corrosive due to their chemical composition and moisture content; others are made more corrosive due to construction procedures that result in mixing of different kinds of materials (through backfilling a trench, for example) and thereby promoting chemical or bacterial activity, or causing a trap for accumulation of fluids. Burying two different connected metals in conductive earth materials will promote an electrochemical reaction. The metal that is more chemically active will react with the conductive earth materials while the less active metal remains free of corrosion. By analogy with a battery, the corroding metal is the cathode. Cathodic protection involves the intentional placing of an active metal in contact with a less active one to protect the system. The protecting metal is periodically replaced. In some areas man accelerates corrosion by unintentionally inducing an electric current into the earth through operation of his various electrical systems.

Disregarding corrosion resulting from man's own operations (the burying of different metals in contact, the mixing of earth materials, and the induction of currents) it is clearly important for engineers to be able to evaluate the natural corrosivity of the various geologic formations and soils with which he is concerned. He must know the distribution of the rock and soil units—which he can learn from a geologic and/or soils map—and their corrosivity. Generally speaking, more conductive earth materials are more corrosive, and where this is the case simple resistivity measurements provide a practical measure of corrosivity—the lower the resistivity the higher the corrosion potential. There are, however, other factors, such as permeability and pH, that also affect corrosivity so that in any particular area the correlation between corrosivity and resistivity needs to be empirically verified. Moreover, between the unaltered substrate and the surface there are various zones within the soil profile where different kinds of chemical reactions occur. This means that resistivity may vary with depth. Seasonal variations in temperature and moisture content of earth materials may also affect rates of corrosion. In the San Antonio area the following corrosion potential classification was used (Tipps, 1964, p. 76):

Resistivity (ohms)	Corrosion potential
<500	highest
500–700	high
750–1000	moderate
1000–1250	low to moderate
1250–1700	low
>1750	very low

Conclusion. The planner concerned with land use probably will never be called upon to make tests or analyses of soils to evaluate their mechanical and hydraulic properties. However, he may on a number of occasions be able to do his job better if he understands the significance of engineering data and can communicate effectively with engineers. Planning will be efficient and successful if, through knowledge, planners can design systems that take advantage of geology. For example, where there is a significant difference in the corrosivity of the rock and soil formations that make up the foundations of a city, it might be advisable to plan pipelines so their greatest possible length lies in the least corrosive earth material. Routing pipelines to exploit the terrain in this fashion might require a slightly longer line and a higher initial cost but result in savings of hundreds of thousands of dollars in maintenance and replacement costs over the long term. Such opportunities will not arise unless the planner knows he needs these kinds of engineering data and recommends to his municipal government studies that will produce the data.

Many reports which present engineering data give a range or an average of measurements made on a particular soil unit. The report itself must be evaluated to determine whether or not the sampling density was adequate and whether or not an average is significant. The report that presents the results of testing in numerical form is in the long term more useful than the report which translates the numbers into qualitative or comparative terms such as "good," "fair," or "poor." Such evaluations on the part of the author of the report presuppose that the author was aware of the entire spectrum of engineering structures which might be placed in or on that soil unit. It is preferable from the point of view of the user of the data to have load-bearing capacity expressed in tons per square foot than to try to interpret what is meant by good, fair, or poor load-bearing capacity. On the other hand, numerical averages can be misleading, particularly if a geologic formation is made up of several facies or members with differing properties.

In general terms, a city or regional planner should know enough about the engineering properties of the rocks and soils that make up his area of responsibility to have knowledge of:

1. the distribution of those soils and rock units which will support large structures without costly and special engineering design
2. the distribution of those soils and rock units that present foundation problems because (a) they are excessively plastic, (b) they have high shrink-swell properties, (c) they are saturated with large volumes of water, or (d) they present the danger of subsidence (p. 39).
3. the distribution of highly corrosive soil and rock units
4. the distribution of impermeable soils
5. the distribution of highly acid or alkaline soils

Publications on environmental geology have attempted to sum up the engineering properties of map units in a particular area so that planners and engineers can take an overview of the limits on land use that are inherent in these properties. Smith (1968, pp. 13–14), for example, presented data on surface materials in McHenry County, Illinois, where the materials are of glacial origin, as follows:

Unit	Probable engineering characteristics
Surficial peat and muck	Compressible Very poor foundation material
Loessial soil	Medium plasticity, high dry strength Moderately slow to drain Would probably swell and shrink upon alternate wetting and drying Material sampled had stiff consistency Inferior foundation material
Accretion gley	High plasticity, very high dry strength Drains very slowly except along joints and fissures Subject to considerable swelling and shrinkage upon alternate wetting and drying

	Little bearing strength when wet Very poor foundation material
West Chicago drift	Mostly granular materials Little or no plasticity Mostly free draining Not subject to shrinkage and swelling Adequate bearing strength in most situations
Clay (Lake County)	Medium plasticity, high dry strength Almost impermeable from a practical standpoint except along joints and fissures Stiff to very stiff consistency Satisfactory as impervious fill for water impoundment embankments Adequate bearing strength if protected from saturation; might develop some plasticity if saturated
Marseilles till	Low to medium plasticity, medium to high dry strength Drains very slowly Stiff to very stiff consistency Satisfactory material for construction of embankments for impoundment of water Adequate bearing strength but might develop some plasticity if allowed to become saturated
Huntley till	Same as for Marseilles till
Gilberts till	Low plasticity, medium dry strength Slow draining Will probably lose some stability if allowed to become saturated Adequate bearing strength when kept dry
Marengo till	Low plasticity, medium dry strength Weathered material has medium plasticity Dries slowly; once saturated, would regain stability very slowly Stiff consistency in upland areas Adequate bearing strength in relatively dry situations, but might lose some stability if allowed to become saturated

Winnebago till   Low plasticity, medium dry strength
                          Very slow to drain
                          Stiff to very stiff consistency; may be hard in dry
                              situations
                          Adequate bearing strength in most situations;
                              might develop some plasticity if allowed to be-
                              come saturated

REFERENCES

CASAGRANDE, A. (1948)   "Classification and identification of soils": *Trans-actions, American Society of Civil Engineers*, Vol. 113, pp. 901–991.

KRUMBEIN, U. C. (1934)   "Size frequency distributions of sediments": *Journal of Sedimentary Petrology*, Vol. 4, pp. 65–77.

KRUMBEIN, U. C., AND PETTIJOHN, F. J. (1938)   *Manual of sedimentary petrography*: D. Appleton-Century Co., New York, 549 pp.

LEGGET, R. F. (1967)   "Soil: Its geology and use": *Geological Society of America Bulletin*, Vol. 78, pp. 1433–1460.

MOORE, R. F. (1966)   "Foundation engineering and the engineering geol-ogist," in *Engineering Geology in Southern California*: Association of Engineering Geologists special publication, Los Angeles, pp. 327–343.

Portland Cement Association (1962)   *PCA soil primer*, 52 pp.

SEED, H. B.; WOODWARD, R. J.; AND LUNDGREN, R. (1964)   "Clay min-eralogical aspects of the Atterberg limits": *Proceedings, American Society of Civil Engineers*, Vol. 90, no. SM4, pp. 107–131.

SMITH, W. CALHOUN (1968)   *Geology and engineering characteristics of some surface materials in McHenry County, Illinois*: Illinois Geological Survey environmental geology notes, no. 19, January 1968, 23 pp.

Soil Survey Staff (1960)   *Soil classification: A comprehensive system—7th approximation*: Soil Conservation Service, U. S. Department of Agricul-ture, 265 pp.

TIPPS, C. W. (1964)   "Corrosion causes and control," in *Soil Handbook for Soil Survey, Metropolitan area, San Antonio, Texas*: U. S. Soil Conser-vation Service, U. S. Department of Agriculture, pp. 72–76.

TIPPS, C. W. (1966)   "Underground corrosion": *Materials Protection*, Vol. 5, no. 9, pp. 9–11.

EARTH
RESOURCES

4

GENERAL STATEMENT ON RESOURCES AND LAND USE

A resource is an asset. It is something that can be used beneficially. From a human point of view, resources may be internal and of a spiritual or physical nature (courage, strength, or intelligence), or they may be external and consist of resources of the environment. If the resources of the environment are to be perceived and utilized in more than a minimal way, the user must possess internal resources such as intelligence, imagination, and a capacity for work.

Man uses the resources of the environment in three ways: (1) for materials, (2) for energy, and (3) to sustain life directly. For building materials, man has used and still uses wood, rock, earth (as common fill and processed into bricks, glass, cement), ice, metals, plastics. For tools and weapons he has used and still uses wood, bone, rock, metal, plastic. Although for highly specialized uses in today's complex industrial culture only special alloys or ceramic bodies have the necessary properties, in general the area of materials offers more possibility for use of alternate materials or substitutions than other categories of resource use. Considering the enormous demand for energy, there are fewer degrees of freedom in utilizing the energy sources of the environment. Wood, streams and rivers (to turn wheels or turbines), fossil fuels, (peat, lignite, coal, oil, and gas), nuclear fuels, geothermal energy (utilization of the earth's heat as natural steam or in heat pumps), tidal energy, and solar energy, are the possibilities. Wood or charcoal made from wood can no longer be considered a significant energy source in terms of modern demand. Known deposits of natural steam offer only local possibilities for development. Solar and tidal energy has not yet been harnessed in any magnitude. Hydropower, fossil fuels, and nuclear fuels remain the energy sources of today and the near-tomorrow.

The life-sustaining resources of the environment are foodstuffs (which can be equated to soil, water, and the agricultural chemicals—nitrogen, potassium, phosphorous), water, and air. There are no substitutes for food, water, and air, no degrees of freedom; these are essential resources.

Within the three categories of resources a distinction can be made between renewable resources and nonrenewable or wasting resources. This is a profoundly important distinction. Forests can be harvested and regrown, even though the span of time for hardwoods may be measured in terms of man's lifetime. Food resources are also renewable through the operation of natural biological processes which produce new schools of fish, new herds of livestock, and new stands of wheat. These processes of natural increase are exploited by man to produce yearly crops. They will continue to operate *so long as the environment remains favorable to their operation, and so long as consumption leaves a sufficient breeding stock to produce seeds, eggs, and young.* There is no guarantee that the biological processes on which man depends will continue to flourish. If air and water are poisoned by toxic wastes, or if runaway populations in the desperation of starvation eat the seed for next year's crop, the so-called renewable resources will not be.

Nonrenewable resources—commonly called earth resources or mineral resources—are at the present time being consumed in enormous quantities. Indeed, the quantity and variety of mineral resources used by a society is a mark of its degree of industrial development (Figure 19). President Kennedy in his 1962 Message to Congress observed that

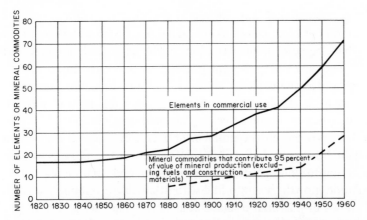

FIGURE 19. **Increase in number of mineral commodities in commercial use.** (After U. S. Geological Survey, Long Range Plan, 1964, Fig. 14.)

in the previous 30 years the United States used more mineral stuffs than all the people of the world had previously consumed. Romney (1965, p. 11) called this steeply rising curve of mineral consumption "the mineral demand explosion." He pointed out that between 1870 and 1957 consumption of minerals in the United States increased by a factor of 41 times where gross national product increased 19.5 times, agricultural products increased 5.21 times and forest products increased 1.57 times. For some mineral commodities the known reserves are sufficient to supply current demand for some hundreds of years, but for others, some metals and petroleum, known reserves are adequate for only a decade or two. New discoveries, lower grade (higher cost) sources, unconventional sources, and substitutions will extend known supplies but even for commodities known to exist in relatively abundant supply the rate of growth in demand provides ample reason for worry on the part of planning agencies (Flawn, 1966, pp. 9–22). As a reminder, demand (or anything else) growing at a rate of 3 percent per year will double in 23.5 years; at 5 percent per year demand will double in 14 years; at 7 percent per year demand will double in 10 years. This same kind of curve also applies to growth of populations.

The gravest question before the world today is, How long can the earth's resources, renewable and nonrenewable, meet the increasing demands of industrial societies and the increasing demands of fast-growing populations? The answer to the question requires many data that we do not have as well as consideration of various levels of support and what degree of human freedom might be possible at these various levels. The kind of governmental system necessary to sustain order among hordes of people at a bare subsistence level does not seem to offer much chance for preservation of human dignity and institutions now cherished by peoples free to plan their own destinies. Many books have been written on the problem of adequacy of earth resources and, as might be expected, the viewpoints range from bleak pessimism to rosy optimism. The pessimists see no likelihood of bringing the world population growth rate into line with attainable economic growth rates and known or potential resource abundance. They see a steadily declining living standard. They predict that the natural laws which have applied to other viable populations that have expanded more rapidly than their food supply, or which have rendered their environment toxic through accumulation of their own waste products, will eventually apply to the human population so that there will be a great die off and a new dark age. This is the Malthusian theory (Malthus, 1798, 1926; Burton and Kates, 1965, Part I). The optimists put their faith in technology (Landsberg et al., 1963, p. 8). They believe that larger populations can be supported at high standards of living through development of new sources of energy and more enlightened exploitation of land and seas. If technologic capabilities are destroyed, however, even the most optimistic resource expert can offer little in the way of encouragement. Harrison Brown and others (1958) have labeled this dismal alternative "point of no return." This is the point where world-wide destruction of technologic capabilities in terms of power, raw materials, manufacturing, and education occurs to such an extent that an irreversible cultural failure takes place. For example, the metal mining industry began at the dawn of history exploiting high-grade, near-surface concentrations of metals. These are now exhausted, but through the use of great earth-moving machines and complex beneficiation systems rock containing a fraction of a percent of the metals which once came from ores ten times richer are being mined and processed. To treat such low-grade ores economically they must be mined at rates of tens of thousands of tons per day. In the event of a dark age caused by nuclear war or failure to balance population with resources, it is difficult to see how a new metal-using culture could develop with only scrap and very low-grade ores to build upon.

Is there an alternative to the industrial culture that consumes such large amounts of the earth's surface and discharges such quantities of poison into earth and atmosphere? Perhaps in the long run the human race would be better off physically and psychologically in a pastoral or agricultural culture that could achieve or come close to living in harmony with nature. A. Russell Wallace (1910, p. 285) wrote in opposition to the trend toward urbanization that was already clearly evident in the early part of this century when London, one of the first great urbs, began reaching out for water supplies to satisfy its fast-growing thirst. He said:

. . . our great cities are the "wens," the disease products of humanity, and until they are abolished there can be no approach to a true or rational civilization.

There is much talk now of what *will* and *must* be the growth of London during the next twenty or fifty years; and of the *necessity* of bringing water from Wales to supply the increased population. But where is the necessity? Why provide for a population which need never have existed, and whose coming into existence will be an evil and of no possible use to any human beings but the landowners and speculators, who will make money by the certain injury of their fellow citizens.

It [Parliament] can justly say: "When you have not a gallon of polluted water in your town, and when its death-rate is brought down to the average standard of rural areas, we will consider the question of your further growth."

These statements show that even as great a natural philosopher as Wallace did not fully appreciate the powerful motive forces driving the world into an urbanized industrial age. An observer looking at Los Angeles half a century or more after Wallace's comments might echo his sentiments and cry, "Where is the need to bring water from northern California more than 400 miles to Los Angeles?" His reasons for wanting to retard the growth of that great metropolis would not be a high death rate due to a higher incidence of common diseases in the city or even a polluted water supply, but he could find ample evidence for poisoned air and perhaps even for a high incidence of psychological and sociological damage to those dwelling within the "wen." City dwellers now have a higher incidence of respiratory disease (lung cancer, emphysema, chronic bronchitis) than rural residents.

But it is hard to sell the concept of an idyllic rural society to the millions of farmers living at subsistence or subsubsistence levels in the underdeveloped regions of the world. Such people, now "enjoying" the pastoral life advocated by some philosophers, are fighting to share the benefits offered by an industrial society: higher living standards (including a more varied and nutritious diet) comforts produced by machines, and leisure time. In the modern world it is the industrial cultures that can support a larger population at a higher standard of living than the pastoral and agricultural cultures; indeed, it is the industrial cultures that have the successful agricultural systems wherein about 20 percent of the population or less engaged in agriculture (5 percent in Great Britain, 10 percent in the United States) (Joslyn and Olcott, 1959, pp. 319–320) can feed the rest. It is difficult to find in the world countries which are not industrial countries and yet which have and enjoy a relatively high standard of living—nonindustrial countries in which farmers are well fed. Iceland, New Zealand, and Finland are among the very few which have successful economies based on fishing, animal husbandry, agriculture, and the harvesting of forest products. Apparently, then, it is not impossible to build a satisfactory economy on this basis; but it is clear that the reason these countries have been successful, while so many others have not, is that these countries have population growth rates that are low to moderate and in rational relationship with their resources. How successful they would be without the markets for their products created by the industrial nations is open to question. By selling the products of their nonindustrial culture to industrial cultures they are able to acquire the machines, medicines, and other technology that make their lives easier.

The purpose of this argument is to demonstrate to the planner and conservationist that he cannot ignore the need of an industrial society to dig into the earth for materials and that however much he would like to preserve vast areas of wilderness, parks, and unscarred suburban and agricultural terrain, all of the pits, mines, and quarries cannot be relegated to someone else's area. Mineral resources are "where you find them." They must be planned around, not planned for.

Thus, inherent in the planning process is a need to make choices between kinds of land use that may be mutually exclusive, at least for the duration of the use. The rationale of decision is based on the benefit that society will derive from use of the land, but a number of factors enter into the decision:

1. *The nature of the land.* It may seem absurdly obvious to point out that land cannot be zoned for agricultural use if it will not

grow crops because of the nature of the soil or terrain. However, recently in Indiana a planning agency zoned land that did not contain any sand and gravel for sand and gravel quarries. Geology and topography are basic controlling factors.

2. *Benefit to society accruing from use of the land.* Real-estate appraisers commonly employ the test of *highest and best use* in land valuation. Highest and best use does not necessarily refer to that use which will produce the highest income per land unit, but rather that use which will be of maximum benefit to the community. Thus a park which produces no revenue may be judged a higher and better use than a high-rise apartment house that would provide housing for a large number of people and at the same time large tax revenue to the community (Table 6). Where multiple uses are possible, it is the measurement of highest and best use that is difficult. The problem was discussed in detail by White (1961). Whereas some uses can be evaluated economically in terms of dollars, it is difficult to place dollar value on all beneficial uses where benefit may be in large part a matter of aesthetics. This point has been argued at length in the drive to create wilderness areas. The congress had to address the question: What is the value of wilderness to American society when the land is actually used by only a fraction of one percent of the population?

TABLE 6. **The Planner's Choice**

Park (public ownership)	Apartment house complex (private ownership)
1. Will require capital investment by city for purchase and development.	1. No capital investment required by city.
2. Only park site easily accessible to 10,000 residents and downtown area.	2. Shortage of housing close to downtown area.
3. Outdoor recreation facilities are needed in this area to alleviate undesirable sociological conditions.	3. Tax revenues from apartment complex will be about $60,000 per year. Sufficient to construct and operate park in more distant area.

3. *United States property laws.* Planners are frequently in conflict
with property owners who want to use their property differently
from that recommended in the planning process. If planners are
to be given broad authority to implement their plans, drastic
changes in United States law will be necessary, even to nationalization of the land. The following discussion of strip mining illustrates the case in point.

As a legacy from English common law, the United States citizen
has been bequeathed the principle of landownership in fee simple,
which includes proprietary rights to the surface, the prism of earth
beneath projected to the center of the earth, and the air space over-
head. The proprietary prerogatives to use the land and earth beneath
it have endured subject to police powers of the State, powers of eminent domain, and conservation laws; a proprietor also is commonly
enjoined, where a court finds sufficient cause for injunctive relief,
against any use of his land which results in damage to his neighbor.

As a result of this legacy from English common law, the United
States citizen holding land in fee simple, unlike many of his counterparts elsewhere in the world, has found himself the owner of an estate
in minerals as well as an estate in the land surface. Some landowners
have sold all or part of the mineral estate, variously called mineral
rights or mineral interest. The act of sale, perfectly within the rights
of a proprietor in fee simple, severs the mineral estate from the surface
estate, and, as a result, the heirs or subsequent owners of the surface
of the land are proprietors of only the surface and obliged to permit
access to the owner of the minerals for the purpose of extracting them.
In modern agreements there is a growing tendency to require the owner
of the minerals to compensate the surface owner for damages sustained
in the extractive process.

As long as the owner of the minerals can economically extract them
through wells or shafts which occupy only a small area of the surface,
the surface owner can farm, ranch, or otherwise develop the surface
contemporaneously with the extractive operations and thus *simultaneous multiple use* of the land is possible. Measured in dollars, extraction
of minerals gives a much higher yield per acre and a more rapid rate
of accrual than most other land uses. Such multiple use is beneficial
to society, and the Government, in administration of the public domain,
has seen fit to encourage it through legislation.

This happy situation does not prevail, however, where the mineral estate is valuable earth materials at or near the surface and the economic mining method is open-pit or strip mining which consumes the surface. In fact, the courts and the congress do not recognize some of the so-called common varieties of earth materials which form the earth's surface as qualifying as a "mineral substance" under the mineral location laws governing the public domain (for example, sand and gravel, stone, and cement materials), nor are they included in general grants or reservations of "minerals." In dealing with private property owners who hold valuable deposits of these "common varieties," the mineral producer either buys the land outright in fee simple or buys the minerals under a special agreement which allows him to break up and remove that part of the surface necessary to his mining operation.

Although recognized as a mineral substance by congress and the courts and not grouped with the "common varieties," coal is increasingly being extracted in strip mining operations which consume the surface. In some areas in the Appalachian coal fields, rights to the coal were acquired from landowners through a conveyance which permits the purchaser of the mineral rights, in the absence of legislation to the contrary, to make whatever use of the land that is necessary to the mining operation, including cutting of timber, establishing road rights-of-way, occupying building sites, and constructing dams. The surface is left open for other use but subject to the mining operation; with rare exceptions there are no provisions for compensation for damages to the surface beyond the original consideration. The landowner who sold the mineral rights in this way thereafter enjoyed and made use of the cash consideration, but he left his heirs a sadly depleted legacy. In those areas where mining continued underground, the surface continued in more or less normal use, *until* changes in economics and technology changed mining methods. Earth moving equipment with previously undreamed of capacities—shovels and draglines, with bucket capacities measured in tens of cubic yards—moved into the coal fields, and coal seams which had been reached by underground workings were opened to the sky. Large tracts of land were covered by barren ridges of spoil, offensive to the eye and generating acid waters. This reduced or eliminated beneficial use of the surface. Technology and the form of the mineral conveyance had made impossible *simultaneous* multiple use of the land.

Those who lived on and used the surface turned their anger against the mining companies; their forbears who sold the mineral rights were for the most part gone. The result was social disturbance.

The extreme alternatives in this case seem to be (1) prevent strip mining by legislation, or (2) do nothing—let the doctrine of *caveat emptor* apply to those who would seek to acquire and use the surface estate where the mineral estate has been severed. Alternative (1) comes up against the economic reality of what the production of about 152 million tons of coal per year at a cost of about $3.50 per ton means to our society. Alternative (2) is perhaps reasonable from the present time forward but clearly inhumane when applied to those persons caught by the change in mining methods. Compensation for damages and aid in relocation seems reasonable. It is vitally important, however, that the owner of a mineral estate engaged in mining perform to the benefit of society in two ways. First, the land in which the operator's mineral estate is vested must be reclaimed after mining to permit *sequential* multiple use; that is, restored to a state where another beneficial use is possible. Second, the mining process should not be allowed to damage neighboring property through release of acid waters or solid wastes. In terms of our example, society will have to bear the cost of reclamation by paying an extra ± 50 cents per ton for coal. If coal is thereby less competitive with other sources of energy and chemical and metallurgical raw materials, mines in some areas will close and local economies will suffer. This is part of the price for restoration in a market economy. Similar changes in response to new technology have occurred in other industries and will occur in the future. Any viable system must strive for efficiency if it is to remain healthy. To add to the problem, surface mining for low-unit value earth materials, such as construction materials, is most common in and around urban areas where competition for land is at a maximum, where large numbers of people are affected by nuisances associated with the mining effort (noise, dust, vibrations, traffic, ugliness), and where they can effectively bring political pressures to close down the mining operation.

Because of technological developments in earth-moving equipment, surface mining has expanded to include deeper and deeper deposits beneath thicker and thicker overburdens. To those with a short-time perspective the great open pits with adjacent cast-aside mountains of overburden constitute permanent ruination of the land. The geologist who has studied the changing earth through geologic time has seen evidence that the earth's natural processes have filled much larger basins and leveled much higher mountains. He understands better than most that nothing is permanent. But conservationists do not want to wait a half a century or more for natural reclamation—and properly so. What man has done, he can undo.

After the extractive operation—or after any exclusive land use—the land can be restored for subsequent beneficial use—at a cost. If the principle of sequential multiple use—as contrasted to simultaneous multiple use—is accepted, the solution to the problem of mineral resources and multiple land use can be stated in terms of three elements:

1. Creation of a legal structure that will require industry-wide performance in land-use practices on an equitable basis. This structure is now being built at all levels of government.
2. Creation of an economic structure that will not only permit but *encourage* the mineral industry to reclaim and restore the surface, prevent subsidence, and prevent deleterious environmental effects from solid, liquid, and gaseous wastes. The tax structure offers a possibility through investment credits, fast write-offs, and "expensing" of conservation costs. Two hundred years of United States' history have demonstrated that incentives get things done.
3. Creation of a social attitude that includes a long-term *sequential* view of the land use and recognizes that in certain areas containing mineral deposits needed by society, exclusive land use is required during the extractive period.

The concept of "damage to a neighbor" is changing in the United States; there is growing opinion that a remedy by injunction against physical damage, such as release of pollutants, or against excavations which induce a neighbor's land to slump or be inundated, is not enough. The conservation movement gaining strength in the United States is concerned with beauty and is suggesting that an affront to the senses is damaging as well. Unpleasant smells and sounds have long been judged as damaging by the courts on the grounds that they constitute a common law nuisance. Now, however, that which is aesthetically obnoxious in terms of the visual sense is popularly condemned with such vehemence that probably very soon the courts will also be asked to judge ugliness as a nuisance. In the case of coal, enforced beautification will further add to the price and further affect the industry's competitive position.

We are being asked to subscribe to the view that society has the right to require beneficial land use in the broadest possible terms, that the land use be made pleasing to the eye, or at least that it should not result in ugliness. But who is to decide whether or not the offensive aspects of a particular land use outweigh the beneficial results? Strip mining of coal continues as a good case in point. Together with the coke necessary to produce steel, the benefits accruing from 152 million tons of low-cost energy, attendant payrolls, property and income taxes, revenues from carriers, and subsidiary and satellite industries which also pay taxes, must be weighed against an ugly, desolate landscape, a terrain bare of vegetation, a terrain without wildlife. But the desolation, however offensive, persists only up to the time when the coal is mined and land reclamation and restoration is complete. The solution of the problem calls for a coal industry that confines its wastes, does not pollute the waters of the land beyond the mining area, and restores the surface.

Certainly the enforcement of "state beauty standards" will significantly erode the right of a property owner to use his property and add to the cost of mining. It is, however, but another extension of a well-established trend; and, indeed, perhaps the burgeoning population will eventually force nationalization of the land. Such an unhappy day will be part of the price of an irrational population policy or no population policy at all. In the world of more extensive government control of land use, it is obvious that decisions on beneficial use cannot be entrusted to local groups with special interests. They must be made by fully informed boards which include scientists, engineers, and economists with the responsibility to plan for the general welfare of the nation. If planning is defined as an intellectual and operational process by which order is brought to change and a beneficial objective is achieved and this process is applied to use of the earth, then earth scientists (geologists and ecologists) and engineers should be invited to join professional planners, architects, recreation experts, and nature lovers on the planning team. The government should formulate and publicize a rational mineral and mining policy so that within the Federal establishment there will be some coordination and consistency in policies. This is one time when we *must* have it "both ways." The government representing the generations to come is the *ultimate* steward of the land; it must look at its trust in terms of centuries and it must follow an educated regional environmental plan—a patchwork with industry-by-industry variances will not produce the "fair land" that makes the difference between existing and living.

HIGH-VALUE EARTH RESOURCES

From the point of view of the planner it is worthwhile to distinguish between high-value earth resources and low-value earth resources because they require different treatment in the planning process. There is little profit in attempting to separate the two groups in terms of an arbitrary dollar value; the distinction is made to illustrate the principle of *place value*. Commodities that have a low value at the pit or quarry commonly do not move very far in commerce. They have value because of their location near a market. Sand and gravel is a good example. As a basic construction material, sand and gravel deposits are very important to growing cities or to large-scale construction projects wherever they are located. In 1968, the value of sand and gravel at the pit averaged $1.08 per ton (U. S. Bureau of Mines Commodity Data Summaries). At haulage rates of 5 or 6 cents per ton mile, the price is doubled to a customer 20 mi from the job site. Long-distance haulage of sand and gravel means higher-priced concrete and therefore increased construction costs. Over a period of years a scarcity of sand and gravel deposits can mean a great deal in dollars and cents to the taxpayers of a city with an ambitious public works program. A deposit of sand and gravel close to the growth parts of a city is a valuable asset, whereas one 100 mi distant may not be a commercial deposit because of the high cost of transporting the material; the corollary is that the existence of large reserves of sand and gravel in a rural county on the west side of a state are not of much significance as resources for the urban region on the east side.

High-value earth resources, on the other hand, are sought and produced wherever they occur and are transported around the world to markets. Petroleum moves around the world in pipelines and tankers; iron ore is afloat on the seas of the world as it moves from South America, India, Africa, and Australia to industrial centers.

Bates (1960, p. 17) classified industrial minerals and rocks into two groups, based on economic and geologic parameters:

Aspect	Group 1	Group 2
Bulk	Large	Small
Unit value	Low	High
Place value	High	Low
Imports and exports	Few	Many
Distribution	Widespread	Restricted
Geology	Simple	Complex
Processing	Simple	Complex

He said:

. . . sand and gravel obviously belongs in Group I. It is produced in enormous tonnages, and brings only a dollar or two per ton. The importance of place value is such that the maximum economic distance between deposit and market is less than a score of miles. Little if any sand and gravel enters into international trade. Deposits are numerous and widely distributed and their geology is relatively simple. . . . Most of these same aspects characterize crushed stone and gypsum. Industrial diamonds, high-grade mica, and quartz crystal, on the other hand, are at precisely the opposite extreme on nearly every count.

The occurrence of a high-value mineral deposit within a planning area can be both a blessing and a nuisance. If the deposit has already been discovered and has a long history of production, the economy of the area is in some degree oriented to the mineral industry. The industry produces a useful product for society, meets payrolls, pays taxes, and supports satellite industries in the form of truck and rail lines, equipment manufacturers, and service industries such as restaurants, laundries, cleaners, and a host of others. It buys water, fuel, and electricity unless it generates or manufactures its own. As a resource-based industry it is digging or pumping "wealth" out of the ground and deserves, in this writer's opinion, to be rated higher than a service industry. On the debit side, its installations may not be aesthetically pleasing, it may emit noise and smoke, and it may be a source of air and water pollutants. Citizens who become aware of the disagreeable aspects of the mineral industry and are not informed about or do not care about the beneficial contributions of the industry, may attempt to attack it through changes in zoning laws, court injunctions, punitive taxes, or excessively harsh pollution-control statutes. Policymakers and planners, better informed on the regional economic importance of the industry, seek remedies based on economic reality. If they are successful, the happy result is an economically sound industry with good community relations.

For example, the Texas Gulf Sulfur phosphate operations at Lee Creek, North Carolina, that began early in 1967 created 670 new jobs with a payroll of $5 million per year. This is more than 20 percent of the entire Beaufort County payroll (*Engineering and Mining Journal*, January 1968, p. 4). When operating at capacity, products from the facility will have a value of four or five times all other manufactured products in the county. The company's investment is some $90 million. However, the North Carolina Board of Water and Air Resources is proposing to restrict the company's water use to prevent intrusion of salt water into the Castle Hayne Aquifer. They charged that Texas Gulf, in pumping 59 million gallons of water per day to keep its pit dry is endangering the quality of the fresh water supply of the region (*Engineering and Mining Journal*, February 1969, p. 128). The company has said that it may find it economically impossible to stay in business if it cannot use the "dry-pit mining system" it has designed. Clearly, there are some hard economic realities to be faced by the leaders of this region and some difficult decisions to be made.

If the high-value mineral resource is a newly discovered one, the governmental agency with authority for planning has the opportunity to design the legal and environmental framework in which the industry can operate. If requirements are too harsh, the deposit will not be brought into production and the area will be denied substantial new tax revenues and a stronger economic base.

Los Angeles provides an excellent example of how a great metropolis can take advantage of a high-value mineral resource. The following information is summarized from an article by A. O. Spaulding, petroleum administrator for the city of Los Angeles (1965).

The first oil field was discovered within the limits of Los Angeles about 1890. By 1965 there were 13 commercial fields within the city and production in the city's fiscal 1964–1965 totaled more than 13,400,000 barrels of oil and about 25,600,000 MCF of natural gas; income to the city from rents and royalties was about $3,500,000. Oil exploration and production within an urban area presents special problems which the city attempted to solve by a Comprehensive Zoning Plan adopted about 1950. This plan permitted drilling within the city, but under closely controlled conditions. As oil companies found that they could operate economically under these conditions, activities increased to the point where in 1957 the city established a Department of Petroleum Management with responsibility in the hands of a petroleum administrator who reported to the city administrative officer. Applications for drilling permits or to create an oil-drilling district are sent through the petroleum administrator to the planning department and thence to the city planning commission and city council for approval. Little or no civic hostility to drilling has been encountered because the companies have made every effort to minimize the nuisance, even to sound-proofing and landscaping the drilling sites and setting the equipment out of sight below ground level (Figure 20). Occidental Petroleum Corporation designed a fluted steel derrick which resembles a modern office building. The rig is 161 ft tall and sky-blue in color; cost to the company was some $30,000 more than a conventional rig (*Oil and Gas Journal,* October 11, 1965, p. 107). The unobtrusive operation of this mineral industry within a busy urban system is a prime example of multiple use of the land. In September of 1966, Los Angeles announced a new discovery underlying some 1600 acres in the Wilshire area of the western part of the city, with reserves of about 100 million barrels valued at $300 million. The city approved six new drilling districts.

Hartsook (1965) examined the history of Huntington Beach, California, which had a population of 5000 in 1959, 75,000 in 1964, and a predicted 150,000 to 200,000 for 1975. The program of the Huntington Beach Company, first a land company, then an oil company, to develop its urban mineral properties while preserving a good community image included extensive studies of geologic, geographic, engineering, economic, social, and political factors affecting successful adaptation of the company to the fast-changing scene.

In Corpus Christi, Texas, there has been strong difference of opinion as to whether or not oil and gas deposits underlying Corpus Christi Bay should be explored and produced. Hutchinson (1966) discussed the situation under the title "Oil and Corpus Christi: A Study of Cooperation," and his remarks are herein reproduced as a case history.

Whenever a controversy exists and a solution is seriously sought, one of the first steps towards solution must be analysis of the differences between

FIGURE 20. A sound-proofed drilling rig in the Los Angeles urban area. (Courtesy of A. O. Spaulding, Petroleum Administrator, City of Los Angeles.)

the opposing parties. Also, a controversy may have many more than "just two sides." Such a controversy presently exists in Corpus Christi as to whether oil companies are to be allowed to drill for and produce oil and/or gas in Corpus Christi Bay. Further, once it became apparent that at least some drilling and producing operations must be allowed, wide differences of opinion arose concerning how, where, when, and to what extent these operations would be allowed. Various special interest groups formed the various sides of this controversy. Of course, the oil industry represents one side and with them is the State of Texas. Another side is the tourist industry of Corpus Christi. This would include the hotels, motels, restaurants, party boat operators, et cetera. Another side is represented by the recreation interests such as the Yacht Club and all private boating enthusiasts. Another side must be the commercial boating and shipping interests which have been represented by the Navigation District and the Corps of Engineers. Real estate developers, city beautification enthusiasts and many others represent additional sides. Each of the various sides of this controversy appears to have a different ax to grind, and it has been a complex operation to gather needed facts, opinions, and judgments, in order to come to some reasonable conclusion.

First, let us look at some of the background. On October 31, 1950, the City of Corpus Christi annexed 88 tracts of submerged lands in Corpus Christi Bay. This amounted to 52,830 acres or about 83 square miles. . . . Prior to this time the city limits had been approximately 6500′ from the shoreline over a limited portion of the Bay. In December, 1950, the City Council passed an ordinance providing for drilling and producing operations within the city portion of Corpus Christi Bay. With minor changes this ordinance remained in effect until April, 1964, when a new ordinance was passed which severely restricted activity compared with the prior ordinance which had relatively few restrictions. The new ordinance, for instance, prohibited the installation of production facilities and instituted some 23 requirements for a city drilling permit. It also provided for a Bay Park and Recreation Area, in which there was to be no oil and gas activity and a limited area near the shoreline outside of this Bay Park and Recreation Area where activity was to be very restricted.

In early 1965, one operator in the Bay made the routine request to the Corps of Engineers that its blanket permit be extended to include additional tracts within the city limits of Corpus Christi. The Corps passes judgments on all structures in the Bay from a navigation standpoint only. Although such permit extensions had been obtained by other oil companies just a few months prior to this time, the request now aroused the public interest and fear. In addition, this same operator had just requested that the city ordinance be revised to allow for the construction of a production platform in the Bay within the city limits. It is quite understandable that the citizens of Corpus Christi who are so very proud of their beautiful Bay became alarmed when coupled with a lack of understanding of the Corps of Engineers blanket permits on these 88 tracts. They imagined that each tract would have an unsightly oil production platform constructed on it. Unfortunately, most of the citizens of Corpus Christi who took an active interest failed to become informed as to what might actually happen. Many demands were made upon the City Council, the Corps of Engineers and any other regulatory body that could be found; these demands took the form of "stop the oil companies." The oil companies on the other hand failed miserably with respect to their public relations responsibility in not properly informing the excited populace of what was really in the wind. Such had not seemed necessary before.

Because of the severe conflict and essentially mass hysteria that arose over this problem of drilling and producing in the Bay, the City Council of Corpus Christi appointed a Bay Drilling Committee to study the entire problem, taking into account the rights of those who hold the leases, in addition to considering the general public interest. The charge to the Committee was to develop a reasonable, restrictive ordinance, but to do so only after thorough investigation of all of the facts, opinions and prejudices that could be uncovered.

The Bay Drilling Committee consisted of three representatives from the oil industry, three representatives from the general pulic and three members of the City Council. This Committee is still working feverishly toward a reasonable ordinance. The Committee well recognizes that no one is going to be completely satisfied with the ordinance. The oil companies are, of course, going to feel that they are unduly restricted, whereas, segments of the general public will undoubtedly want greater restriction.

Unfortunately, the oil industry which primarily created Corpus Christi as the metropolis that it presently is, has been cast into the unwanted role of the villain. Let us for a moment examine this industry. Its employees and families represent better than ten per cent of the population of Corpus Christi, or well over 20,000 people. This does not include service station operators or those people who depend entirely upon the oil industry for their jobs and which are an ancillary part of the industry, such as the various service and supply companies. These oil industry families are good citizens of the city. They contribute more than fifteen percent of the United Fund, the payroll amounts to well over $45,000,000 per year, and the industry provides over two-thirds of the tonnage which goes in and out of the port of Corpus Christi for which we are very proud. Members of the industry are very active in civic affairs. The oil industry brings many people on a transient basis to this city for business, conventions, and other meetings. Last year from Nueces County better than $60,000,000 worth of oil and gas was sold. This represented a royalty interest to private and State lease owners of over $8,000,000. Nueces County provides the most money for the State Permanent School Fund of any county in the State of Texas.

The purpose of pointing out all of the above is simply to identify the significant contribution which this industry has made to the city and county, and is continuing to make. Of course, we might also look at personal property taxes in which everyone has a very subjective interest. On January 1, 1965, the total evaluation taken from the Board of Equalization for Nueces County amounted to some $377,000,000. The oil industry evaluation was $114,000,000 or 30% of the total. A large portion of our tax bill is being borne by this industry.

Now that we have identified the oil industry in a role not as the villain but actually as a very prominent contributor, if not the major contributor, to Corpus Christi's growth and economy, we should briefly look at the other participants in this controversy. Broadly, they are categorized as "the general public" but actually represent a number of special interest groups as well as a "broad general interest" of the entire population. The more vocal of the special interest groups have been the tourist industry, the private recreation interests, and the city beautification interests.

The tourist industry believes, rightfully, that the major attraction for tourists to Corpus Christi is the water, its beauty and recreational advantages. They, of course, do not want any of this attraction to be lessened. The tourist industry at present is represented to be drawing income to this city of about $20,000,000 per year. It is anticipated that this will increase dramatically in the future. The private recreation interests are primarily the small boat operators as represented by the Yacht Club. Their desire, of course, is to maintain the Bay and yachting areas with as few obstructions as possible. In addition, they desire that these obstructions be clearly visible so that they will not run into them at night or in bad weather. It is impossible to determine how many obstructions, how widely spaced, are tolerable from a boating standpoint. Wide differences of opinion have been expressed. The oil industry contends that it is a very poor yachtsman that cannot steer his boat between structures that are spaced more than one-half mile apart. There is a conflict between the boating groups and the beautification groups in that one would like to be able to see any obstructions in the Bay clearly, whereas, the other would like the obstruction to be as invisible as possible. The fishermen love these obstructions because fish gather around the shell foundations. The structures are also anchorage and tie-up spots for these fishermen. A great many small boats can be found almost any day in the areas of Mustang Island and Redfish Bay, where there are numerous well structures.

From the standpoint of the maintenance of the aesthetic quality of Corpus Christi Bay, there are numerous opinions also. We might note at this point that very few people realize that over the years more than 60 wells have been drilled within the city limits of the Bay. Thirty-nine of these wells have been completed as producers and 30 are still in the Bay, producing gas. These structures are relatively small and the closest one to the shoreline is well over a mile out. On exceptionally clear days they can be identified, but much of the time they are not obvious to the person standing on the shore. It did not appear that these structures created any problem before the recent hysteria concerning the Bay. We might ask ourselves that if 30 such structures do not bother us at the moment, how many structures might there be, and would these bother us? Of course, if they were all close to the shoreline a given number would bother us much more than having the same number scattered over the Bay.

The primary problems the Bay Drilling Committee had to investigate were first, whether any additional drilling was to be allowed in the Bay, and second, whether present and/or future producing wells would require the construction of production platforms. Quite rapidly it became apparent that the rights of the State of Texas were involved. The State has mineral interests to the submerged lands and has leased these rights under a competitive system to the various oil companies. An ordinance which completely forbade drilling operations would essentially represent confiscation of the rights of the State and of the oil companies who held the leases. Thus, there was no question as to whether drilling could be absolutely prohibited. It could not. Unrestricted drilling and producing operations were, however, recognized as not being proper. The city has its police power jurisdiction to look after the general well being of the citizens of Corpus Christi. Unregulated oil operations within the Bay might not harm the public interest, but there was no absolute assurance of this; therefore, regulations as restrictive as could be reasonably imposed were a goal.

Simple economics dictate that the oil industry drill as few wells as possible to efficiently recover any hydrocarbons that should be discovered within the Bay. Those present subterranean formations that might contain oil and gas to a depth of 6000 to 8000' have already been investigated by the more than 60 wells that have been drilled to date. No oil is presently being produced, nor is there any indication that commercial oil is to be found. The formations below this depth have recently been penetrated by several wells and potentially large gas reservoirs have been discovered. No oil, however, is apparent, and it would not be expected at these depths based on the tremendous amount of experience that has been gained along the Gulf Coast in this geologic province. It is fortunate from Corpus Christi's standpoint that we are apparently confronted only with the development of gas reservoirs since a gas reservoir will require a significantly smaller number of wells for depletion. We can anticipate that, on the average, these deep gas reservoirs will be developed on the basis of one well every square mile, with a few exceptions where two wells may be necessary. It is the oil industry's contention that on an average of one well per square mile the Bay would not be cluttered from a boating standpoint nor would the number of structures in the Bay be sufficiently increased to detract significantly from its aesthetic qualities. The oil industry immediately recognizes, as does everyone else, that the closer the wells are to the shoreline, the more undesirable they are from an aesthetic viewpoint. It is, therefore, quite apparent that a no drilling zone should be established along the shoreline and such a zone with a width of about one mile has been agreed upon in the Bay Drilling Committee. For the area further into the Bay, there is great pressure on the oil industry to agree that the number of surface locations should be restricted to at least no more than one cluster of wellheads every square mile. Thus, there might be a number of wells drilled from essentially one surface location. There is some pressure to increase this spacing even larger. The question that must be resolved is whether the requirement of wide spacing of well clusters is reasonable when the benefits derived therefrom are compared to the costs and risks involved. If it is necessary to cluster the wellheads, it will also be necessary that the oil companies use directional drilling techniques to spot their bottom hole locations within the proper points of the various reservoirs. Such directional drilling is costly and has numerous inherent risks, not only to the oil companies but also to the general public. Forgetting for a moment the risks involved, we can look simply at the minimum additional costs that are imposed by directional drilling even when no trouble in drilling is encountered. It has been estimated that, on the average, this directional drilling will increase the cost of drilling and completing a well by 50% or more. Thus, a 13,000′ well in the Bay which will cost over one-half million dollars if drilled vertically, will cost three-fourths of a million dollars if drilled directionally. If some 50 additional wells are to be drilled in the Bay, and this is probably an outside limit on that number, we could immediately see that this involves an expense to the oil industry of over $12,000,000. Is it worth it? This is particularly pertinent when we consider that some of these directional wells will be as much as 8 to 10 miles out in the Bay and that the only people that will see them are the boating group. This is a tremendous price to placate the interests of a relatively small group. Nevertheless, it is apparent that some degree of clustering will be required, and it is at this point that the Bay Drilling Committee is now studying what spacing of surface well locations will be permitted.

Some of the reservoirs that have been discovered in Corpus Christi Bay are gas condensate reservoirs from which large quantities of liquid hydrocarbons may be extracted. Such extraction requires producing equipment such as separators, stabilizers, dehydrators, and compressors, located near the scene of the production. This requirement precipitated the request to the City Council that the present city ordinance be amended to provide for the construction of these producing facilities within the Bay.

The Bay Drilling Committee has investigated several possible and many impossible suggested producing schemes, concluding that some production equipment will be necessary, and fortunately that the number of producing structures in the Bay can be significantly limited by requiring joint operations amongst the various producers. This, of course, would have come to pass without ordinances since such joint operations are undertaken elsewhere simply from the standpoint of economics. It would appear that no more than 3 or 4 such producing platforms would ever be required and that probably no more than 2 would be located south of the ship channel. The Committee is presently recommending that one platform with dimensions of approximately 30×100′ be permitted now in the eastern end of

State Tract 62, which would place this platform over three miles from the shoreline. Many people have been surprised to find that such a platform already exists at approximately this location but that its dimensions are about one-third the size of the proposed structures. It is not believed that the proposed installation will be a blot on the landscape because of its distance from shore.

The Bay Drilling Committee has studied numerous alternate proposals for the producing facilities that are needed within the Bay with the thought that actual platforms might not be required. One proposal that attracted the imagination of many people of Corpus Christi was the possibility of making man-made, landscaped islands within the Bay on which all equipments could be located below the surface. Such islands have been built in California and the Committee visited these islands and investigated their applicability for Corpus Christi. It was concluded that for numerous reasons, these would not be acceptable to the people of Corpus Christi nor to the oil industry. From the oil industry's standpoint, the chief problem involved the tremendous cost of construction (several millions of dollars each) and the operating problems that are associated with an operation both on water and land. From the city's standpoint, it is apparent that the islands would not look natural, would constitute a much larger blot on the landscape, would also create a larger hazard for navigation, and would not be as readily removed when the operations ceased. In the investigation, the Committee found that the oil producing operations in the Bay off Los Angeles are very much different from the gas producing operations in Corpus Christi Bay and that the techniques employed in Los Angeles could not be used in Corpus Christi.

The Committee also studied the possibility of prohibiting any producing facilities in the Bay and requiring that all production be brought to shore before it is processed. It found that this is a very inefficient producing technique and would result in the irretrievable loss of large amounts of hydrocarbons. The Committee did find, however, that the platforms in the Bay could be spaced relatively far apart and it has determined that these platforms should be no closer to each other than three and possibly four miles. Further, the platforms should be at least three miles from the shoreline.

The Committee has not worried much about transient structures such as rigs but has studied closely the possibilities of making permanent platforms and well protective structures more attractive.

There has been considerable misunderstanding throughout the uninformed segment of the general public as to what structures are relatively permanent and what are purely transient. When the industry has spoken of the permanent Christmas trees that will be placed on the producing wells, many of the general public have assumed that these trees are the rigs that they see drilling the wells. This is typical of the lack of understanding. Thus, the Committee has faced an education problem which is still to be met head-on with respect to informing the general public about offshore operations. This will be a major education undertaking, but if properly accomplished, can well lead to a better understanding between the citizens of Corpus Christi and the city's major industry.

The Bay Committee is presently working with a firm of lawyers in Houston to draft a proposed bay drilling ordinance. Incorporated in this ordinance will be the provisions for clustering of wells, joint operations of producing structures, and spacing of well clusters and structures. In addition, there will be many other less important items which will include lighting requirements for all structures in the Bay, maintenance of equipment (including specific camouflage painting), regulations on pollution of waters, and safety in general. The Committee has also worked with the Corps of Engineers and the Navigation District to try to develop ideas with respect to future channel needs in the Bay. It will, of course, be quite difficult to remove wells or platforms once they are drilled; therefore, in considering well and platform locations, the Committee must also consider needs of the water transportation groups.

It is believed that a secondary contribution that the Bay Drilling Committee will make to Corpus Christi is the dissemination of accurate information to the general public concerning operations in the Bay. An informed populace will then be able to understand and not fear the oil industry's activities. The ordinance that will be developed will undoubtedly be unacceptable to everyone; however, it does appear that a reasonable compromise will be reached within which both the city and the industry can live.

LOW-VALUE EARTH RESOURCES:
WATER AND CONSTRUCTION MATERIALS*

Low-value earth resources of principal interest to planners are water and construction materials. Currently, government at all levels is preoccupied with water—water supply and water quality. The lion's share of government money spent on conservation, reclamation, and resource development is spent on water projects. No human society can exist without water. The human body, performing a moderate amount of

* Parts of this section have appeared previously in other publications (Flawn, 1966).

work in a temperature climate, requires 5 to 6 pt per day; commonly 3 pt are consumed as fluid and the remainder is made up of the water content of food (Swenson and Baldwin, 1965, p. 22). Maxwell (1965, p. 100) added to the direct consumption of fluids the amount of water necessary to produce the food necessary to sustain an individual and concluded that ". . . Something between 300 and 3000 gallons per day would appear to be the bare subsistence water-cost for one human being." These figures are derived from data that indicate that 300 gal of water per day are transpired by enough wheat to produce grain sufficient for a daily allowance of 2.5 lb of bread and that a diet of 1 lb of meat per day has a water cost of 2900 gal of water per day in water consumed by the steer and the alfalfa which fed him. In primitive rural societies water use was probably about 5 gal per day per person; in the modern industrial society of the United States, household use has climbed to 60 or 70 gal per person per day (Swenson and Baldwin, 1965, p. 22). This generous allowance is made possible by municipal water prices averaging 35 cents per 1000 gal. Much water is wasted by excessive washing, rinsing, flushing, and sprinkling. At prevailing prices, there is little incentive for more conservative practices. Per capita use in United States cities ranges from the household average in nonindustrial communities to 175 gal per person per day in cities where big water-using industries are located. In the United States about 340 billion gallons of water per day are drawn from all of the various sources (1964). Divided by a populations of 192 million, the total withdrawal is 1770 gal per person per day. This does not include the water necessary to produce food, fibers, timber, etc. Maxwell (1965, p. 101) estimated total per capita daily use in these terms as in excess of 15,000 gal per day. Slightly more than half of the total withdrawn for consumption is used by industry, about 40 percent is used in agriculture (irrigation) and about 9 percent is used for municipal and rural supply. A distinction is made between water "drawn" from various sources and water "used" or "consumed" because much of the water withdrawn is returned to the system and again becomes part of the supply. For example, very little (about 1 percent) of the large volume of water used to cool power plants is actually used up but a relatively high percentage (50 to 60 percent) of water spread on fields for irrigation is consumed (*U. S. Bureau of Mines Minerals Yearbook*, 1964, Vol. I, p. 1159).

Water is, of course, the prime municipal resource, and with few ex-

ceptions the availability of water controlled the original site of settlement. In the early history of community growth, water supply was
usually the first municipal service provided after provision for maintenance of law and order. From a community spring or well, water supply
was improved by distribution systems, and its quality was controlled to
meet public health standards. In nearly all cases the early city water
systems tapped local sources—streams, rivers, lakes, shallow aquifers. As
demand grew, cities were faced with the problem of expanding the water
supply for both residential, commercial, and industrial users and it soon
became clear that an abundant supply of cheap water was an attraction
to industry and a mechanism for achieving community prosperity.
Expansion of supplies through construction of new reservoirs, deeper
well fields, aqueducts to more distant surface sources, and treatment
plants required large capital investment and cities turned to bond
issues for financing. Some communities in dry regions with no surface
water and limited prospects for ground-water development had such a
serious water problem that growth stopped. As population and demand
grew, conflicts between cities and prior water users and between one
city and another became more common and more heated. In the mid-
1960s for the first time large-scale desalination of sea water or saline
ground water appeared to offer future hope of water at costs of 20 to 30
cents per thousand gallons (p. 177). This new source could solve many
of the problems of coastal cities and some inland cities in sedimentary
basins containing large volumes of saline ground water.

Because of this "reaching out" for water on the part of established
users, water is an exception to the general rule that low-value mineral
commodities do not travel very far in trade. The aqueducts of Rome
are perhaps the most widely known engineering works designed to solve
a city water-supply problem. Beginning about 312 B.C., Rome began to
construct aqueducts to tap new sources of water and by A.D. 226 eleven
of these structures, ranging in length from 11 to 62 mi and totaling about
336 mi, had been completed. However, the Roman efforts were not the
first. Much earlier, Egyptian, Babylonian, Assyrian, Phoenician, Persian,
and Greek communities went after both surface and ground water with
systems of canals, aqueducts, tunnels, and wells. Tolman (1937, p. 12)
described the water-collecting tunnels or kanats of the Middle East as
the greatest water works of the ancients. The oldest one cited by Tolman
is the tunnel of Negoub built in 800 B.C. to supply water to Nineveh. The
tunnels, connecting a series of shafts, are driven in water-bearing strata,

commonly alluvial sands and gravels. The city of Teheran is underlain by a network of kanats as much as 16 mi long and 500 ft below the surface (Tolman, 1937, p. 12). Los Angeles and surrounding counties and communities in Southern California began reaching out with aqueducts shortly after the turn of the century and soon put the Romans in second place. The First Los Angeles Aqueduct, composed of the Owens River Aqueduct constructed between 1907 and 1913 and the Mono Basin Extension constructed between 1934 and 1941, is 338 mi long with 36 reservoirs and 76 mi of tunnels; it can deliver 490 cfs or about 0.32 billion gallons per day (Wilson and Mayeda, 1966). One of the most bitter water controversies in the United States grew out of construction of the Owens Valley Aqueduct and the appropriation by Los Angeles of water used by farmers in Owens Valley. As Outland said (1963, p. 32):

By 1924 the hatred and hostility in Owens Valley toward Los Angeles had reached the breaking point. Taking the law into their own hands, settlers began a campaign of sabotage against the Los Angeles Aqueduct that would keep the valley in an intermittent state of siege for three years. It was violence in the best tradition of the Old West but rarely seen after the beginning of the twentieth century. Captured headgates, seizure of Los Angeles representatives by masked men, forcible rides out of the valley under armed escort, illegal stopping and searching of automobiles, and wholesale dynamiting of the aqueduct made the Owens Valley fight the most magnificent water brawl of all time.

The Second Los Angeles Aqueduct was started in 1965 and projected for completion in 1969. It is 153 mi long with only 1.6 mi of tunnels and can deliver 210 cfs or .14 billion gallons per day. The Colorado River Aqueduct constructed in two phases, 1933 to 1939 and 1951 to 1961, is 244 mi long with 11 reservoirs and 92 mi of tunnels and a capacity of 1605 cfs or slightly more than 1 billion gallons per day (Proctor, 1966).

Because water is a fluid, it can be moved relatively cheaply through canals, aqueducts, and pipelines. Because it is essential to the functioning of a community, it is judged economically prudent to invest large sums in water transport rather than restrict the growth of a town or city or, in a more drastic case, to abandon the site. Because modern municipal economies are geared to a delivered price of 20 to 60 cents per thousand gallons, water costs cannot be raised so as to defray the entire cost of water supply projects; these are commonly financed through municipal bonds paid for out of general revenues. The consumer commonly pays only a fraction of the real cost of delivering water to him. Because city authorities are utterly committed to continuing growth, it is not likely that the collective municipal thirst in the United States will diminish—indeed, the reverse is true, for growth is equated with prosperity, jobs, business profits, and increasing real-estate values. The concept that there might be an optimum size for a city in terms of resources and other environmental factors is anathema to Chambers of Commerce. Very large concentrations of people have political power and can use it to achieve their objectives. There is, however, an alternative to the Chamber-of-Commerce view that regards regional population growth as an independent variable and requires huge investment and environmental modifications to bring water to an area. Populations are mobile; perhaps if the water is not supplied in the quantities demanded, the regional population growth would be slowed as people moved to the area of abundant water supply and the overall needs could then be revised downward. It is unlikely that such an alternative could be implemented unless absolute authority were vested in a national master planning commission, and this is of course not possible in a democratic system. In late 1966, a Committee of the National Academy of Sciences-National Research Council published a report entitled "Alternatives in Water Management"; to this writer's knowledge, it was the first time an official and prestigious group challenged the Chamber-of-Commerce philosophy that water must be brought to people. The committee said (1966, p. 27): "Once people 'need' to live in Los Angeles they 'need' water, but to what extent does the nation need to subsidize the delivery of water to Los Angeles?"

Regional water plans: California, Texas, and the North American Water and Power Alliance. One ambitious water project on the current scene is the California Water Plan, designed to meet the immense water needs of urban southern California. The first stage, known as the State Water Project and financed by a $1.75 billion bond issue, will construct the dams, aqueducts, power plants, and pumping stations necessary to move large volumes of water from north to south. The aqueduct is 444 mi long. Engineering is complicated by earthquake hazards.

The first Texas Water Plan, announced in a tentative and summary form in May of 1966, proposed to solve Texas's water problems by large-scale transport of water from the well-watered east across drainage basins to the dry southwest. Units A and B of the State Water Project envisioned a 980-mi conduit to bring water from the Sulfur River, Red River, and Cypress Creek basins in the northeast part of Texas southwest through a series of new reservoirs, canals, natural drainage channels, and pumping stations to the Rio Grande irrigation system in south Texas, satisfying municipal, industrial, and agricultural demands along the way. Units C and D of the plan called for construction of additional reservoirs and two barriers against salt water. Altogether, these four units required construction of 53 new reservoirs, modification of 6 existing reservoirs, and construction of the two barriers at a total capital cost estimated at nearly $3 billion. Units E and F of the plan were concerned with additional navigational and flood control facilities, hurricane protection, pollution-control projects, phreatophyte-control projects, and projects to import water for the western parts of the state which would not benefit directly by the redistribution of in-state water. The first water plan was opposed by eastern and central parts of the state which would lose "surplus" water and the western parts of the state which were "left out." Representatives of the High Plains and Trans-Pecos regions, which now depend in large part on limited supplies of ground water, argued that their agricultural economy had to be provided for and that the state plan had to contain provisions to increase their supplies. Other critics challenged the wisdom of building such a high-cost system to put an additional 1 million acres of land into cultivation in south Texas. Is such additional crop capacity really needed? What for? If it can be demonstrated that this additional capacity will be needed in the future to produce food the argument is persuasive; the need for more cotton production is not so compelling. Some ecologists and biologists were perturbed about the environmental consequences of the plan in terms of changes in the coastal environment where reduction in the inflow of fresh water could markedly change the salinity of Texas bays. Effects of such changes on biological activity in Texas bays and estuaries, which serve as a breeding ground for fish and shrimp, are not known. Would the plan, which envisaged large-scale surface storage of water, result in weather modification? Would engineering advances in the design of large-scale dual-purpose nuclear plants for producing electric power and desalted water make it economically more feasible to produce new fresh water in south Texas from saline water than to import water from the northeast? All of these questions were considered by architects of the plan. In many cases they were forced to make judgments on very little hard data; the environmental data do not exist and development of them would require years of scientific study.

Following a state-wide series of meetings, in which the plan was discussed by concerned parties, a new and much more ambitious Texas Water Plan was conceived. It was unveiled at a public meeting in Austin late in 1968 and currently is under consideration by the Texas legislature.* It recognized that the needs of the High Plains and Trans-Pecos irrigation districts cannot be met unless the state's supplies are augmented from an outside source. The new plan is based on importation of Mississippi River water into northeast Texas and distribution of it from storage reservoirs in that area through a canal running westward through the Dallas and Fort Worth metropolitan areas, with western branches to Lubbock in the High Plains and to El Paso in Trans-Pecos. The main distribution system of the first plan, a coastwise canal, was retained. The estimated cost of the new plan is more than twice that of the first, or approximately $7 billion.

Even more imaginative plans have been suggested; one, the North American Water and Power Alliance, costing perhaps $100 billion, would transport water from the northwestern North America, including Canada, eastward into the Great Lakes and southward into the dry southwest of the United States. NAWAPA would redistribute water among three nations, including 7 Canadian provinces, 35 states of the United States, and 3 states of the Republic of Mexico. The environmental consequences of this plan are considered on p. 173.

Another very interesting example of man's ambition to making large-scale changes in the environment in order to improve water supply is the recently proposed plan to convert Long Island Sound into the largest fresh-water reservoir in the United States (Gerard, 1966). The scheme calls for isolating the Sound from the sea by construction of dams (which would also serve as bridges) at the east and west ends and reducing water salinity over a period of years through inflow of the Connecticut and Housatonic rivers until the water became potable. (See

* A constitutional amendment that would authorize the Texas legislature to issue up to $3.5 billion worth of bonds to finance the Texas Water Plan was defeated by the voters on August 5, 1969.

p. 176.) Economic growth of dry areas ultimately will have to reflect the resource base of the area; there is a practical limit to supplementation of the indigenous resources by imports.

Clearly a planner responsible for the design of a regional eco-system must know what kind of questions to ask before he approves engineering projects with such major environmental consequences.

Construction materials. There are few cities that have not grown over and around peripheral sand and gravel pits, stone quarries, clay pits, or cuts from which fill has been taken. The relationship between the city and the urban mineral industry is embodied in the concept of place value (p. 93). The construction materials resources which are of concern to a city are used in large volumes but have a low value per unit of production. Of paramount importance, then, is their location with respect to a city's growing areas. The operator producing minerals for the urban market is constrained by transportation economics to locate the closest deposit to the urban area that is satisfactory from the mineral product standpoint. The occurrence of mineral deposits, however, is determined by geologic factors and not by the shape and symmetry of the growing city. Deposits of sand and gravel and of stone suitable for aggregate and base material are not ubiquitous, and around many large cities they either never existed in adequate quantities, have been depleted through use, or have been rendered unavailable through unplanned urban growth. The planning group of a city that becomes concerned about depletion of sand and gravel or crushed stone sources cannot simply find the least desirable land in the city—the old dump —and zone it for quarry sites. Mineral resources cannot be created by administrative decision or legislation. Intelligent planning for and management of urban mineral resources must be based on sound information about the occurrence of the resources. Detailed knowledge of the geology of a city is basic to any resource or environmental planning, and of first priority is an accurate and detailed geologic map or model. The same kind of advance planning used by city departments concerned with power, traffic, sewage, and parks should be applied to mineral resources. Such is already the case in regard to water; no city can be managed efficiently without long-range water planning. This concept needs to be extended to the construction materials. If sand and gravel must be hauled in from distant points, the price of concrete will go up, construction costs will go up, and the city's bill for municipal projects will be higher.

Some years ago (1950) the sand and gravel industry of Indianapolis in Marion County, Indiana, was threatened by a county-wide metropolitan zoning plan which would have relegated mineral producing industries to remote parts of the county. The following case history was supplied by John B. Patton, state geologist of Indiana (personal communication, 1966). In the original version of the plan it was assumed by the planners that sand and gravel was equally distributed in the area and that one tract was as good as another for production of aggregates. The Indiana Mineral Aggregates Association reacted against this naive assumption and called upon the Indiana Geological Survey for factual data on the occurrence of sand and gravel in the county. The Indiana Geological Survey explained the geologic controls of sand and gravel deposits in the area to the planning group. Indianapolis is situated at the confluence of Fall Creek and the West Fork of White River, both of which were glacial sluiceways during the Ice Age. The major sand and gravel resources of Marion County are valley train deposits along these streams. Small to medium-sized pockets of sand and gravel occur in many other parts of the county, largely as kames associated with moraines,* but the quantity and character of these deposits would not support a modern large-volume aggregate industry. Deposits also occur along Eagle Creek, another glacial sluiceway, but they are thin and not of commercial interest at present. Much of the business district, certain industrial areas, and residential areas ranging from exclusive neighborhoods to slums overlie the valley train deposits through the heart of the city and thus have put large volumes of sand and gravel out of the reach of the industry. Reserves are further limited in that dams for municipal reservoirs have removed substantial parts of the old glacial channels or sluiceways from mineral resource development. Also pertinent to planning is the fact that the center of Indianapolis is approximately the dividing point between good gravel deposits and poor deposits because downstream from the center of the city there is a decrease in coarse and medium sizes and a high sand ratio. Some operators

---

* A *kame* is a mound of stratified glacial drift composed chiefly of sand and gravel deposited in contact with glacier ice by meltwater streams; a *moraine* is a general term for glacial drift built up by deposition from and thrust of glacal ice. *Drift* is an inclusive term which embraces all earth material transported and deposited by glacial ice or in bodies of water adjacent to and receiving meltwater and glacial debris.

in this area are forced to blend crushed stone with the naturally occurring material to make specifications.

As a result of information about the location, size, and quality of the
deposits, and of the beneficial contributions of the aggregates industry,
the planning group revised their original recommendations. Significantly,
they also became aware of the value of geologic information in land-use
planning and established a close relationship with the Indiana Geological Survey. Mineral deposits are not equally distributed through the
earth and even a common commodity like sand and gravel is in this
respect similar to gold—it is where you find it. In terms of geologic
history, there is always a reason why mineral deposits occur in a particular location and once the reason is understood it is possible to classify
other lands as potential hosts to the same kinds of deposit. Geologic
data, however, cannot be developed overnight—they require painstaking
mapping, sampling, testing, and analysis.

Demographers predict that a large number of fast-growing urban
areas in the United States and elsewhere will merge into giant cities,
or megalopoli, in the near future. In the United States about 1 million
acres of land per year are being converted to residential home sites and
most of this land is in and around existing population centers. Every
mile of federal highway consumes about 40 acres. Planning, zoning, exercise of eminent domain, and condemnation of private land in the
public interest are natural results of population growth, increased competition in the human hive, increasing conflicts between potential land
users, and increasing the overall pressure for land. The dismal alternative
to planned urban complexes are urban jungles such as exist around the
old nuclei of New York and Chicago, and which cost society so much
in so many ways. It is cheaper to plan in advance, and the mineral
producer must have a place in the planning. He competes for land in
the urban area and is restricted in the area he can use by the natural
occurrence of the mineral deposit. He is not regarded as a desirable
neighbor—he scars the land, detonates explosives, makes noise with
heavy equipment, spews dust over the landscape, and is a terminus for
fleets of trucks. Many of these nuisances can be modified or controlled,
but at extra cost. According to Ahearn (1965) "zoning ordinances have
treated sand and gravel operations with the junk yard, rendering plant,
trash incinerator, stockyard, and sewage treatment facility."

In the first half of this century, when deposits were more abundant
and the city's perimeter expanded at a relatively slow and predictable

rate, the quarry or pit operator could more easily locate in an area where he bothered few neighbors and where he could count on an adequate period of time to work the deposit. In the second half of the century, with many deposits already depleted, his chances of being engulfed by a much more rapidly expanding perimeter and closed down by high taxes, restrictive zoning regulations, or even injunctions are greatly increased. He now needs the protection of a city authority. Citizens who do not understand the importance of an abundant supply of cheap construction materials, and commonly led by uninformed groups who regard the pit and quarry operator as a "despoiler" or "plunderer," need to be better informed. The operator needs to look at his public relations and to make plans to reclaim and restore the land after the minerals have been harvested. In the United States, the National Sand and Gravel Association, through its committee on public relations, has been a leader in establishing standards for rehabilitation of sand and gravel pits and demonstrating to the producer the import- ance of maintaining high standards of operation; at the same time it has effectively explained the importance of sand and gravel to modern society and the harm that can be done through reckless and punitive community action to drive away the producer (Schellie and Rogier, 1963; Ahearn, 1964). Through a research project at the University of Illinois, the association has sought ways to improve pit rehabilitation practices (Bauer, 1965; Johnson, 1966). Planners should familiarize themselves with these publications. Case histories of Lincoln Lakes, Illinois, and Sansabar Estates, Indiana, were presented by Bauer (1965); these are two wet pits which have been transformed into a privately operated recreation center and a water-oriented residential community, respectively. Johnson (1966) described the planning procedures involved in the development of the Three Lakes Community, south of Denver; here a plan was developed to create a community of 212 dwelling units on 106 acres of sculptured land surrounding 100 acres of water in a former sand and gravel pit.

The obvious answer to urban land shortage is multiple use. Los Angeles has included mineral deposits in its planning. The city surveyed a number of sand and gravel deposits in San Fernando Valley, evaluated them by drilling, and zoned a number of gravel pit sites. After the deposits are quarried, the pits will be first used for waste disposal, and then restored for normal urban development.

REFERENCES

AHEARN, V. P. (1964)   *Land use planning and the sand and gravel producer:* National Sand and Gravel Association, 30 pp.

AHEARN, V. P. (1965)   "Urbanization, land use controls, and the mineral aggregate industry": Paper presented at the annual meeting of American Institute of Mining, Metallurgical and Petroleum Engineers, Chicago, February 17, 1965.

BATES, R. L. (1960)   *Geology of the industrial rocks and minerals:* Harper & Row, New York, 441 pp.

BAUER, A. M. (1965)   *Simultaneous excavation of sand and gravel sites:* University of Illinois and National Sand and Gravel Association project no. 1, 60 pp.

BROWN, HARRISON; BONNER, JAMES; AND WEIR, JOHN (1958)   *The next hundred years:* Viking Press, New York, 193 pp.

BURTON, IAN, AND KATES, R. W. (1965)   *Readings in resource management and conservation:* University of Chicago Press, 609 pp.

FLAWN, P. T. (1966)   *Mineral Resources:* Rand McNally, 406 pp.

GERARD, R. D. (1966)   "Potential fresh water reservoir in the New York area": *Science,* Vol. 153, no. 3738, pp. 870–871.

HARTSOOK, E. A. (1965)   "Population pressure and mineral industries": Paper presented at the annual meeting of American Institute of Mining, Metallurgical and Petroleum Engineers, Chicago, February 17, 1965.

HUTCHINSON, C. A. (1966)   "Oil and Corpus Christi: A study of cooperation": *Corpus Christi Geological Society Bulletin,* Vol. VI, no. 6, pp. 7–16.

JOHNSON, CRAIG (1966)   *Practical operating procedures for progressive rehabilitation of sand and gravel sites:* University of Illinois and National Sand and Gravel Association project no. 2, 75 pp.

JOSLYN, M. A., AND OLCOTT, H. S. (1959)   "Food consumption and resources," in *Natural Resources,* edited by Martin R. Huberty: McGraw-Hill Book, Inc., New York, pp. 288–327.

LANDSBERG, H. H.; FISCHMAN, L. L.; AND FISHER, J. L. (1963)   *Resources in America's future:* Resources for the Future, Inc., The Johns Hopkins Press, 1017 pp.

MALTHUS, THOMAS R. (1798)   *An essay on the principle of population:* J. Johnson, London, 396 pp.

MALTHUS, THOMAS R. (1926)   *First essay on population, 1798,* with notes by James Bonar: Macmillan & Co., Ltd., London, 396 pp.

MAXWELL, J. C. (1965) "Will there be enough water?": *American Scientist*, Vol. 53, no. 1, pp. 97–103.

National Academy of Sciences Committee on Water (1966) *Alternatives in water management*: National Academy of Sciences-National Research Council, publication no. 1408, 52 pp.

OUTLAND, CHARLES (1963) *Man-made disaster, the story of the St. Francis Dam*: Arthur H. Clark Company, California, 249 pp.

PROCTOR, R. J. (1966) "The Colorado River aqueduct," in *Engineering Geology in southern California*: Association of Engineering Geologists special publication, pp. 73–80.

ROMNEY, M. P. (1965) *Minerals in the life of man*: Utah Mining Association, Salt Lake City, Utah, 16 pp.

SCHELLIE, K. L., AND ROGIER, D. A. (1963) *Site utilization and rehabilitation practices for sand and gravel operations*: National Sand and Gravel Association, 80 pp.

SPAULDING, ARTHUR O. (1965) "Drilling in city brings on no civic hostility": *Oil and Gas Journal*, March 8, 1965, Vol. 63, no. 10, pp. 198–203.

SWENSON, H. A., AND BALDWIN, H. L. (1965) *A primer on water quality*: U. S. Geological Survey, Washington, D. C., 27 pp.

TOLMAN, C. F. (1937) *Ground water*: McGraw-Hill, Inc., New York, 539 pp.

WALLACE, A. RUSSELL (1910) *The world of life*: Chapman and Hall, London, 400 pp.

WHITE, GILBERT F. (1961) "The choice of use in resource management": *Natural Resources Journal*, Vol. 1, no. 1, pp. 23–40.

WILSON, R. R. AND MAYEDA, H. S. (1966) "The first and second Los Angeles aqueducts," in *Engineering Geology in Southern California*: Association of Engineering Geologists special publication, pp. 63–72.

MAN AS A GEOLOGICAL AGENT: THE GEOLOGICAL CONSEQUENCES OF INDUSTRIALIZATION

5

Introduction. The subject of this chapter, geological consequences of human activities, was introduced in the chapter on geologic processes (Chapter 2) where subsidence of the surface as a result of man's withdrawal of support was described and where it was pointed out that in some areas works of man have changed the natural equilibria of slopes and caused landslides. In this century, the energy and machines available to society, together with the demands of society for energy, materials, and a controlled environment, have given rise to a level of use of the earth and a consumption of earth materials whose magnitude can scarcely be measured and whose consequences are not yet apparent. No one really knows how many irreversible reactions have been triggered through the application of human energies to (1) changing the contour of the land and modifying its physical properties, (2) changing the chemical composition of the land, waters, and atmosphere, and (3) changing the natural thermal regimen. Effects on the biosphere have, of course, been enormous, and in some cases devastating, but are not discussed herein except insofar as they cause geological changes.

There is some tendency in the modern context to view a pristine wilderness as "good" and any modification of nature by man as "bad." This writer does not pretend to omniscience, and will not attempt to investigate psychological and sociological consequences of swelling populations, industrialization, and urbanization. It is assumed that society will continue along presently established trends, desirable or not, for some decades at least. The main concern here is what is happening to the earth because of the expanding human colony and what the ultimate consequences might be. Judgments will be limited to the general thesis that human activities that render the environment less habitable over the long term are bad and human efforts that make the environment more habitable are good. The writer admits to sympathy for the position that habitability should not be defined solely in terms of food supply, potable water, and breathable air. There must be some consideration given to aesthetic values. A feedlot is eminently habitable for cattle; standing shoulder to shoulder at the trough they get fatter than on the open range. An urban dweller in his cubicle supplied with three ample meals a day and breathing an artificial atmosphere is likewise in an environment that is, physically at least, habitable. It is, in the final analysis, up to society itself to define what is habitable and set up specifications for habitability. But let us hope there will always be room somewhere for those mavericks who find it impossible to adapt to life in the urban hive. There is already some indication that those who successfully adapt to urban environments develop characteristics antipathetic to those living in small towns and rural areas. There is potential for a deep sociological schism between urbanites who live in a manufactural environment and those outside of the hive in the natural environment. With political control vested in the growing majorities of urban regions, and with the urban voter increasingly out of touch with the more natural world outside, the stage is set for an increasingly serious political schism as well.

The consequence of industrialization, of intensive use of the earth, are manifest in three general areas:

1. Physical, chemical, and biological alterations of the earth environment as a result of diverse activities such as urban construction,

water resource projects, creation and disposal of wastes, agriculture, and mining.

2. The accelerating consumption of earth resources. Whereas area 1, above, is concerned with environmental effects of resource extraction and use, area 2 is concerned with the capacity of the earth to supply the variety of resources needed to support an industrial society.

3. The vulnerability of increasingly complex engineering systems to damage or destruction by natural geologic processes either operating independently of human activities or set in motion by them; such processes are commonly called geologic hazards. They have been considered at length in Chapter 2.

ENVIRONMENTAL ALTERATIONS

It is difficult to separate in a meaningful way purely physical effects from purely chemical or biological effects for many of the changes brought about through human activities. A good example is coal mining, where excavation changes the contour of the land and at the same time exposes to the air large volumes of coal containing pyrite (FeS_2). Oxidation of pyrite produces acids which, if they escape into local drainage systems, lower the pH to the point where water quality is adversely affected and aquatic life is destroyed (p. 165). Thus the following discussion attempts consideration of the spectrum of physical, chemical, and biological changes associated with enterprises such as (1) highways; (2) cities; (3) waste production and disposal; (4) mines, quarries, and well fields; (5) water-resource projects; (6) coastal installations; and (7) agriculture.

The highway. An observer flying over an industrialized country cannot fail to note that the landscape is everywhere pitted, scraped, leveled, heaped up, or otherwise scarred. Although the evidences of man's ability to move earth and rock are more intense around population centers, even in rural districts, in isolated forest, and in desert ranch lands, scars—chiefly roads—are everywhere. In the most sparsely populated area of the United States, for example, the Great Basin country of Nevada, California, Idaho, Utah, Colorado, New Mexico, Arizona, and western Texas, there are roads to mines, ranches, isolated windmills, microwave towers, and aviation beacons; there are roads along pipelines and railroads; there are roads into recreational areas. The infrequently used unpaved roads do not have serious direct environmental effects; they only promote local erosion by breaking turf cover and channeling run-off water. However, they make possible the movement of energy and machinery to almost any point and thus indirectly contribute to major engineering modifications of the land. Where man goes, he builds a road. Graded and paved roads, ranging all the way from county roads to the great concrete ribbons of the Interstate system, require moving large volumes of earth—cuts and fills, rerouting of drainage, stabilization of the subgrade, the laying of base-course material and pavement. Whereas roads used to follow the contour of the land, winding through valleys and climbing hills along spurs, the modern highway cuts straight across the landscape, slicing through deep cuts in hills and riding on massive fills in valleys. Limited access Interstate highways are effective barriers to traffic moving at angles to the great artery. In cities there have been complaints that the "freeway" separates neighborhoods as efficiently as a high wall; in the country, some farmers and ranchers whose land has been divided complain that the highway has made it more costly to work the odd-sized tracts that have been created. Along the route of the major highway are pits and quarries, for the most part abandoned, from which base material and concrete aggregate were obtained during construction. If local sources were not available during construction, base material and aggregate were transported from the nearest source, thus leaving a bigger hole somewhere else. On clay formations, large volumes of lime are commonly used to stabilize the subgrade, thus physically and chemically changing a strip of countryside.

Unlike the large permanent crushed stone quarries and sand and gravel pits where the trend is toward reclamation and rehabilitation of the pit or quarry for subsequent beneficial use after the construction material is depleted, the excavation opened up for road materials during highway construction and abandoned when the portable crushing and screening plant moves on is likely to remain as a hole in the ground until reclaimed by natural processes. In humid regions, soil creep and vegetation may in a few decades convert the hole into a gentle depression; in more arid areas, the pit may remain as an unhealed scar on the landscape for generations. In some places these abandoned pits fill with water and are an asset to the farmer or rancher, in others they are used as a dump. This is a beneficial use if the refuse-fill is eventually covered.

The most serious consequence of major highways results from use and is chemical, rather than physical. The highway is the locus of the internal combustion engine. Combustion of gasoline containing tetraethyl lead has caused a "lead halo" along heavily traveled roads. Lead is a well-known poison; the bloodstream level where its toxic effects are evident as "lead poisoning" in the human organism is 0.5 ppm (p. 137). The deleterious effects of this highway lead halo have not yet been evaluated, but sampling indicates that farm produce grown within 2 mi of major highways contains anomalous concentrations of lead (p. 137). Many other noxious products of the internal combustion engine are spewed into the air along highways; their effects on the environment are described on pp. 130–140.

Cities. As pockmarks and scrapes on the land surface increase in number, the air traveler can be sure he is approaching an area with a higher density of human beings, that is, a town or city. At night these colonies shine as brightly colored ornaments with ribbons of lights radiating outward from a center like some flamboyant piece of costume jewelry. In daylight, however, the larger communities are covered by a low-lying mantle of smoke or haze. The observer notes a great deal of motion in and around a city. Things are coming in by highway, railroad, and pipeline, and through air terminals and river or sea ports; things are going out by the same means and also through smokestacks and exhaust pipes and fans.

A large volume of the traffic into the city is earth materials, either crude or processed to some degree. Water comes in through a natural system such as a river, or is brought in through aqueducts, pipelines, or well bores. Some of the water is consumed, taken in by people or used up in a manufacturing process; some is simply used—for example, for washing or cooling—and then returned to the environment through a waste-disposal system. It is rare, indeed, for this water to leave the city with the same high quality as it entered. Energy comes into the city as natural gas, oil, coal, or electricity; it comes in pipelines, tank cars, trucks, and transmission lines. Some of it is put to work; some of it, converted to heat, raises the ambient temperature and leaves the city in rising air masses; some of the products of combustion are discharged into the air as gaseous waste products of varying degrees of noxiousness; the residues of combustion in the form of solid wastes are transported to a dumping ground in or out of the city where their steady accumulation poses a vexing problem for the future. Rarely, as in the case of fly ash, the waste is processed into a useful product. Ores, concentrates, and industrial minerals flow into the city in amounts dependent on the industrial orientation of the area. Processing and refining of minerals and manufacture of mineral products produce gaseous, liquid, and solid wastes in varied amounts. These add to the load carried by city waste disposal systems. Some of the minerals and elements concentrated in the urban environment are notorious poisoners (p. 135).

Construction materials move in large quantities into any viable community. Because of their low unit value most of them are locally mined or quarried. Sand and gravel and crushed stone are shipped for long distances only when a city has depleted more conveniently located supplies or inhibited local production through punitive zoning ordinances and tax policies. Brick, tile, and dimension stone commonly move longer distances because their acceptance is in part governed by architectural and aesthetic considerations. Most cities have dredged, quarried, or otherwise mined large volumes of sand, gravel, and stone from their environs. Reining (1967) calculated that in Los Angeles per capita consumption of sand and gravel was 4 tons per year. In the past little effort was made to rehabilitate or otherwise reclaim these peripheral depleted pits and quarries. More recently, however, as residential areas crowd close to old pits and quarries, efforts have been made to exploit the man-made irregularities of the terrain. Where the pits extended below the water table, small-lake oriented residential and resort areas are planned (Bauer, 1965: Johnson, 1966). Schellie and Rogier (1963) described other recreational, residential, institutional, and industrial uses. In some areas pits have been filled with refuse and then topped with earth fill for eventual restoration to other beneficial use. In Austin, Texas, in 1967 a recently evacuated stone quarry was landscaped and is now the site of a new junior high school and playground (Figure 28).

Production of natural aggregates (sand and gravel, crushed stone) in the United States is growing at a rate of about 5 percent per year; in volume, sand and gravel outrank any other mineral product. Despite their low value, sand and gravel plus crushed stone make up about 10 percent of the total mineral production value in the United States, including metals and fuels. The U. S. Bureau of Mines (1965a, pp. 787, 892) predicted that 1980 production would be 1.8 billion tons of sand

and gravel and 1.5 billion tons of crushed stone, but based on a 1965 production of .91 billion tons of sand and gravel and .77 billion tons of stone this estimate may be on the low side. Another U. S. Bureau of Mines projection (*Minerals Yearbook*, 1965b, p. 11) estimated a growth rate of 6.8 percent for sand and gravel and 6.9 percent for crushed stone between 1964 and 1975. If the 5 percent growth rate is maintained for the 25-yr period 1965 to 1990 that quarter century will see production of 43.4 billion tons of sand and gravel and 36.7 billion tons of crushed stone. This is a staggering volume, amounting to almost 20 cu mi— enough to spread a layer 5 ft thick over New Jersey, Connecticut, and Massachusetts or enough to fill nearly 500 times over the off-farm grain silos of the United States now empty because of the government's "success" in getting rid of "surpluses." However, sand and gravel deposits around major consumption areas have already been seriously depleted in many areas. In Dallas and San Antonio, for example, sand and gravel has been replaced in large part by crushed stone. Those areas with large stone deposits are fortunate to have an alternate source of natural aggregate. Risser and Major (1967, p. 7, Table 1) showed how production of natural aggregates is concentrated in the big urban counties of the United States (Table 7 and Figure 21).

With this background information it is appropriate to consider the consequences of depletion of aggregates in the big consuming areas.

The first effect of depletion of deposits of natural aggregates near urban centers is rising construction costs within the urban area as consumers assume the increased costs of haulage from more distant sources. Aggregate (fine aggregate plus coarse aggregate) makes up about 75 percent (by volume) or 80 percent (by weight) of average concrete. An increase of $1 per ton or $1.50 per cu yd for aggregate would not appear to result in a serious increase in the cost of an average residence where concrete is used principally in the foundation, driveway, walks, etc., because the amount of concrete in residential units seldom exceeds 60 cu yd. The increase due to higher aggregate cost would be only about $70. For a large building concrete requirements might be on the order of 10,000 to 30,000 cu yd of concrete. In this case the additional cost of aggregate could make a significant difference in total cost and could very well result in consideration of alternative materials. To go further, Reining (1967) estimated that 75 million tons of aggregate will be needed in the three-county Los Angeles area over the next 10 years to build highways alone. In this case, a dollar increase in aggregate cost will add $75 million to the total. This amount of public funds could measurably improve other public services.

Under the practical laws of economics, when a commodity becomes so expensive that it substantially raises the costs of the products in which

TABLE 7. **Examples of Extreme Concentration of Industrial Mineral Production in or Adjacent to Urban Areas in the United States**

Commodity	Geographical area	Percent of state area	1964 tonnage (millions)	Percent of state tonnage
Stone (crushed & broken)	Cook County (Chicago), Ill.	1.7	12.2	31.6
Limestone (crushed & broken)	Dade County (Miami), Fla.	3.7	10.2	32.3
Stone (all types)	St. Louis County, Mo.	0.7	5.2	16.5
Sand and gravel	Chicago Metropolitan Area (Cook, Will, Kane, DuPage, McHenry, and Lake Counties)	6.6	12.6	41.6
Sand and gravel	Los Angeles County	2.6	26.2	23.2
Sand and gravel	Los Angeles Metropolitan Area (Los Angeles, Orange, and San Diego Counties)	8.2	39.2	34.7
Sand and gravel	Detroit Metropolitan Area (Livingston, Washtenaw, Oakland, Macomb, and Wayne Counties)	5.7	18.7	36.0
Sand and gravel	Suburban Long Island (Nassau and Suffolk Counties)	2.5	10.6	27.0
Sand and gravel	Denver Metropolitan Area (Adams, Denver, Arapahoe, Boulder, and Jefferson Counties)	3.5	6.3	30.1

SOURCE: Risser and Major, 1967, p. 7, based on data of U. S. Bureau of Mines and U. S. Bureau of the Census.

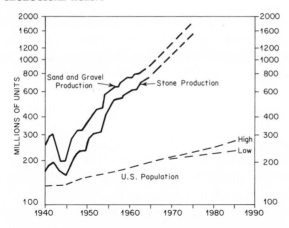

FIGURE 21. **Rates of growth for sand, gravel, and stone production, 1940–1975, and for total United States population, 1940–1985. Based on data of U. S. Bureau of the Census, 1967, and U. S. Bureau of Mines, 1965.** (After Risser and Major, 1967, p. 6.)

it is traditionally used, other commodities or other products begin to penetrate the market. For example, as the price of copper rises, aluminum moves into its market. However, this cannot happen unless there are other materials with similar properties so that substitutions are feasible. In the case of concrete, manufactured aggregates compete with natural aggregates, but they in turn are made from clay or shale which are subject to depletion. There are substitutes for concrete in some of its uses. Brick can substitute for concrete in some applications. Poreen brick and silicalcite, two manufactured construction materials, have recently entered the market as competitors with concrete. However, they are also made of earth raw materials such as sand, lime, cement, and water (*Chemical Week,* 1963, p. 94). Steel substitutes for reinforced concrete in beams and other structural members. For massive structures such as dams abandonment of concrete would require radical new methods of construction. In flexible-base highway construction with asphaltic paving, the asphalt binds an aggregate, thus substitution of asphalt for concrete does not solve the aggregate problem.

The urban area that has used up its own mineral resources will have to bear the financial burden of transportation from distant sources or of higher-cost substitutes. Scars from urban and suburban mineral production are healable. So it is reasonable for a city to make the most advantageous use possible of the strategically located supplies of construction materials.

Wastes. Man creates wastes wherever he goes. In sparsely settled areas without large industrial installations the volume of waste and the problem of disposing of it do not threaten the pattern of living. Waste that is combustible is burned on the premises and the resulting gaseous wastes are carried off and diluted by the atmosphere. The volume is small and the people affected are few. A farmer or rancher hauls those wastes that he cannot burn to a small pit on his own property, or he may use them to fill depressions or gullies. Organic animal wastes are beneficially applied to fields; in some areas of the world this includes human organic wastes, but in rural United States human wastes are disposed of in septic tanks or through a privy into specially constructed pits. A producer of waste in large volume, such as a large mine or a power plant, located in sparsely settled areas encounters few to complain. The atmosphere dilutes and disperses the gaseous wastes and those immediately downwind from the stacks move away or protest impotently. Solid wastes accumulate in large piles that may offend some through their unsightliness, but complaints based on aesthetic considerations do not yet convince courts that injunctive relief is in order, particularly in the light of the large economic contributions made by extractive enterprises. Only when solid and liquid wastes pollute local water supplies or threaten a substantial recreation and sportsman-oriented section of the economy do the inhabitants of sparsely populated regions rise up against the waste-producer.

Consider how the problem is compounded when people come together in large numbers. The amount of waste produced by each person is increasing and the number of people living in urbanized regions is increasing. In the United States a "wasteful" society has developed. Through planned obsolescence, throw-away containers, hard selling of "new models," and high labor costs that make it uneconomic to re-collect, reclaim, and reprocess, the burden of waste grows increasingly heavy. As McGauhey (1968) pointed out, wastes are not just the tailings of production but, eventually, the product itself. Our affluence has reached the point where thrift costs too much. Few remember the depression days when many unemployed collected and sold scrap metal, tinfoil, newspapers, and bottles. At present it is estimated that daily per capita production of solid wastes is on the order of 6 to 8 lb; the cost to U. S. cities for collection and disposal of solid wastes is estimated at $3 billion per year (Alexander, 1967).

Gaseous and liquid wastes are still largely ejected in the air or natural drainage systems. It is clear that this is no longer satisfactory, but the cost of alternative systems is not yet known. The spacecraft earth is doomed to travel as an essentially closed system carrying the wastes of the human culture along with it. Although man has succeeded in shooting some metallic matter outside of the atmosphere, most of it is still traveling along with the earth. Moreover, the cost of putting objects into orbit makes it unlikely that this is a potential mechanism for waste-disposal. We are left with the alternative of living with our wastes. We can convert wastes from one state to another—for example, we can reduce the volume of solid waste by high-temperature incineration, plus the cost of collecting it, plus the cost of the fuel, plus the capital cost of the incinerator—but we then have the problem of disposal of the gaseous wastes and the remaining solid. If we cannot tolerate a close association with our solid wastes, we can haul them off and stack them up in a pile, bury them, or fill in a natural depression—in short, get them out of the main stream of human activities. However, in recent history, we have had a way of catching up with our wastes or having our wastes catch up with us. Even the simple solution of seacoast cities barging wastes out into deep water and dumping them into the sea may in the long run turn out to be an unfortunate expedient. We can simplify the problem by producing less waste, by using and reusing until a thing is used up. But this makes the economist throw up his hands in horror. He sees no acceptable alternative to an ever-expanding economy.

Gaseous wastes—the new atmosphere. Man evolved as an air-breathing animal with sensory and respiratory organs adapted to a gaseous environment composed (at sea level and excluding water) of approximately 78 percent nitrogen, 21 percent oxygen, nearly 1 percent argon, and about .03 percent carbon dioxide. Water vapor ranges from near zero to as much as 4 percent. He has, on the average, a tolerance for natural deviations from the preindustrial atmospheric norm and, at least for limited periods, can survive in heavy concentrations of dust, water vapor, pollen, bacteria, and spores. Dwellers in swamp regions have been exposed to hydrogen sulfide gas produced naturally by decaying organic matter. Over millenia tolerance to such additions to the atmosphere was undoubtedly increased by selective survival—those with asthmatic or emphysematic tendencies and those with powerful allergies did not survive. However, the fact that human populations living near volcanos have in the past been overwhelmed and exterminated by dust and gases and those caught up in grass and forest fires have been asphyxiated show that man's tolerance to deviations from the atmospheric norm is limited. The heavy concentrations of smoke produced by early users of fire in caves, dugouts, tents, huts, and other primitive dwellings must have been injurious to eyes and respiratory systems. But life spans were short and exposure sporadic so that man survived these early poisons from combustion of wood. Now, in crowded, heavily industrialized areas there is a chronic and much more varied and complex deviation from the pre-industrial atmosphere in which man evolved. There is a persistent haze, a persistent array of industrial odors (that, indeed, may be noticeable only to the visitor), concentrations of particulate matter, and a variety of gases not present in nonindustrial areas.

The industrial atmosphere is an aerosol, a suspension of fine liquid and solid particles. In a typical urban aerosol particles range in diameter from 0.01 to 100 μ (1 μ is 1 micron = .001 mm). Particles less than 10 μ stay in suspension in the atmosphere a long time. When inhaled some particles are filtered out by nasal hairs, some are trapped in oral and bronchial passages, and some find their way into the lungs (Rich, 1967, p. 800). Some of the constituents of industrial atmospheres are toxic, some are merely irritants. Some nontoxic particles absorb toxic gases. There is considerable work under way to determine the levels or concentrations at which these substances are hazardous to health, but little is known about the cumulative effects of many decades of exposure to these aerosols in which concentrations of poisonous substances are substantially below those at which large numbers of people start dying. In all probability selection is already working to favor the survival of urban dwellers (man, other animals, and plants) with higher tolerance for the new atmosphere. There is developing, however, ever-increasing contrast between "inside" atmospheres and "outside" atmospheres. Dwellings, working places, and vehicles are air conditioned. Noxious substances are filtered out. The filters interposed between man's living and working habitats and the increasingly noxious outside atmosphere will work against selective evolution of a race that can tolerate the new atmosphere.

Although wind systems, topography, and solar radiation work to mix the lower part of the atmosphere, there is a rough stratification in terms of pollutants. The new industrial atmosphere is more or less limited to the bottom 6 mi of the atmosphere (which is nevertheless about 70 percent of the total air mass); within the bottom layer, the air in direct contact with urban regions contains higher amounts of gaseous wastes and aerosols than air over wilderness regions. Moreover, the atmosphere is not a permanent sink—over a period of time through chemical reactions and agglomeration pollutants are changed in form or settle out under the influence of gravity. Therefore, if all sources of pollution were to cease, the atmosphere would eventually cleanse itself; even the CO_2 content would reach an equilibrium. The new atmosphere is maintained by the ever-increasing discharge of pollutants.

The empirical approach to air pollution in the past has been to expel industrial gases through tall stacks to get the waste out of the immediate breathing area, depending on normal atmospheric processes to disperse the pollutants and dilute the waste to acceptable levels. This has worked fairly well where the volume of pollutants was low and the atmosphere was willing to cooperate by moving the air around and not "inverting" or stratifying so as to put a lid on upward movement. However, the volume of pollutants has steadily increased while the co-operativeness of the atmosphere has remained the same. A great part of the gaseous pollutants, moreover, are not susceptible to the tall-stack method of first-stage dispersal. One of the major causes of pollution, the internal combustion engine, is a ground-level poisoner.

Inasmuch as the atmosphere is no more helpful than it was, and the volume of pollutants shows no sign of abating, the obvious approach is to strip the more noxious substances out of the gaseous waste before ejecting it and thus keep the pollutants at "acceptable levels." "Acceptable" is rarely defined honestly in terms of health standards alone, for it normally means a level at which both the individual and the economy can survive. And so we have devices to attach to automobiles and smokestacks. There is an alternative—to strip out the noxious substances at the human intake end by equipping the urban dweller with a gas mask. However, it is difficult to put gas masks on birds, crops, trees, and grasses.

The principal substances in the "new atmosphere" that either did not exist in preindustrial atmosphere or now exist at significantly higher concentrations are:

1. Water vapor: produced in large volume by combustion but not a pollutant. It enters the hydrologic cycle, and precipitates out of the atmosphere.

2. Carbon dioxide: a product of combustion. In 1890 the average CO_2 content of the atmosphere was 290 ppm. It has now increased about 10 percent to 315 ppm. It is estimated that doubling the CO_2 content will raise the average surface temperature of the earth about 3.8°C (Conservation Foundation, 1963). The current rate of increase is 0.7 ppm per year. About 10 times as much CO_2 comes from combustion as from breathing by animals (Air Conservation Commission, 1965, p. 79). This is not a pollutant in the sense that it is directly injurious to life, but it may prove to have great geologic significance in terms of altering the environment (p. 139). Biological productivity increases with increase in temperature and CO_2 content. Increase in temperature increases the volume of sea water and raises sea levels through melting of ice caps (Conservation Foundation, 1963).

3. Carbon monoxide: a product of incomplete combustion contributed chiefly by the internal combustion engine. Approximately 3 lb. of CO are produced per gallon of fuel burned (Environmental Pollution Panel, PSAC, 1965, p. 67). Breathing of atmosphere containing as much as 120 ppm of CO for an hour is damaging to health. For many individuals lower concentrations are injurious —100 ppm commonly causes dizziness and headache (Air Conservation Commission, 1965, p. 74). Goldsmith and Landaw (1968) reported on a study of carbon monoxide in human health. They concluded (p. 1359) that cigarette smoking is the principal source of exposure to carbon monoxide and that the median concentration for one-pack-a-day smokers who inhale is a serious threat to health in persons with "underlying vascular insufficiency." They further concluded that community air pollution may produce this same level of concentration in nonsmokers. Concentrations of 72 ppm have been measured in Los Angeles, 100 ppm in Detroit, and it is believed that during peak times in most metropolitan areas concentrations of CO reach 100 ppm (Presi-

dent's Science Advisory Committee, 1965, p. 67; Abelson, 1965b, p. 1527; McGaughey, 1968, p. 18). Studies of carbon monoxide concentrations in New York City in different places and at different times of the day showed a correlation with the normal activities of the business day (Johnson et al., 1968, pp. 67–68). Total daily emissions from vehicle exhausts for the city were estimated at 4140 tons of carbon monoxide, 560 tons of hydrocarbons, and 160 tons of oxides of nitrogen. Midtown and lower Manhattan were the main sources. A probe at 110 East 45th Street, 15 ft above the pavement and 5 ft from the curb, measured average hourly concentrations of more than 15 ppm of carbon monoxide between 9:00 A.M. and 7:00 P.M. from January–May and August–September of 1967. These amounts are in excess of the recommended maximum under New York State standards.

4. *Sulfur dioxide and sulfuric acid:*   produced from combustion of sulfur-bearing fuels, mainly from power plants, smelters treating sulfide ores, and from sulfuric acid plants. These substances are present in much smaller quantities than carbon dioxide and carbon monoxide but are much more toxic. Concentrations rarely exceed a few parts per million. SO_2 does not accumulate in the atmosphere because it converts to sulfuric acid and sulfates; its atmospheric life is generally a few days. Primary emissions are as SO_2. In the presence of oxygen, sunlight, and water vapor, SO_2 converts to SO_3 and then to H_2SO_4 (sulfuric acid). However, SO_2 is very irritating to the upper respiratory tract, and inhalation of sulfuric acid mist damages sensitive tissues. Sulfuric acid mist at concentrations of 5 mg per cu m and SO_2 in the range 1 to 5 ppm are damaging to health. Exposure to concentrations of 5 ppm of SO_2 for an hour causes choking. Combinations of SO_2 with aerosols seems to increase toxic reactions. Sulfur compounds are considered to be the most harmful agents in the deadly smogs that have taken a large toll of life. In the London smog of 1952, held responsible for 4000 deaths, SO_2 concentration reached 1.34 ppm (Air Conservation Commission, 1965, p. 61). The sulfur pollutants are also very damaging to crops and other vegetation. Sulfurous smelter pollution at Ducktown, Tennessee, Anaconda, Montana, and Sudbury, Ontario, has almost totally destroyed vegetation (President's Science Advisory Committee, 1965, p. 204). Prolonged exposure to SO_2 and SO_3 causes corrosion and etching of various building

materials, particularly copper alloys and building stone, concrete, and mortar containing carbonate.

In industrial counties SO_2 is spewed into the atmosphere in large volumes. In the United States alone it is estimated that 25 million tons per year are emitted. The solution is (1) to use fuels naturally low in sulfur, (2) to remove the sulfur from the fuel prior to combustion, or (3) to recover the sulfur from gases as a marketable by-product. Fortunately, there is economic incentive for collection, because sulfur is a valuable industrial mineral and can be sold to recover part of the cost of collection or even at a profit. At present, from an economic point of view, removal and recovery of sulfur from stack gases seems more attractive than removal of sulfur in the form of pyrite from coal prior to combustion. A study by Arthur D. Little and Dorr-Oliver authorized by the National Center for Air Pollution Control indicated that coal operators would have to charge $1.10 to $1.20 per ton more for desulfurized coal, but the users, the power companies, can expect only about 30 cents per ton increased value from the desulfurized coal. The difference of 80 to 90 cents per ton is the cost of pollution abatement, and it is not clear who is going to pay it or how (*Chemical Week*, 1968c p. 37).

The Air Quality Act of 1967 required the Department of Health, Education, and Welfare to set air quality standards. Standards set for SO_2 call for a concentration of no more than 0.1 ppm for any 24-hr period. Maintenance of these standards world require massive reductions of SO_2 levels in major cities— 80 percent in New York and 50 percent in Philadelphia (*Wall Street Journal*, Nov. 22, 1967, p. 12). New York and New Jersey have moved to reduce pollution by limiting the sulfur content of fuels burned. In New Jersey, effective May 1968, no fuel oil containing more than 1 percent sulfur may be purchased for use; by October 1971, the allowable content drops to 0.3 percent sulfur. State regulations on fuel sulfur limits as of 1968 are summed up in Table 8.

Early in 1969 it was announced that a $10-million desulfurization plant scheduled to go on stream in 1971 in the New York–New Jersey metropolitan area could make 50,000 to 100,000 tons of sulfur available per year by processing Venezuela crude oils (*Chemical Week*, January 25, 1969, p. 13). Fuel industries, faced with the need to switch to low sulfur fuels or desulfurize traditional fuels, say that the standards will cause economic havoc and are lower than those really necessary for health. Coal and fuel oil commonly contain 1.5 to 3 percent sulfur, and it will be necessary to reduce the sulfur content of fuels to less than 0.5 percent. Costs of desulfurizing are shown in Figure 22. Capital costs for desulfurizing of residual oils from the Caribbean region are estimated at $750 million (*Chemical Week*, 1967a, p. 78).

5. *Hydrogen sulfide and other sulfur compounds (mercaptans)*: produced by industrial processes and accumulation of industrial wastes in stagnant waters. This is mostly a local nuisance, accounting for bad odors, and does not constitute a hazard except in extraordinary circumstances, such as a massive escape of gas due to accidental releases or equipment failures. Bacteria produce hydrogen sulfide by reducing sulfates and the gas is released to

TABLE 8. **State Regulations on Sulfur Limits in Fuel**

Date	Sulfur limit	Fuel user
NEW YORK[a]		
October 1, 1968	1.0%	Power plants in New York, Bronx, and Kings counties
October 1, 1969	1.0	Power plants in the remaining New York City metropolitan area
October 1, 1969	0.3	All residual fuel oil users except power plants
NEW JERSEY[b]		
May 1, 1968	1.0	All residual fuel oil users
October 1, 1970	0.5	All residual fuel oil users
October 1, 1971	0.3	All residual fuel oil users
MARYLAND[c]		
July 1, 1968	1.5	All residual fuel oil users
July 1, 1969	1.0	All residual fuel oil users

SOURCE: *Chemical Week*, 1968b, p. 20.
[a] Applicable to the New York City metropolitan area. [b] Except for certain rural counties. [c] For Montgomery and Prince Georges counties; ordinances of certain northern Virginia communities in the Washington, D.C., area provide for identical limits.

the atmosphere all over the world as a result of this natural process. Except around industrial centers, H2S levels probably are not appreciably higher now than in the past.

6. *Oxides of nitrogen (mainly nitric oxide and nitrogen dioxide):* produced in industrial urban areas with large numbers of motor vehicles and power plants. Nitrogen and oxygen combine when combustion takes place at high pressures; the internal combustion engine is the main source of these pollutants. However, the manufacture of nitric acid and other such chemical processes also produce oxides of nitrogen. Nitric oxide is the main gas produced by combustion, but in the atmosphere photochemical reactions convert much of it to nitrogen dioxide, a more toxic brownish gas that reduces visibility and contributes to smog. So-called photochemical smog is the result of such oxidants as ozone and peroxyacetyl nitrate formed by photolytic reactions of nitrogen oxides, hydrocarbons, aromatics, and aldehydes in the presence of sunlight. See Figure 23. Damage to plants and injury to health of animals, including man, results from concentrations of nitrogen dioxide at 5 ppm for 1 hr or combinations of ozone, nitrogen dioxide, and hydrocarbons at concentrations of 0.15 ppm for one hour. Ozone is extremely toxic. It is not emitted into the atmosphere as such, but is formed photochemically as described above.

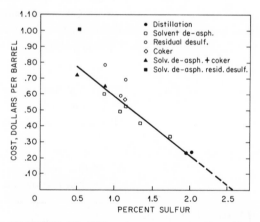

FIGURE 22. **What it costs to cut the sulfur content of fuel oils.** (After *Chemical Week,* 1967a, p. 78.)

Vehicle exhausts contain some 1500 ppm of oxides of nitrogen; the goal is to reduce these to at least 350 ppm. NO_2 reacts with water vapor to produce highly corrosive nitric acid. Los Angeles "smog" has been found to contain peroxybenzoyl nitrate which is a powerful eye irritant (*Wall Street Journal*, March 29, 1968).

7. *Organic gases:* produced by vehicle exhaust and chemical process industries. Organic gases participate in the photochemical reactions with oxides of nitrogen, as described previously, and are also damaging to health of plants and animals in their own right. Ethylene in concentrations of only a few parts per billion damages trees. Olefins, aldehydes, mercaptans, and "solvents" are other organic gases entering the industrial atmosphere.

8. *Hydrogen fluoride:* produced in the manufacture of superphosphate from fluorine-containing phosphate ores, in the manufacture of aluminum, and in smelting of fluorine-containing ores. This extremely toxic gas is particularly dangerous because it is taken out of the air and concentrated by plants. Concentrations as low as 1 part per billion are damaging to some species. A few parts per million of fluoride in plants indicates atmospheric contamination. When high-fluorine vegetation is ingested by livestock a disease called fluorosis appears.

9. *Particulate matter:* (1) dust (soil and rock particles); (2) soot (finely divided carbon commonly carrying heavy hydrocarbons); (3) ash from combustion; (4) oily photochemical smog particles; (5) lead and lead salts and other metals and metal compounds,

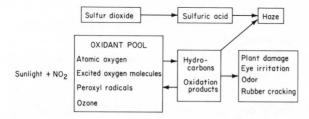

FIGURE 23. **Complex reactions in photochemical air pollution.** (After Air Conservation Commission, 1965, Fig. 4, copyright 1965 by the American Association for the Advancement of Science.)

such as chromates, nickel carbonyl, cadmium, titanium, mercury, manganese, zinc, copper, beryllium, and vanadium; (6) asbestos; (7) miscellaneous particles from local manufacturing, metallurgical, and agricultural industries; (8) "resuspended" finely comminuted particles of a multitude of products—rubber, newspaper, paint, glass, etc.; (9) insecticides and herbicides; and (10) radioactive materials. Larger, heavier particles ($>10 \mu$) settle out of the atmosphere more or less rapidly, depending on turbulence and precipitation, but smaller particles tend to remain in suspension for longer periods. Particles $<1 \mu$ behave similar to gases. Vehicle exhausts emit particles of which 70 percent are in the range 0.02 to 0.06 μ.

In addition to affecting plants and animals, a large volume of aerosols affect weather and climate. Although the carbon dioxide added to the atmosphere by internal combusion has a tendency to raise the temperature of the earth (p. 139), the large amount of particulate matter added to the atmosphere as smoke or dust particles by human activities has the opposite effect. Of particular concern is the volume of exhaust that is to be expected from the proposed supersonic jet transports operating in the upper atmosphere. These "contrails" trigger the formation of cirrus clouds. The total effect of smoke, dust, and increased cirrus cloud cover is to contribute to a climate change toward a cooler earth.

Some particulate substances induce injurious chemical reactions in animals and plants, some harsh and abrasive substances cause physical damage to sensitive tissues, and some do both. The effects on plants and animals of many particulate substances remain to be learned. Lead, a well-known poisoner, has been killing people for thousands of years. The earliest documented case was that of the ancient Greeks, who mulled wine in lead containers. Although we have learned to avoid lead cooking vessels and utensils, we continue to spew lead into the environment at a great rate. In 1966, 1.3 million tons were consumed in the United States— 37 percent in manufacture of batteries, 18 percent in gasoline additives, 6 percent as red lead and litharge, and 5 percent as calking lead. Nearly 600,000 tons a year collected as scrap are recycled. Most of the lead dispersed into the atmosphere is the lead added to gasoline as tetraethyl and tetramethyl lead, lead contained in coal and other natural fuels, lead emitted by smelters, lead in the form of arsenate in dusts and sprays, and lead contained in trash that is burned. Tetraethyl lead was first added to motor fuels in 1923, so we have nearly half a century of increasing volume of dispersal mainly concentrated in cities and along major highways. The U. S. Public Health Service permits lead concentrations of up to 4 cc/gal in motor fuel, but most refiners use between 2 and 3 cc. To make gasoline with equal performance specifications without lead will cost from 1.1 to 2.9 cents per gallon more and require investment of $1.5 to 3 billion (*Oil and Gas Journal*, 1967b, p. 43) with some estimates of capital costs as high as $4.2 billion (*Oil and Gas Journal*, 1967a, p. 74). Since 1923 enough lead has been emitted to contaminate the surface of the Northern Hemisphere to the extent of 10 mg per sq m (President's Science Advisory Committee, 1965, p. 205). Grasses and vegetables collected near highways show an abnormal concentration (President's Science Advisory Committee, 1965, p. 205). Larger particles fall out on and become concentrated in pavements. In New York City, concentration in street dirt rose from 1190 ppm in 1924, to 1760 ppm in 1934, to 2650 ppm in 1953 (Air Conservation Commission, 1965, p. 125).

There is a direct correlation between lead content of the atmosphere and city size. Los Angeles is highest, with 5 μg per cubic meter, other communities larger than 2 million inhabitants have concentrations of about 2.5 μg per cubic meter, and communities of less than 1 million show concentrations of from 1.5 to 2 μg per cubic meter (Air Conservation Commission, 1965, p. 125). Fortunately, only a small amount of the total lead content emitted from automobiles is in a highly toxic organic state. Most is in the less-dangerous form of bromides and chlorides. The more lead there is in the air that a person breathes the higher the concentration of lead in his blood and urine. Those working in high-lead environments (automobile garages and tunnels, for example) show highest concentrations and are closest to the threshold for lead poisoning, 0.5 to 0.8 ppm (*Chemical Week*, 1965b, pp. 24-25).

Tobacco and the soils it is grown in were in the past contaminated by lead arsenate sprays (no longer used). Although the sprays were discontinued, the soils remain contaminated. Smokers have higher lead content in their red blood cells than nonsmokers.

There is currently a controversy over the seriousness of asbestos particles as a pollutant. According to an article in *Chemical Week* (September 10, 1966, p. 32), 40 percent of all Americans have mild chronic cases of asbestosis through inhalation of small fibers (1 x 3 μ) from (1) asbestos-lined ducts in air-conditioned buildings, (2) asbestos insulation, (3) brake linings and clutch plates, (4) auto undercoats, (5) ceiling and floor tiles, (6) shingles and siding, (7) fitting, cutting, and removing of asbestos-containing wallboards, pipes, flooring, and insulating materials, (8) incineration of asebstos-filled scrap, and (9) dust from asbestos processing plants. The article quoted the U. S. Public Health Service to the effect that asbestos-related cancer has increased sixfold. The fibers have a capacity to absorb other toxic substances and carry them into lungs. The article was subsequently challenged by an officer of the Johns-Manville Corporation (*Chemical Week*, October 8, 1966, p. 7), who stated that no evidence indicates that even 1 percent of Americans have mild chronic asbestosis and that the claim of a sixfold increase in asbestos-related cancer cannot be substantiated.

In summary, it is estimated that some 125 to 150 million tons per year of pollutants are cast into the atmosphere over the United States through combustion. Seventy percent of the total are CO and SO_2; the remainder are oxides of nitrogen, hydrocarbons, and particulate matter of varying composition. About 60 percent of these pollutants come from vehicle exhausts, 17 percent from industry, 14 percent from power plants, 5.5 percent from space heaters, and 3.5 percent from refuse burning (Rich, 1967, p. 796; *Oil and Gas Journal*, 1967b, p. 43). Other pollutants, such as asbestos and pesticides, are in addition to the combustion-produced pollutants. The chief villain is the motor vehicle, which emits CO_2, CO, gasoline, oxides of nitrogen and nitrogen-containing organics, aldehydes and acids, phenols, and particularly matter including lead, nickel, phosphorous, and boron compounds (President's Science Advisory Committee, 1965, p. 67). It is clear that the "new" atmosphere is being produced largely through combustion and that from the point of view of habitability of the environment for existing species of plants and animals the changing composition is undesirable. Although the principal industrial contaminants—CO, CO_2, SO_2, and oxides of nitrogen—can be reduced through more careful control, to produce complete combustion of CO and the re-moval of the deleterious constituents (SO_2 and oxides of nitrogen) prior to emission, CO_2 will continue to increase as long as combustion of fossil fuels continues. Moreover, combustion uses up large volumes of oxygen. It is appropriate, therefore, to examine the oxygen-carbon dioxide balance of the atmosphere and to consider combustion in terms of alternatives.

The oxygen in the atmosphere is the result of an interplay of its production by photosynthesis in plants and its removal by animals, combustion, and oxidation reactions in surficial and near-surface earth materials. The supply is completely renewed over a period of several thousand years. The main threat to the oxygen supply is not increasing use by animals and combustion but the possibility of destroying the great corpus of oxygen-producing plants through nuclear war, biological war, or sheer population pressure (Air Conservation Commission, 1965, p. 24). However, LaMont Cole of Cornell University was quoted in the Conservation Foundation Letter of February 23, 1968, to the effect that we may be approaching the point at which the rate of oxygen burned in fuel combustion exceeds the rate at which oxygen is liberated in photo-synthesis—if this happens, the oxygen content of the amosphere will begin to decrease. Carbon dioxide is used up in natural biological and chemical processes. Plants extract it from the air in photosynthesis; weathering of rocks and minerals fixes carbon dioxide in new minerals; much CO_2 is taken out of sea water by chemical and biological pre-cipitation of calcium carbonate; much is stored in carbonaceous deposits (peat, coal, lignite). However, oxidation, natural or through com-bustion, releases CO_2 back to the atmosphere. By burning fossil fuels, man releases suddenly CO_2 that was absorbed by plants and animals over millions of years and stored in coal and petroleum deposits deep in the crust. Large amounts are also contributed by volcanos. The oceans absorb CO_2 at a very slow rate. It is clear that more is being added than is being removed by natural processes (p. 130).

Principal concern about this progressive accumulation is its possible effect on the earth's heat budget, because CO_2 is one of the substances (water vapor and ozone are the others) that absorb some of the heat radiated toward space from the earth, in the same way as the glass in a green house holds heat these gases hold heat in the atmosphere. The question is, will the increase in CO_2 warm up the earth to the point of effecting climatic changes? One corrective mechanism is likely to slow down the change, because increase in CO_2 plus increase in temperature increases biological productivity and results in a larger plant mass, and this in turn requires more CO_2 and produces more oxygen. However, rapidly rising levels of combustion might overwhelm this braking mechanism. Estimates indicate that by the first decade of the next century the combustion of fossil fuels could have produced an amount of CO_2 equal to 20 percent of what is now in the atmosphere. Combustion of the reserves of all the known fossil fuel deposits will produce an amount of CO_2 equal to 17 times the present amount in the atmosphere. If only half this amount stays in the atmosphere this will drastically change its composition. If rising earth temperatures result in melting of ice caps the traditional living and food producing area for the expanding human culture—the land area—will be drastically reduced. There will be slow but inexorable evacuations of coastal areas and painful social readjustments. Thus, this geologic consequence of industrialization could be far-reaching.

Forgetting for the moment the great economic dislocations attendant upon any reduction in combustion, are there technological possibilities that would suggest alternatives to combustion? The answer is, of course, yes. Nuclear-fueled power plants are a reality and can replace those fired by fossil fuels. The development of breeder reactors will solve the nuclear fuel problem. One alternative to the internal combustion engine is the fuel cell or battery, but the technological road to equal efficiency will be a long, hard one and a successful engineering solution will open up formidable raw material problems. Batteries are made from metals and production of any of those now under consideration in the numbers required for the present vehicle population would result in severe material shortages, except for the sodium-sulfur (with sulfur coming from nonconventional sources such as gypsum)or zinc-air batteries. According to Chemical Week (1968a, p. 43) the following metal batteries are under consideration to power vehicles: lead-acid (300 lb), lithium (75 lb), nickel-cadmium (125 lb), and silver-zinc (300 lb).

Considering the vehicle population of the United States as composed of 100 million automobiles, the consumption of metals, if this entire vehicle population were battery operated, would be staggering. The total 1967 world production of these metals was: cadium, ~30 thousand pounds, lead ~3 million tons, lithium ~5 thousand tons,* nickel ~0.5

* This figure is approximate because production figures from some lithium-producing countries are not available.

million tons, silver ~250 million troy ounces, and zinc ~5 million tons. Concern over the volume of pollutants emitted by the internal combustion engine has revived interest in vehicles propelled by steam power plants wherein the fuel is more completely consumed; in May 1968 it was reported that the United State Senate would study "steam cars" as a possible solution to air pollution (*Wall Street Journal*, May 27, 1968).

For many manufacturing processes the elimination of combustion and elimination of CO_2 discharge would be impossible or present great difficulties. Portland cement manufacture is a clear case. Blast furnace iron production using coke is another. Again, ignoring the economic upheavals, many metallurgical processes could use heat from nuclear reactors to promote the necessary reactions or go to electrolytic processes. Space heating could be nuclear-electric or through heat pumps. An all nuclear-electric society that prohibited burning of fossil fuels could probably achieve an atmosphere with a stable CO_2 content.

Liquid wastes. The traditional method of disposing of liquid wastes has been the simple one of discharging them into the surface drainage system—streams and rivers—where they are diluted by the normal flow of the system and eventually find their way into the ultimate basin for liquid wastes, the ocean. In some drainage systems, such as the tributaries to the Great Lakes, the wastes accumulate in a lake basin and, from the geological view, are temporarily stored. In this century some liquid wastes have been injected into subsurface reservoirs. Substances discharged into water courses either as liquids or as slurries, sludges, and sediment include (1) domestic sewage—wastes with a high demand for oxygen, (2) infectious agents—largely eliminated in the United States, (3) plant nutrients—mainly nitrates and phosphates, (4) organic chemicals—detergents, pesticides, insecticides, (5) other minerals and chemicals, (6) sediments from erosion, (7) radioactive substances, and (8) heat (Committee on Pollution 1966, pp. 12-13). Wastes dumped in surface water systems, depending on their concentration and chemical composition, undergo some changes in transit and affect some changes in transit, reacting with the dissolved salts in the natural water, with the suspended sediment load (including organic matter), and also affecting the aquatic life in the water system. Effects on living organisms can be beneficial—for example, increasing their food supply—or deleterious—consuming the oxygen supply, changing the pH of the solution, destroying the food supply, or directly poisoning the organisms. Heavy discharge of nutrient wastes (mainly human sewage, animal wastes, phosphate-rich detergents) results in a process called *eutrophication:* the superabundant nutrients, principally excess phosphate, cause overwhelming growth of algae and aquatic plants that choke open water, destroy potability, decompose and foul the air, and consume the deep-water oxygen necessary to sustain fish and animal life. Bacteria are unable to convert the great mass of dead organic matter into plant and animal food as rapidly as it accumulates.

As the volumes and variety of liquid wastes increase, the dilution capabilities of many natural systems are overwhelmed and the deleterious effects are obvious even to the casual observer. The Potomac Estuary receives 200 million gallons per day of waste water (only partly treated) and 3 million tons per year of sediment (U. S. Geological Survey press release, May 1, 1966). Waste-bearing waters from domestic, industrial, and agricultural sources are forecast to reach nearly 750 billion gallons per day by the year 2000, an increase of 400 percent since 1954 and about two-thirds of the total estimated volume of stream flow in the continental United States (Committee on Pollution, 1966, p. 177).

The Chicagoland Deep Tunnel Project is a plan to control pollution in Chicago. Floods and associated pollution come from overflows of storm water. During storms the capacity of the sewer system is insufficient to handle both sewage and storm water, and raw domestic and industrial sewage is discharged with storm waters into Illinois waterways and during occasional severe storms, into Lake Michigan. This polluted water causes a health hazard. In addition, the inability of the system to carry the required volumes results in flood damage. The deep tunnel project will divert the polluted overflows so they will drop through vertical shafts into a network of concrete-lined tunnels. The tunnels will conduct the overflow into two large reservoirs mined out of the Galena dolomite 600–800 ft below the surface. It is proposed to construct the deep tunnel system over a 10-yr period at a cost of about $1.27 billion (Koelzer, Bauer, and Dalton, 1968).

In areas where pollution problems are most acute attempts have been made to diminish the volume and toxicity of wastes by treatment prior to discharge. For example, one company that used to dispose of zinc slurry now precipitates the zinc as oxide and disposes of it as a solid. In coastal areas, in an attempt to remove the wastes from heavily populated areas, river systems and estuaries are avoided and wastes are barged out to sea and dumped offshore. At Tom's River, New Jersey, the Tom's River Chemical Corporation built a 10-mi-long underground pipeline to bypass the river and discharge the wastes 3500 ft offshore (*Chemical Week*, 1966a, p. 95). New Jersey has recently announced a plan to construct a series of regional sewage treatment plants along 100 mi of its coast line. Effluent would be pumped as far as a mile out to sea to prevent contamination of shellfish in the near-shore environment (*Environmental Science and Technology*, November, 1967, p. 871).

Barging and offshore dumping of liquid chemical wastes is increasing (*Chemical Week*, 1967b). National Lead, Shell Chemical, U. S. Steel, Standard Oil of California, American Cyanamid, Du Pont, Jet Propulsion Laboratory, and others are actively dumping wastes off the Atlantic, Pacific, and Gulf coasts of the United States. The Federal Water Pollution Control Administration is watching the situation and has commented that so far waste disposal at sea has proceeded in a cautious and careful manner (*Chemical Week*, 1967b, p. 133).

In addition to the caution exercised by companies engaged in ocean disposal (several large companies employ oceanographic consultants), there are local rules. Off New York, the harbor supervisor has set a minimum distance of 15 mi for acids and 125 mi (beyond the edge of the shelf) for toxic materials. Wastes currently dumped include such diverse substances as sodium salts, iron acid solutions, mercaptans, organic phosphate pesticides, phosphorous compounds, sulfur compounds, carbon tetrachloride, methanol, halide salts of antimony in zinc slurry, phenol derivatives, chlorinated hydrocarbons, and cyanides. A waste consisting of a dilute solution of iron sulfate and sulfuric acid with a 30-percent-solid slurry of insoluble silica and titanium oxide is produced in titanium metallurgical operations. Both Du Pont and National Lead dump these wastes from barges. National Lead's disposal area is checked periodically for harmful effects by Woods Hole Oceanographic Institute. Some wastes are discharged directly in liquid form, some are packaged in drums. However, eventually the drums disintegrate and the solution is released. Ocean waste disposal is not cheap. It is regarded by many as the "last resort" method of waste disposal. Costs of special 5000-ton capacity barges are about $1 million and overall disposal costs have been calculated at $2 to $4 per ton of waste (*Chemical Week*, 1967b, p. 133).

It is difficult to secure accurate figures on the volumes of liquid wastes now dumped directly into the ocean. The order of magnitude off the United States' coasts is probably at the level of hundreds of millions of gallons per year. Compared to the total volume of the oceans, about 33×10^6 million cubic miles, a yearly increment of 100 million gallons or 1×10^{-4} cu mi is insignificant. But, of course, the wastes are not dispersed evenly in the great volume of sea water. They are concentrated in local areas and some are so toxic that concentrations of a few parts per million are deadly to living organisms. The long-range effects of continued dumping of wastes on the composition of ocean water and living marine populations remains to be seen.

Large-scale use of water for cooling in power plants and in industrial processes results in discharge of water at a higher temperature than it entered the facility. Conversion of a cold-water stream or river upstream from a facility to a warmer stream or river downstream is, in modern parlance, *thermal pollution*. The effects are biological—coldwater species die; the stream, with a reduced oxygen content, no longer has the capacity to support the bacterial action necessary to clean up wastes, and algae growth chokes the water. If there should be a general increase in temperature of water entering a coastal region, the result might well be extinction of some species, migration of others, and a disruption of fishing industries. The Mahoning River in Ohio is an extreme case where summer water temperatures as high as 120° F have been measured (*Wall Street Journal*, December 1, 1967). This is about 30° above the tolerance of most aquatic life. There is currently controversy about a potential thermal threat to Lake Cayuga, New York, from a proposed 830-megawatt natural fluid steam generating plant for electricity (Carter, 1968).

The principal source of heat is the power plant, specifically the steam condenser. Commonly the temperature of cooling water is raised 10-30° F above normal; during summer months discharges may be at 100-115° F. The problem is becoming more urgent because nuclear power plants, for safety, operate at lower steam pressures, are less efficient, and thus discharge more heat through the condensor system. A single large nuclear plant may require as much as 7 billion gallons of cooling water per day. Considering the number of nuclear power plants either proposed or already under construction, it is estimated that the deluge of hot water might reach 100 trillion gallons annually by 1980, double the current production (*Wall Street Journal*, December 1,

1967). One solution to the problem is to air-cool the water in a cooling tower before discharge, but this is expensive and adds to the cost of electric power. Conservationist groups have proposed limits on the discharge of hot water—the temperature of water in rivers designated as cold water fisheries could not be raised above 68°, and temperature in warm water fisheries could not be raised above 83°. At present (early 1968), construction of a nuclear facility on the Connecticut River at Vernon, Vermont, is held up because the company's original plans contemplated raising the river temperature by 20°. Probably Vermont Nuclear will install cooling towers to meet temperature requirements.

Subsurface disposal of liquid wastes. One earth resource that seldom comes to mind is the space that exists below the surface. As room on the surface becomes more and more precious, it is certain that subsurface space will become more and more valuable to society. Subsurface space is of two kinds, (1) natural subsurface space, existing mostly as pores in granular rocks, dissolved cavities in carbonate rocks, and fractures; and (2) artificially created subsurface space either as cavities mined or dissolved out of the rock, or as pressure-induced fractures. In all deep subsurface strata below the water table, natural openings—pores and fractures—are already filled with fluids. Depending on the porosity and permeability, however, space can be created by pressure injection, which forces the existing fluids to move out. Where these fluids go and how fast is considered in studies of the hydrodynamics of the formation.

By far the greatest volume of liquid wastes disposed of through injection into subsurface formations occurs in oil fields, where the waste is salt water. Some highly toxic chemical wastes are disposed of underground and considerable research has gone into investigation of subsurface disposal of radioactive wastes (p. 159). It should be emphasized that there is more to subsurface waste disposal than pouring fluids into a hole in the ground. A three-dimensional geologic and hydrodynamic analysis is required to locate a formation with sufficient porosity and permeability to receive the waste fluids and to predict where the fluids will go when they enter the disposal reservoir. The American Association of Petroleum Geologists has recently published a study of subsurface waste disposal in geologic basins (Galley, 1968*b*). The association's study was brought about by the Atomic Energy Commission's request for assistance in evaluation of geologic criteria for secure subsurface waste disposal. Other studies include reports by Warner (1967) and the Interstate Oil Compact Commission (1968).

In many oil fields the wells produce a mixture of oil and salt water. In Texas, on the average, 2.5 barrels of salt water are produced for every barrel of oil, or about 2.5 billion barrels of salt water (42-gal barrels) per year. The oil and salt water are separated at the well and salt water then presents a waste disposal problem. In the early days of the industry, the practice was to dispose of the salt water in surface pits; the pits frequently leaked, and the result was pollution of surface water and groundwater and contamination of pasture or farm land around the pit. Subsequently salt-water disposal pits were more carefully constructed and lined to prevent leakage. The increasing concern about environmental pollution, together with the declining pressures in many oil reservoirs, promoted development of technology for re-injection of large volumes of salt water into the reservoirs. Injection wells are drilled to repressurize reservoirs, for waterflooding reservoirs in secondary recovery operations, and simply to dispose safely of brines in subsurface formations that do not contain fresh water. In Texas, some 5 million barrels per day of oil-field brines are already reinjected, 440,000 barrels per day in the East Texas field alone. Over the nation, nearly 20 million barrels per day are injected. The Texas regulatory authority (Texas Railroad Commission) has ruled that as of January 1, 1969, no new permits for open-pit disposal of brines will be issued; thus, subsurface disposal of salt water will increase sharply.

Subsurface waste disposal can have unforeseen effects. The Rocky Mountain Arsenal in Denver manufactures a variety of chemical products under the direction of the U. S. Army Chemical Corps and has a waste-disposal problem. From 1942 until 1961 contaminated waste water was disposed of through evaporation in surface reservoirs. There was contamination of local ground water through leakage of the reservoirs, and attempts to render the reservoirs watertight were not successful. In 1961 an injection disposal well was drilled to 12,045 ft. In March 1962 pressure injection of wastes began with disposal of 4.2 million gallons. In 1½ years (to September 1963) over 100 million gallons of fluids were injected. In April 1962 the Denver area began to experience a series of earthquakes. They are continuing to this date. David M. Evans (1966) noted an extraordinary correlation between the earthquakes and the injection of fluids in the disposal well (p.

22). Thus, he presented a convincing case for a cause-and-effect relationship. Rising of fluid pressures in the reservoir lowered frictional resistance to shear stress along fracture planes and resulted in slippage and man-made earthquakes. Evans suggested that this mechanism might be used to release elastic wave energy in seismic areas and thus perhaps avert the stress build-ups that cause major earthquakes. However, at the time of this writing, December 1967, a year after the arsenal stopped pressure injection, the earthquakes were continuing. Clearly the stress relationships are not such as to permit earthquakes to be "turned on or off" through pressure injection or cessation of injection. Once an equilibrium has been unbalanced, it cannot be restored in a geologic microsecond.

There are, in general, three methods of waste disposal which take advantage of subsurface space: (1) injection of waste liquids into deep permeable formations, (2) the incorporation of waste liquids in cement slurries which are injected into artificially created fractures in shale formations, where they harden and become a solid part of the formation, and (3) storage of solids in caverns in salt formations. In the first method, the disposal formation should be some thousands of feet below the surface and contained top and bottom by impermeable beds which prevent vertical movements of the injected fluids. The point of injection and pressures used must be such that injection does not induce vertical fractures that would permit escape of fluids. Moreover, the hydrodynamics of the formation must be such that the fluids do not migrate up-dip and enter the shallow groundwater system. In such environments permeabilities are low and natural rates of fluid flow rarely exceed 3 ft per yr. Thus in 1000 years fluids under the natural gradient would not travel more than one mile. Stratiform units with intergranular porosity are preferred over fracture porosity because the limits and hydrodynamics of fracture porosity systems are difficult to determine. Judging from the performance of the oil industry, which currently pumps nearly 20 million barrels of salt water per day into subsurface formations, large volumes of wastes can be disposed of in this manner. In the second method, the thickness, lithology, and structure of the shale unit, the depth of the unit, and the injection point should be such that the slurries are injected into horizontal fractures rather than vertical fractures which would permit escape of the slurry into overlying or underlying formations. Probably as much as 1 million gallons per year can be disposed of at one site (Galley, 1968a,

p. 8). The third method, disposal of solids in caverns in salt, is the most expensive because it requires preparation of a cavity. However, it is an excellent method for disposing of relatively small quantities of very toxic wastes. Salt is an ideal material in which to isolate such wastes because it is impermeable and therefore insulates the waste from groundwater systems. It is also easy to mine. Because it is plastic and flows, cavities will close around wastes if supports are removed.

Solid wastes. Geologic consequences of solid waste accumulation are (1) changes in physical contour of the land due to concentration—filling—in a small area and (2) chemical changes in the environment due to concentration of a mass of chemically diverse substances. The volume of the earth's crust affected by the concentration depends on whether or not the accumulation is stable or gases and leachate from the concentration move out into surface drainage systems and groundwater basins. The social problem is simply where to put the stuff. Considering that the largest volume of wastes is produced in urban areas—where there are already great pressures for more land for highways, dwellings, industry, public buildings, and recreation—and that the cost of transporting large volumes of waste must be borne by the producers, the problem is a serious one.

In the United States the average citizen produces 6 to 8 lb per day of waste. This includes his direct contributions plus a pro-rata share of industrial and agricultural wastes. According to present projections, this could be double in 20 years. Per capita production of waste is increasing at 2 percent per yr and population is growing at about the same rate (Committee on Pollution, 1966, p. 176). Cities spend some $3 billion per year on refuse collection and disposal (Alexander, 1967, p. 149). It costs New York $30 per ton to collect, transport, and dispose of wastes. This is three times the cost of a ton of coal mined in West Virginia and delivered in New York. Los Angeles has costs of only $12 per ton, among the lowest. New York reduces the volume of solid wastes through high-temperature incineration, but contributes to air pollution by doing so. Every year it uses up 150 acres in south Staten Island for sanitary land fills. During the 1968 strike of sanitation men, garbage accumulated in New York at the rate of 10,000 tons per day. Recently, New York announced a $75-million plant to burn waste and produce steam for sale to a utility (*Wall Street Journal*, Nov. 1, 1967). There are plans for construction of a privately-owned central waste disposal unit on the Houston ship channel (*Oil and Gas Journal*, 1967c, p. 41). Liquid and solid wastes will be burned to produce steam and "clean" land fill. A 400-ft-high stack will discharge the gases. Capacity is 10,000 tons per month of waste delivered by barge, rail, and truck.

With or without prior incineration, the so-called sanitary landfill is the principal means of solid waste disposal. What makes the landfill "sanitary" is the practice of covering each day's accumulation of waste with a compacted layer of earth so that gases and fluids produced by chemical and biological action are restrained from escaping into the atmosphere, surface water, and groundwater, and so that insects, rodents, and other animals are denied continued access to the wastes. The objective is to contain and isolate the fill.

The pollution potential of a landfill depends on (1) the reactivity of the waste itself as measured in content of organic matter, soluble inorganic constituents, easily oxidized substances, etc.; (2) the physical stability of the refuse in terms of volume change (mostly shrinkage) as decomposition advances; (3) the geological and hydrological parameters of the site—the porosity and permeability of the formation in which the fill is located and whether or not the water table intersects the fill; (4) how efficiently the upper surface of the fill is protected from insects, animals (mainly rodents), and exposure to wind and rain; and (5) climate—chemical reactions are inhibited by low temperatures, and in areas with little rainfall leaching of fills is slight.

The most permeable earth materials are sand, gravel, jointed and fissured rocks such as limestone and dolomite, and some vesicular lavas; least permeable are unjointed clays and shales. Wastes from incinerators where much of the original refuse has been gasified are less subject to biological action than wastes which have not been so processed, but they may contain substantial amounts of soluble constituents. Where there is an original separation of food wastes (garbage) from nonfood wastes (trash or refuse) the resulting nonfood accumulation is more stable than a mixture of the two. Where the landfill is located well above the water table in a relatively impermeable formation, fluids produced by leaching of the fill by rainfall do not percolate downward into the ground-water system. Where daily accumulations are compacted and protected by a well-compacted earth layer, the amount of rain percolating downward is reduced and the volume of leachate is reduced. A well-compacted cover also cuts down on production of gases by oxidation and decomposition of organic matter. However, compaction alone will not protect the fill from rain if the covering material used is permeable. A compacted clayey layer is much less permeable than a compacted sandy layer. A flat-surfaced fill in England was covered by 18 in. of soil and the entire mass compacted by a vibrating roller to a depth of 5 ft. Nevertheless, some 10 in. of rainfall out of a total of 25 in. penetrated the fill and produced a leachate (Hughes, 1967, p. 7). If the fill cover is impermeable, gas produced in the fill will be forced to move laterally into the surrounding formations instead of escaping into the air.

Hughes (1967) summed up investigations of the production and movement of pollutants from landfills that have been made in Great Britain, New York, California, and Illinois and presented a useful bibliography. Studies have been made of contaminants produced in ash dumps, leachates from domestic garbage landfills, the effects of refuse fills on ground water, the composition and shrinkage of refuse, the gases produced in landfills, comparisons of saturated and unsaturated fills, and the efficiency of filtering of leachates passing through natural formations and engineered gravel systems. The following discussion is condensed from Hughes (1967).

Decomposition of fills begins in contact with air, and decomposition processes are aerobic; after burial anaerobic processes predominate. Rain water or ground water moving through the fill dissolves the soluble components, including CO_2 produced by decomposition. The weak acid thus produced increases the solvent power of the solution. Principal gases produced are CO_2 and methane. Gas production is at a maximum early in the deposition of the fill and decreases as the fill ages. Table 9 presents the composition of some leachates. Natural purification occurs by filtering of contaminants in sand and gravel formations and by ion exchange in clay formations. If contaminating leachates do reach the ground-water system, they may remain undetected for years because of the generally slow movement of ground water, and a large reservoir of contaminated water may build up before corrective action can be initiated.

Bergstrom (1968, p. 3) presented sketches showing geologic environments in which ground water is safe from contamination by surface waste disposal and those in which contamination is likely to occur. In Figure 24a the dry climate and deep-water table makes it unlikely that any leachate from the landfill will find its way into the zone of

TABLE 9. Percentages of Materials Leached from Refuse and Ash, Based on Weight of Refuse as Received

Materials leached	Percent leached					
	1[a]	2[a]	3[a]	4[a]	5[a]	6[a]
Permanganate value						
30 min	0.039					
4 hr	0.060	0.037				
Chloride	0.105	0.127		0.11	0.087	
Ammoniacal nitrogen	0.055	0.037		0.036		
Biologic oxygen demand	0.515	0.249		1.27		
Organic carbon	0.285	0.163				
Sulfate	0.130	0.084		0.011	0.22	0.30
		(as SO_4)				
Sulfide	0.011					
Albuminoid nitrogen	0.005					
Alkalinity (as $CaCO_3$)				0.39	0.042	
Calcium				0.08	0.021	2.57
Magnesium				0.015	0.014	0.24
Sodium			0.260	0.075	0.078	0.29
Potassium			0.135	0.09	0.049	0.38
Total iron				0.01		
Inorganic phosphate				0.0007		
Nitrate					0.0025	
Organic nitrogen	0.0075	0.0072		0.016		

SOURCE: Hughes, 1967, p. 6, Table I.
[a] Sources of data and conditions of leaching:
1. Ministry of Housing and Local Government [Gt. Brit.] (1961), p. 117. Analysis of leachate from domestic refuse deposited in standing water.
2. Ministry of Housing and Local Government [Gt. Brit.] (1961), p. 75. Analyses of leachate from domestic refuse deposited in unsaturated environment and leached only by natural precipitation.
3. Montgomery and Pomeroy (1949), pp. 4 and 19. Refuse from Long Beach, California. Material leached in laboratory before and after ignition.
4. Engineering-Science, Inc. (1961), p. 39. Estimate based on data reported in "Final Report on the Investigation of Leaching of a Sanitary Landfill" (Sanitary Engineering Research Laboratory, 1954). Domestic refuse in Riverside, California, leached by water in a test bin.
5. Engineering-Science, Inc. (1961), p. 73. Based on data reported in "Investigation of Leaching of Ash Dumps" (Sanitary Engineering Research Laboratory, 1952). Leaching of California incinerator ash in a test bin by water.
6. Enginering-Science, Inc. (1961), p. 73. Based on data reported in "Investigation of Leaching of Ash Dumps" (Sanitary Engineering Research Laboratory, 1952). Leaching of southern California incinerator ash in a test bin by acid.

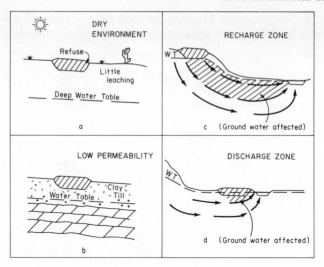

FIGURE 24. **Surface waste disposal and ground-water contamination.** (After Bergstrom, 1968, Fig. 1.)

saturation. In Figure 24b the ground water is protected by the impervious clay host which does not transmit the leachate. In Figure 24c, leachate from the landfill is free to percolate down slope into the zone of saturation and contamination occurs. In Figure 24d the high water table intersects the landfill so that part of the fill is within the saturated zone.

Generally, a satisfactory site would be above the water table or zone of saturation. The permeability of earth materials should be low enough to retard movement of contaminants, and the contaminates produced should be either unable to reach any ground water reservoir or should be removed or attenuated to acceptable levels before entering such a reservoir. If such a site cannot be secured within an economically attractive range of the waste-producing center, then special engineering to protect the site is necessary. Impermeable clay layers can be used to line the fill site and to cover it. Subsurface barriers to movement of leachates can be constructed, and where gases and leachates are thus impounded they can be diverted to a collection point and treated. If favorable sites are rare, it is possible to reuse proven sites by excavating old, stabilized, nonreactive wastes and using them as fills in more sensitive environments. Of course, this increases handling costs. Decomposition and stabilization proceeds most rapidly where moisture content is high and temperatures are warm. In any case, geologic and hydrologic investigation of the site is necessary for protection of the public.

With suitable sites for sanitary landfills rapidly filling up and incinerators forced to shut down or limit activities because of air pollution problems, American cities are investigating radical proposals for solid waste disposal. One proposal is high-pressure, high-temperature compression of wastes into stable bricks about one-tenth the original volume. They could either be sheathed and used for construction or disposed of in fills requiring only one-tenth the space of the original, uncompressed waste. Another proposal, advocated by the cities, is long-distance rail transport of solid wastes to refill the country's abandoned mines. San Francisco is studying a system that would involve shipping trash 375 mi by rail to a sanitary land fill in the high desert of Lassen County in northern California (*Wall Street Journal*, November 12, 1968, p. 14). The *Wall Street Journal* (November 12, 1968, p. 12) also carried a story on a study by the city of Chicago to "purify" garbage by atomic radiation and then pump the irradiated sludge out of the city for dumping on open ground.

In 1965, after passage of the Solid Waste Disposal Act, the Bureau of Mines began a campaign to alert the nation to the possibilities for beneficial use of wastes. According to Carl Rampacek, research director of the bureau's Maryland Metallurgy Research Center, there are more than $1 billion worth of metals in urban trash accumulations. The Bureau of Mines is working on methods to recover metals from incinerator residue, including iron, aluminum, zinc, copper, lead, tin, and precious metals (U. S. Bureau of Mines press release, April 2, 1968). According to Earl T. Hayes, then deputy director of the Bureau, mine dumps present opportunities for beneficial use and are really man-made ores (U. S. Bureau of Mines press release, April 3, 1968). A national survey of solid waste practices by the Department of Health, Education, and Welfare concluded that it will be necessary to spend an additional $7.3 billion over the next five years to produce a satisfactory system for collection and disposal of garbage, household refuse, and other solid wastes. This is over and above the $4.5 billion now spent each year for solid waste disposal. In more detail, the program calls for $2.75 billion for upgrading collection systems, $225 million to increase incinerator capacity, $300 million to upgrade land disposal operations, and in excess of $500 million to convert open dumps to sanitary land fills. Solid wastes include 360 million tons of household, commercial, and industrial solid wastes, 2 billion tons of agricultural solid wastes, and 1 billion tons of mineral solid wastes (*Environmental Science and Technology*, January 1967, p. 13).

Urban debris. Solid wastes are accumulating on the earth's surface in other than the planned sanitary landfills. Modern cities slowly raise themselves on a mound of debris in the same way as long-occupied middens and ancient towns and cities. New structures and pavements rise on the leveled debris of razed earlier structures and even though there are massive excavations for foundations of large buildings with basements and subbasements, the area of a city builds up as a low mound of fragments of stone, brick mortar, asphalt, glass, metal, wood, ashes, clinkers, cinders, sewage sludge, paper, bone, and a wide diversity of cast-off manufactured substances and products called rubbish. The great flow of raw materials, foodstuffs, and manufactured products into a city is always more than the flow out, and inevitably the wastes accumulate. From an engineering point of view, the result is to increase the stability of the surface and make a better overall foundation for the city much in the same way as a foundation engineer lays down a pad of sand and gravel on which to pour a slab foundation. Sherlock (1922, p. 189) estimated that London was building upward at about one foot per century, a rate consistent with that estimated by archeologists for ancient cities. On the periphery of cities, and indeed in the decaying hearts of some, are the junk yards, ugly but fascinating accumulations that are a catalog of man's industrial past and a reserve of materials, mostly metals, for the future when the economy will return to reprocessing and recycling to make maximum use of materials resources. It is interesting to consider what has happened to metals originally distributed in natural concentrations or orebodies in a layer of the outer continental crust about 2 mi thick. These concentrations were diligently sought out over 5 or 6 millenia, at first very selectively and in relatively few areas of the globe where metal-using cultures developed. The deposits found were those intersected by the land surface, and they were followed downward. With the passage of time the variety and volume of metals sought increased exponentially and the area of search broadened to include all of the continents except those under the ice caps. Using geophysics, geochemistry, and geology, deposits that are not exposed at the surface have been located by probing drills. In the present decade the search has expanded to include the ocean bottoms and the ice-covered land masses.

Metalliferous wastes. The great volume and variety of mined metals from over the world was and is shipped to industrial manufacturing nations. It has been concentrated in the metallurgical and manufacturing centers of the world. Then it has been redistributed in products all over the world, and metals extracted from a shell of rock some 2 mi thick are now concentrated on the surface of the earth. It is true that there is a greater concentration of metalliferous objects in the industrial nations, but even in the less-developed areas there is a surprisingly wide distribution of cans, drums, wire, and tools. Some metal objects reflect the fact that wars have been fought over wide areas of the earth, developed and nondeveloped alike, and some reflect the natural-resource operations conducted by industrial nations in less-developed regions. In any case, if a world-wide geologic event were to cataclysmically entomb the present surface, the irregular "unconformity" would be one marked by a very high concentration of metals. Even outside of population centers, anyone who has walked over an area that has been farmed or ranched for a century cannot help but note the ubiquitous fragments of wire, cans, corrugated roofing metal, nails, screws, bolts, and machinery parts (along with the persistent bottles and glass that do not oxidize).

Walter R. Hibbard, Jr., director of the U. S. Bureau of Mines (press release, February 22, 1967) said that the mounting piles of scrap that litter America's landscape represent a major source of future mineral supply and that scrap heaps and other secondary sources must be considered on the same terms as conventional mines. He pointed out that the mineral values such sources contain often greatly exceed those of a natural mineral deposit. To this observation can be added the point that these metals have already been mined and transported to a central collection point and thus have in them a substantial handling cost. Under the authority of the Solid Waste Disposal Act of 1965, the Bureau of Mines is investigating a variety of metallurgical processes that will make it economic to recover the metal content of scrap, particularly scrap automobiles, and at the same time eliminate the ugliness of these accumulations. The bureau has proposed construction of a large rotary kiln to combine 50 tons per day of auto scrap with 500 tons of ore to produce a higher-grade product (U. S. Bureau of Mines press release, February 16, 1967).

The mining industry looked at mineral waste utilization at a symposium in April 1968. It was pointed out that the some 5 million tons per year of "red mud" wastes produced in aluminum ore processing might be used as a building material, soil conditioner, or source of iron; phosphate slimes have potential as a source of alumina and phosphate, as a medium for disposal of radioactive wastes, or as a raw material for making light-weight aggregate; tailings from underground mining operations are more and more used to backfill and support the workings (*Engineering and Mining Journal*, May 1968, p. 110). According to a U. S. Bureau of Mines press release (March 2, 1968) several thousands of tons per day of alumina are now being discarded in waste solutions from copper leaching plants, uranium plants, and clay processing plants. Preliminary laboratory data suggests that this alumina could be recovered for $51 to $58 per ton, a cost very close to that of Bayer-process alumina (average cost $56 per ton as of the date of the press release). See Table 10.

Animal wastes. It might seem far-fetched to consider animal wastes in a geologic context. They are certainly a nuisance while they are decomposing, but bad odors, large fly populations, and their disease-producing potential are short-term effects. However, a consideration of the tremendous volumes of wastes produced by large populations in industrial societies and the methods of disposal of them suggests that these organic accumulations may well have long-ranging geologic significance, if not for the land itself, then for the biosphere. Throughout history and currently in large areas of the world, animal wastes, including human wastes, have been collected and applied to fields to furnish crop nutrients and maintain soil fertility. The problem in the United States is really that of a superabundance of highly nutrious natural organic wastes that are not put to useful purpose because it is easier and cheaper for farmers to use manufactured fertilizers. McGauhey (1968, p. 41) stated that in California alone some 20 million cubic yards per year of animal wastes are produced at the point of impact between urban and rural areas in dairies, feedlots, and poultry farms, and that the droppings from one cow in one day have the potential of producing 200,000 flies. Animal wastes that enter streams, rivers, lakes, and estuaries are a major source of water pollution through pathogens common to animals and man. Animal wastes together with municipal and industrial sewage, treated and untreated, are high in phosphorous, nitrogen, and other plant nutrients. When these are discharged into surface-water systems there is an overfertilization of streams, rivers, lakes and estuaries. This promotes an exuberant plant growth that consumes oxygen, kills aquatic animal life, and otherwise reduces the quality of water, making it unfit for domestic, industrial, and recreational use (p. 142). These nutrients, together with other municipal and industrial wastes, are changing the composition of surface waters in the same way that gaseous wastes are creating a new atmosphere.

Special municipal and industrial wastes. Some industries produce large quantities of rather special wastes. The volume is so great that disposal is a problem where these industries are in urban areas. Metallurgical

TABLE 10. **Waste Produced by Processing Minerals and Fuels in 1965 (In Thousands of Short Tons)**

Industry	Mine waste (other than surface mine overburden)	Mill tailings	Washing plant rejects	Slag	Processing plant wastes	Total
Alumina					5,350[a]	5,350
Anthracite	[b]		2,000			2,000
Bituminous coal	12,800		86,800			99,600
Copper	286,600	170,500		5,200		462,300
Iron and steel	117,599	100,589		14,689	1,000	233,877
Lead and zinc	2,500	17,811	970			21,281
Phosphate rock	72		54,823	4,030	9,383	68,308
Other	[c]	[c]	[c]	[c]	[c]	229,284[d]
Total	419,571	288,900	144,593	23,919	40,233	1,122,000

SOURCE: U. S. Bureau of Mines Publication, *Wealth out of Waste* (1968).
[a] Of this total 1.7 million tons are discharged directly into the Mississippi River annually by two alumina production plants in Lousiana, annual accumulation thus is 3.65 million tons.
[b] Total not available, but quantities are negligible and are included in washing plant wastes.
[c] Not available.
[d] Wastes of remaining mineral mining and processing industries—20 percent of total wastes generated.

industries that produce slag heaps are an example. Slags accumulate around smelters, and the cost of hauling them away is formidable. Moreover, many of them contain sufficient quantities of metals such as manganese to constitute a low-grade ore for the future. Some slags are sold as a raw material for making rock wool and these, of course, present no waste disposal problems. Fly ash produced by installations that burn large tonnages of coal, chiefly power plants, is another example. Much effort has been put into research to find a beneficial use for fly ash so that it becomes a by-product instead of waste. Some 20 million tons a year are produced by U. S. power plants. Fly ash can be used as a concrete additive (pozzolan), brick additive, filler, or soil stabilizer. Consolidated Edison, a major New York utility, converts fly ash into an aggregate marketed under the trade name "Edicrete." But at present the United States only utilizes about 4 percent of the fly ash produced, whereas France uses 50 percent and Britain 40 percent (*Environmental Science and Technology*, 1967, p. 201). Trash-burning municipal incinerators produce about 500,000 tons of fly ash and 14.5 million tons of clinker and other residue each year, and the number of municipal incinerators is increasing. The incinerator product may be a source of metals, depending on the nature of the wastes burned (*Wall Street Journal*, January 8, 1968); for example, fly ash from wastes containing photographic chemicals, film, solders, electronic components, and costume jewelry would be expected to be high in silver. It remains to develop a satisfactory process for assaying the incinerator products and recovering the valuable metal. In Germany, the Bayer company invested $4.5 million in an incineration plant. It has a yearly capacity of some 40,000 metric tons of chemical wastes. Although costs of disposal are high, $20 to $25 per metric ton, up to 25 metric tons of steam per hour can be recovered. Previous costs of disposal by burial were only $3 to $4 per ton, but this method did not meet new environmental control standards (*Chemical Week*, 1968d, p. 59).

A survey of United States oil refineries conducted by the American Petroleum Institute in 1968 indicated that refinery effluents contribute on the order of 4.2 million pounds of contaminants per days to the environment in the following distribution: biochemical oxygen demand, 800,000 lb; chemical oxygen demand, 2.5 million lb; oil, 360,000 lb; phenol, 55,000 lb; and suspended solids, 500,000 lb (*Oil and Gas Journal*, 1968, p. 59). According to the *Wall Street Journal* (April 3, 1968) Standard Oil Company of California has made a "conservation breakthrough" in a process to purify oil refinery waste waters. Hydrogen sulfide and ammonia, the major pollutants, are removed so that the water can be recycled. Both the hydrogen sulfide and ammonia are useful products and are marketable.

Radioactive wastes. Atomic fission produces a variety of radioactive substances that differ in half-life and the kinds of radiation emitted. Some of these elements and isotopes were present in natural sources in the preindustrial environment, for the most part in and around natural deposits of radioactive minerals, but the great majority of them at present are man-made contributions to earth, water, and atmosphere. They come from explosions of nuclear devices, from the nuclear-fuel cycle, from use of nuclear energy as propulsive power, and from the use of radioactive materials in industry, agriculture, medicine, and scientific research in general (Air Conservation Commission, 1965, p. 58). By far the largest volume is from explosions of nuclear devices and the nuclear-fuel cycle. Testing of atomic weapons and projects designed to explore peaceful uses of nuclear explosions in engineering and mining projects have produced large quantities of radioactive substances in the atmosphere and in the ground. A nuclear device was detonated in 1967 in the San Juan basin in New Mexico (Project Gasbuggy) to test the possibility of increasing natural gas yields by nuclear fracturing of a tight reservoir rock. Results are not known but preliminary indications are encouraging. A second attempt (Project Rulison) took place in 1969 in Colorado.

Unconfined explosions in the atmosphere have spread radioactive substances all over the world, making "fallout" a common word in nuclear-age vocabularies. Strontium 90, with a half-life of 28 yr; cesium 137, with a half-life of about 30 yr; and carbon 14, with a half-life of 5600 yr, commonly accumulate in the soil. The C^{14} is present in soil organic matter; Sr^{90} and Cs^{137} are held by clay. Animal populations are principally affected by strontium 89, strontium 90, cesium 137, carbon 14, and iodine 131. The concentration of cesium 137 in eskimo populations exemplifies meteorological and biological factors operating together to produce an anomalously high concentration. Fallout has been at a maximum in high latitudes. Concentration of cesium 137 in snow resulted in a widespread cesium 137 build-up in lichens growing in northern latitudes. This is the principal forage for caribou, which in turn form a large part of the eskimo diet.

Wastes produced in the nuclear-fuel cycle by controlled fission in reactors and by reprocessing spent fuels, mostly liquid wastes, are classified as low-level, intermediate-level, and high-level wastes. Low-level wastes are for the most part treated through flocculation, ion-exchange, evaporation, or other chemical processes to bring the radioactivity below a level considered safe for discharge into traditional disposal systems, surface-water drainage systems. One problem is that some natural processes tend to selectively reconcentrate the dilute wastes discharged into rivers and estuaries. For example, a 5-yr study of waste waters released from Oak Ridge National Laboratory into the Clinch River in eastern Tennessee showed that some isotopes, in particular the long lived cesium 137, but also including cobalt 60, ruthenium 106 and strontium 90, are adsorbed by clay minerals and concentrated in bottom sediment (U. S. Geological Survey press release, May 20, 1966).

More highly radioactive solids are commonly solidified in concrete or adsorbed on zeolites or vermiculite and packaged in 55-gal drums for land or sea burial. In sea disposal, care is taken to be certain that containers will be structurally sound, will withstand burial in water more than 1000 fathoms deep, and will resist sea-water corrosion for about 10 years. For many contaminants, containment for 10 years will reduce the radioactivity to very low levels. There have been some attempts to dispose of intermediate-level wastes by pressure injection through wells into a secure subsurface host. A slurry of radioactive waste, clay, and cement is pumped into an impermeable formation under pressure so as to fracture the formation and make room for the waste material. Subsurface disposal is used by Nuclear Fuels Services, Inc., at its reprocessing plant at West Valley, New York (*Chemical Week*, 1966b).

Large volumes of high-level radioactive waste, on the order of 100 million gallons, are currently stored in underground steel tanks at Atomic Energy Commission facilities at Savannah River, South Carolina, Hanford, Washington, and the Idaho National Reactor Testing Station. Tank storage of these very long-lived, highly radioactive liquid wastes can only be considered an interim solution to the problem. One method of ultimate disposal is solidification to render the radioactive wastes less mobile, either by conversion to a nonleachable glass, adsorption on zeolites, evaporation and calcination, or radiant spraying, followed by burial in mined cavities in secure formations (such as salt domes) where they will be isolated from the biosphere. Salt is perhaps the best possibility because it is impermeable and has good thermal conductivity. Of course, burial grounds for radioactive wastes, whether on land or at sea, must be continually monitored to make sure that the radioactive materials are "staying put." As with other pollutants, with radioactive wastes we really do not know what long-range effects they will have on the environment and biosphere, but, again as with other pollutants, we cannot wait around to find out before disposing of them. Unlike other pollutants, however, radioactive substances can definitely induce mutations in living species. Inasmuch as society looks to cheap nuclear energy to solve many of its resource problems in the future (p. 140), it is likely that the volume of radioactive wastes will increase sharply. The long-term effect of wide distribution of radioactive substances on plant and animal populations might well be drastic.

One problem with geologic consequences is the way dilute radioactive wastes are reconcentrated by biological processes or by selective adsorption. Another geologic problem is that if solid or solidified wastes are disposed of in quantity, the heat that they produce tends to raise the thermal gradient, to heat up ground waters, and generally to increase chemical and physical activity in the storage area. If heat builds up faster than it can be conducted away there is the possibility that the radioactive materials and containing materials could be melted and remobilized to generate lethal local magmas. In one demonstration, 400,000 c of mixed radioactive materials in 350 gal of waste were converted to a phosphate glass; the decay of radioactive materials in the glass gives off 1500 w of heat (*Chemical Week*, 1967c).

The idea that large volumes of radioactive wastes could be injected underground and then forgotten—out of sight, out of mind—was a matter of great concern to many petroleum geologists with experience in the migration of subsurface fluids. The question was, "In what parts of and at what depths in various basins could radioactive wastes be stored so as to be permanently out of man's environment?" Between 1959 and 1964, the Research Committee of the American Association of Petroleum Geologists, under contract from the Atomic Energy Commission, undertook a study of six basin provinces to develop data on their hydrodynamic regimens (Galley, 1968b). At first the study was concerned with disposal of small volumes of very-high-level wastes, but subsequently interest shifted to disposal of large volumes of low-level wastes, storage in salt strata for very dangerous materials, and fixation of cement slurries containing radioactive materials in fractures in thick shale sequences.

Mines, quarries, and well fields. Selective withdrawal of earth substances from below the surface for use on the surface inevitably must result in a change in the composition of the surface. And because the use to which some of the extracted material is put results in a change of state and dissipation as gases or aerosols, the change in composition is extended to the atmosphere (p. 128). The United States consumes more mineral products than it produces, thus what is consumed in this country includes subsurface withdrawals from other parts of the world.

In the United States about 3 billion tons of rock (metallic ores, nonmetallic industrial rocks and minerals, coal, clay, stone, sand and gravel) is mined each year, and approximately 85 percent of the tonnage is from open pits. Probably two or three times as much earth and rock, perhaps as much as 9 billion tons, is moved around to get at the desired substances. The world total for rocks and minerals mined is near 9 billion tons but world over the percentage mined by open pit methods is lower than in the United States, perhaps about 70 percent (*Mining Engineering*, 1967, pp. 107–108). According to a 1967 Department of the Interior report (pp. 39–42) there are some 3 million acres (about 5000 sq mi, or 0.13 percent of the total surface area) in the United States that have been affected by surface mining and that of these some 2 million stand in need of reclamation. At present 150,000 acres per year are involved in surface mining, but only 30 percent of this total is included in reclamation programs.

The total amount of metal used each year in the United States, including new metal plus recycled scrap, both domestically produced and imported, is on the order of 200 millions tons. Nearly 95 percent of the total is iron. The consequences of annual use of 200 million tons of metals cannot be evaluated from available data. Some metals are inocuous as far as the biosphere is concerned. Oxidation and leaching of scrap metal—for example, rusting of iron—introduces metal ions into the environment. Slow enrichment of some metal ions in soils is beneficial to plants, but other metals are toxic. There are few guidelines to what is "safe" as far as plants and animals are concerned, except for such notorious poisoners as lead, selenium, and radioactive isotopes. Dissipative uses of metals, such as burning of lead or nickel in motor fuels, or disposal of waste solutions high in metal ions, disperses metals widely through the environment, and intuitive judgements indicate that this is not beneficial. Wastes produced by mining, beneficiating, refining of metalliferous ores, as well as the terrain changes induced by the excavation, are also of concern. Some smelters are located in populous areas where their gaseous discharges, commonly high in SO_2 from sulfur-rich ores, add greatly to air pollution problems (p. 131). Other smelters in relatively isolated mining districts disturb only the company employees and vegetation downwind from the installation. Liquid wastes, mainly highly mineralized acid mine waters, can do a great deal of environmental damage if they are released into surface drainage systems without treatment. Neutralization and demineralization of mine waters prior to release does not completely solve the waste problems. If metals such as iron are precipitated in a settling basin, disposal of the sludge presents a problem. One solution is to back-fill pits or underground workings with such wastes. Of course, all of this adds to costs. One experimental program of neutralization, precipitation, and sludge disposal anticipated a cost of 5 cents per 1000 gal of acid water treated (*Chemical Week*, 1965a, p. 94).

Bailly (1966, pp. 17–21) analyzed the land requirements for a typical large (400-million-ton), low-grade (0.7 percent copper, or 14 lb of copper per ton) open-pit copper operation as follows: pit, 1 sq mi; mine waste dumps, 2 to 4 sq mi; mine leach dumps, .5 to 2 sq mi; mill waste or tailings pond, 1 to 3 sq mi; plants, offices, parking, etc., several acres. The total area required ranges from 5 to 10 sq mi. He pointed out that in certain mines where there is a sharp boundary between the "ore" and country rock the workings can be backfilled with waste to fill up the hole and restore (open-pit) or support (underground) the surface; however, metalliferous ore bodies are commonly surrounded by an envelope of weakly mineralized rock that might be of economic interest in the future. If the mine workings are backfilled, this marginal or submarginal ore is rendered inaccessible. This is poor conservation practice. Immediate reclamation, therefore, cannot be regarded as desirable for all mines. Structures or waste dumps should not be built above extensions of ore bodies even though the extensions are now of only marginal or submarginal grade. Moving the structure or waste will add to the cost of obtaining the marginal material if it should in the future become needed.

Bailly (1966, Figure 15) noted that 672,000 acres, or 1050 sq mi, in the United States (0.06 percent of total area) is occupied by metal mines and auxiliary facilities.

With regard to the enormous volume of nonmetallic rocks and minerals and construction materials, the principal problem is occasioned by the alteration of the terrain as a result of the operation of pits and quarries. Where sand and gravel is extracted from the modern drainage system there is a resulting change in the regimen of the stream as well as local modifications of aquatic populations. In some mineral extraction operations—such as sand and gravel pits, stone quarries, some oil wells, gas wells and coal mines—virtually all of the material extracted is a useful product. In other operations, only a small part of the material mined or pumped is a useful, saleable product and it must be separated from the unusable material. In most industries, the waste is separated at or close to the mineral source. For example, in the oil industry the salt water is separated at the well, and at metal mines the ore is milled to make a concentrate. At very large operations the concentrate is further refined at or near the mine. There is thus produced a volume of solid, liquid, or gaseous waste around mining centers—crushed and ground waste rock; waste water from mining, milling, and refining operations; and waste gases from refining operations. This waste, together with the breaking of the ground surface and shifting around of overburden, has caused the public in general to label mining industries as "despoilers."

About 3 billion barrels of crude petroleum and 2.5 trillion cubic feet of natural gas, helium, and carbon dioxide are produced from United States wells each year. The domestic annual ground water withdrawal is on the order of 6 million acre feet. All of these withdrawals can be expected to increase, except perhaps crude oil. Although the United States retains the capacity to increase production of crude oil from known deposits, an analysis of the reserve situation suggests that this country is close to the inflection point on the total resource curve and that production of domestic crude oil will decline if present conservation practices are continued (Hubbert, 1962, 1966, 1967). New discoveries in Alaska and offshore, together with improved secondary recovery practices, make it difficult to predict with exactitude just when the decline will begin. However, the decline in production of domestic crude oil will force development of alternative sources of liquid fuel, namely, tar sands, shale oil, and coal, and thus increase large-scale open-pit mining.

Geologic consequences of fossil fuel withdrawal (coal, lignite, oil, and gas) are the result of (1) combustion that releases a variety of gases (mainly CO, CO_2, SO_2 and oxides of nitrogen) into the atmosphere; (2) the solid, liquid, and gaseous wastes produced by mining, benefication, and refining; and (3) changes in the landscape as a result of open pit or strip mining. In the United States, combustion of fossil fuels releases about 20 million tons of SO_2 into the atmosphere each year. On a world-wide basis, combustion of fossil fuels results in annual discharge into the atmosphere of about 10 billion tons of CO_2 (Air Conservation Commission, 1965, p. 78).

The Appalachian coal mining region is a good example of undesirable environmental consequences of mining. Stripping of the coal seams exposes to air and water large quantities of rock high in iron sulfides. On oxidation, this pyrite breaks down into ferrous sulfate, ferric sulfate, ferric hydroxide, and sulfuric acid. The pH of exposed spoil banks is as low as 3. The high acidity inhibits vegetation growth until the pyrite has been oxidized and the acids leached from the spoil. Experiments on revegetation of backfill strip mines conducted by the Bureau of Mines showed that application of lime to bring the pH up to 4.5 (decrease the acidity) increased the survival of many plant species (Manguson and Kimball, 1968). During the time that high acidity keeps them barren the spoil banks are subject to rapid erosion, thus in addition to having acid water, streams are choked with sediment. The Monongahela River, which drains parts of Pennsylvania and West Virginia, discharges the equivalent of 200,000 tons of sulfuric acid each year into the Ohio River. The Ohio is able to neutralize this acid through a flow of about 170 mi. The solution is containment and treatment of acid waters and stabilization of spoil banks, followed by grading and replanting of the stripped, mined-out areas.

Costs of reclamation vary greatly depending on terrain, but available data indicate a range of from 1 to 2 cents per mined ton of coal (about $50 per acre) for grading alone to 40 or 50 cents per mined ton of coal (about $2500 per acre) for complete reclamation and reforestation (Brooks, 1966, p. 27). Inasmuch as coal sells for about $4.50 per ton, it is clear that the higher costs of reforestation cannot be borne by industry without a price increase on the order of 10 percent or more. Such an increase would result in major economic effects in the highly competitive fuel industry.

An unexpected dividend of strip mining was noted in Indiana by

Truax (1965), who reported that the cast overburden from strip mines is an important ground-water reservoir during times of drought.

Solid wastes—mine dumps, mill tailings, slags, cinders, and ashes—accumulate in huge piles around big mines. If these wastes are contained, either by the natural terrain or by engineing design, the only environmental effect is a man-made hill, a minor addition to the topography. However, if large amounts of unconsolidated materials are allowed to accumulate without proper engineering supervision, they may become unstable and subject to mass movements. A slide in a mountain of coal mine wastes at Aberfan, Wales, in October 1966 destroyed a school and took many lives. If solid wastes are allowed to enter wind or surface water transport systems they can choke a stream channel, thereby provoking a flood hazard, or provide a source of rock dust for distribution by wind. The problems of solid wastes from mines are not newly upon us as a result of industrialization. Old Roman legal codes indicate that the problem of mine waste disposal existed in the Roman Empire. In the middle of the eighteenth century, the old mining town of Guanajuato, Mexico, where mining began in 1550, suffered a series of disastrous floods because the river channel became choked with waste rock from the mines. A report in 1749 by a mining engineer recommended immediate construction of retaining walls to hold the dumps and tailings and cleaning out of the river channel (Autúnez Echagaray, 1964, p. 54). What is of growing concern to society is the increase in the number of local environmental disturbances caused by mining.

Over the long term, a river or stream works to clear its channel of the sediment load. Gradients steepen and the carrying capacity of the system thereby increases. Aquatic life adjusts to turbid waters, but some species cannot adapt and die. Thus it cannot be argued that there are large-scale geologic consequences arising from the production of solid wastes from mining. However, while the geologic adjustment is taking place, man's aesthetic senses are offended and the recreation potential of the waterway is lessened.

Geologic consequences of withdrawal of large amounts of ground water are difficult to evaluate. Most of the water enters the hydrologic cycle. Precipitation, run-off, and downward percolation from irrigated fields works to return water to subsurface reservoirs unless geologic conditions are such as to prevent natural recharge. In many irrigation districts (and most of the ground water withdrawn is used for irrigation) withdrawal is so much greater than natural recharge that there is a yearly net deficit.

However, if pumping were to cease, most of the reservoirs eventually would be recharged. Probably the greatest environmental consequence of ground-water withdrawal occurs through this heavy and continued irrigation of croplands. Over a period of years there is a change in composition of irrigated soils through a build-up of alkali elements. All ground water contains some dissolved salts. Through evaporation of water applied to fields, these salts become concentrated in the soil, reducing its fertility and eventually rendering it unfit for cultivation. Thus, dissolved salts originally dispersed through a large volume of water are, through man's actions, concentrated in a relatively thin layer of the earth in a limited area. They can to a degree be redissolved and flushed out by massive applications of fresh water, so the build-up is not a permanent change in soil composition.

Water resource projects. There is an interrelationship in any area between climate, landforms, flora and fauna, and the amount of water available to the area as precipitation or surface water and shallow groundwater. The interdependency of climate, precipitation, and landforms is impressed on anyone who has compared the bold, rugged landscape of arid lands with the softer, rounded contour of humid lands. In the broad view, rain and snow are but one of the parameters of climate, but in the local view the amount of precipitation strongly influences microclimate. Rock weathering and soil formation is controlled by climate, topography, and geology (structure and composition of rocks and other surficial earth materials). Fauna and flora adjust to the total environment but are most sensitive to water supply. Landforms also tend toward equilibrium with the water budget, but are less sensitive to short-term change than is the biosphere. Clearly, any change, increase or decrease, in the amount of water in an area is going to result in an environmental change; any change in the temperature of the water is going to result in an environmental change.

All over the world, man is busily engaged in changing natural water systems. Until now his capabilities have limited him to changing surface and ground water systems, but he has made a start on changing atmospheric systems—inducing precipitation, preventing nucleation of hailstones, and so on (p. 191). Most of the environmental consequences of water projects are attributable to (1) impoundment of water behind dams; (2) long-distance transport of water by canal, aqueduct, or pipeline from one region to another; (3) large-scale extraction of subsurface water; (4) modification of natural stream and river channels; and (5) desalting water. All water projects have biological effects—on aquatic life, waterfowl, and vegetation, on the size of the human population in a region, and on land use. When a new large supply of irrigation water changes thousands of acres from a complex natural eco-system to the simple eco-system of the farm, or when large areas of swamp are flooded to destroy a large natural eco-system, the biological consequences are large scale, whereas the geologic consequences are small scale. The concern here is mainly with geologic consequences and those biological consequences that in themselves are profound enough to result in geological effects over the long term.

1. *Storage or impoundment of water behind dams in reservoirs.*
   a. The load on the crust is increased in the local area. This may or may not result in failure of earth materials, depending on the existing stress patterns, the strength of the materials, existing rock structures, and amount of load. Following impoundment of Lake Mead by Hoover Dam there were minor earth tremors and settlements. Leggett (1968) described a minor earthquake that occurred during construction of a large dam on the Arapuni River in New Zealand. Structures were shaken and tilted. A large crack some 2000 ft long and 2 in. wide opened up along the valley wall. Failure was attributed to loss of strength due to wetting through leakage from the headrace canal.

   Large dams on major waterways are nearly all constructed under engineering supervision and geologic studies are undertaken prior to construction to determine the geologic nature and feasibility of the site. However, with the increased capabilities of earth-moving equipment and the encouragement given to soil and water conservation and to recreation projects, there has been, in the United States at least, a great increase in the construction of small dams. For the most part these are simple earth dams with crests seldom over 100 ft high and impounding a few hundred to a few thousand acre feet of water. However, notwithstanding the limited scale of these impoundments, a failure can cause loss of life and substantial damage downstream. Many, if not most, of these dams are constructed without geologic and engineering supervision, and state regulatory responsibilities are extremely variable. In February of 1968 the Missouri Geological Survey, in an editorial, summarized recent small dam failures in Missouri and identified some 21 dams in danger of failure (*Missouri Mineral Industry News*, 1968*a*). In April 1968 the Missouri Survey followed up with another editorial increasing the "danger list" to 28 and pointing out that of the 14 dam failures in Missouri in the 10-yr period 1958–1968, 8 failed because of inadequate spillways and 6 failed because of poorly constructed embankments. The potential failures have inadequate spillways, poorly constructed embankments, or poor foundations. A 75-ft-high earth dam impounding a 35-acre lake near Bonne Terre was used as an example; according to geologists with the Missouri Geological Survey, failure of this deteriorated structure would send a 20-ft wall of water over a downstream residence within 10 to 11 min after collapse. The editorial cited an example in New England, where in early 1968 a 30-ft dam gave way under the pressure of heavy rains, killed two persons, destroyed or damaged 11 houses, damaged a manufacturing plant to the extent of some $8 million, eroded half a mile of U. S. Highway 20, and destroyed other minor structures (*Missouri Mineral Industry News*, 1968*a*). Because of the trend toward construction of small lakes by private individuals and the clear need for engineering and geological supervision, legislation is pending in Missouri to regulate the design, construction, and maintenance of dams and reservoirs.

The findings of the U. S. Committee on Large Dams were summed up as follows:

(1) Thirty-three states participate in the design and construction of dams.
(2) Seventeen states provide on-site inspection during construction.
(3) Twenty-nine states review the preliminary plans and designs.
(4) Thirty-two states require that contract plans and specifications be reviewed.
(5) Twelve states have a roster of dams readily available for public inspection.
(6) Some states have no record or list of dams at all.
(7) Five states require no permit or license for construction of a dam.
(8) Eleven states require no construction supervision.

(9) Nine states require no supervision or review of any kind.

(10) Thirteen states require no filing of application for construction.

(11) Fifteen states have no control over dams once they are built.

(12) Ten states do not require that the design of a dam be supervised or approved by a registered professional engineer.

b. Water tables behind the dam are raised and water tables downstream decline. In addition to freshening springs and seeps in one area and drying them up in another, agriculture may be stimulated upstream by shallower (cheaper) and more abundant water and discouraged downstream by increased pumping costs. In the lower Rhone valley in France, a canal was constructed to cut off a great meander in the river and provide a head or increased gradient for power generation. The abrupt change in the level of the stream thus induced under normal circumstances would have raised the ground water level upstream from the powerhouse and lowered it downstream. But in order to maintain the status quo of the ground water-based agriculture, pumps were installed to pull the water table down above the power plant and a series of porous-bottomed canals (canals of réalimentation) were constructed downstream so as to maintain the water table through intentional leakage (Legget, 1968, p. 31).

c. Evaporation and transpiration are increased through formation of an artificial lake. About 70 to 75 percent of the precipitation that falls on land areas evaporates rather quickly; approximately 4.3 trillion gallons per day fall on the United States, and of this about 3 trillion gallons per day return to the atmosphere through evaporation from surface water bodies, soil, and transpiration through vegetation (Nace, 1967a, p. 4; Dykes, Bry, and Kline, 1967, p. 780). The net runoff or streamflow in the United States is therefore about 1.26 trillion gallons per day. The flow is irregular. Minimum dependable flow is perhaps half the total, or 630 billion gallons per day. Half of this is required for navigation, waste discharge, recreation, fish, and wildlife. This leaves 315 billion gallons per day for public and industrial consumption and agriculture. But of this only 1.38 billion gallons per day is actually consumed or used up—the rest is used again and again. This explains why daily consumption—356 billion gallons per day— can be more than the average 315 billion gallons per day available (Dykes, Bry, and Kline, 1967, p. 780). Of course these average figures do not mean very much in any particular area, but they do suggest that the United States is already using a substantial fraction of the water in the surface-water system. It is clearly desirable to conserve as much as possible. There is no big surplus to waste.

The storage of water in large and relatively shallow reservoirs increases the area of the evaporation surface and thus increases the evaporation. Increased vegetation growth around reservoirs increases transpiration. Thus in attempting to store surface water for use we actually decrease the amount of net stream flow by the amount of increased evapotranspiration. Of course, water is stored for other reasons—for flood control, navigation, power generation, and recreation—but considering only the water needs of municipalities, agriculture, and industry, it would be more desirable to store water in narrow, deep reservoirs or underground to hold back the maximum amount of surface water from evapotranspiration for as long as possible.

Is the amount lost by evaporation from reservoir surfaces really significant in terms of (a) water loss and (b) microclimate changes? Texas is a state that ranges from arid in the west, where annual rainfall averages less than 10 in., to well-watered in the east, where annual rainfall averages more than 50 in. Over the 25-yr period 1940–1965 the average annual gross lake surface evaporation ranged from about 100 in. in the driest part of the State to 40 in. in the wettest part (Kane, 1967). The greatest number of reservoirs occur in the area where average annual gross lake surface evaporation is between 40 and 80 in. Ignoring the myriad small farm and ranch ponds or "tanks" in the region, and considering only the surface area of existing major reservoirs with capacities more than 5000 acre feet (total surface area at conservation level is ~1.34 million acres), and average evaporation of 60 in. per yr, the amount of water lost to the atmosphere by evaporation from reservoirs in Texas alone is nearly 7 million acre feet, or more than 2 trillion gallons per year. This is almost three times the current annual consumption for municipal and industrial purposes. With construction of the additional reservoirs in the Texas Water Plan this figure will double. Whether or not this amount of water is sufficient to cause microclimate changes remains to be seen. Certainly it is significant in terms of overall supply and demand, and in terms of stream regimen.

d. Decrease in the flow of water downstream. Impoundment of water upstream, with resulting increased loss through evapo-transpiration and use for agricultural, industrial, and municipal purposes, inevitably reduces the amount of water in the down-stream segment and thus changes the regimen of the stream. The dam not only cuts down on the total flow, it eliminates the storm flood surges that work to clean out the channel. It may be argued that if regular amounts of water are released to the downstream segment the flood-drought extremes of flow are eliminated and the result is beneficial to aquatic life. However, if flow is sub-stantially reduced, the amount of fresh water entering bays and estuaries is reduced. In Texas, many biologists fear that the dams contemplated in the State Water Plan will reduce the fresh-water flow to the Texas coast, raise the salinity of the estuaries and bays, and destroy the bays as the spawning ground for shrimp and many food fish. Others believe that a controlled flow to bays and estuaries will reduce the extremes of low and high salinities and improve the spawning ground.

e. Impoundment of the normal sediment load carried by the stream. It is well-known that the working life of many dams is governed by sediment build-up in the reservoir. Eventually the reservoir is filled with water-saturated sediment instead of water. The result of unloading the stream by trapping the sediment it carries is to increase its erosive power and sediment-carrying capacity down-stream. At St. Louis the Mississippi River averages yearly about 260 tons of sediment for every square mile in the drainage basin upstream. The figure for the Colorado River at Grand Canyon is 670 tons per sq mi drained. The geologic consequences are (1) a change in the long profile of the stream, (2) a change in focus of erosion, with the new sediment load coming from that part of the drainage basin lying below the dam, and (3) a possible change in the character of sediment transported, depending on the nature of the rocks below the dam as contrasted with the upper part of the basin.

2. *Long distance transport of water from one region to another.* The geologic effects of the long distance transport of water through canals, pipelines, aqueducts, or by modifying existing water courses to transport larger volumes than the natural flow, depend on the amount of water moved in relation to the supply in both ends of the transport system and the use of the water in the receiving area. Clearly, if 5 percent of the average flow of a major stream were diverted into a canal and moved to another area, the effect on the source area would be much less than if 50 percent of the average flow were tapped away. Likewise, if the water were transported to augment by 5 or 10 percent the municipal supply in a well-watered region, the effect on the receiving area would be much less drastic than if the transported water increased the supply to an arid region by several orders of magnitude. If a small amount of water were brought into an arid region to supply the municipal requirements of a small town, the effect would be much less than if large volumes were brought in to nourish a vast irrigation project. The so-called North American Water and Power Alliance provides an example of an extreme.

The North American Water and Power Alliance is the name given to a $100+ billion proposal conceived by the Ralph M. Parsons Company (Abelson, 1965a; Nace, 1967b). It would transport large volumes of water ($\sim 800 \times 10^9$ cu m/yr or about the same number of metric tons, since a cubic meter of water is 264.2 gal and weighs about 1 metric ton) from northwestern North America, much of it from the Peace and Yukon rivers, through a series of reservoirs, lifting stations, tunnels, and canals to the Great Lakes, southwestern United States, and Mexico, affecting in some way 7 provinces of Canada, 33 states in the United States, and 3 states in the Republic of Mexico. The amount of water involved is about 13 percent of the total surface-water crop of North America and about 91 percent of the amount in the drainage area that would be tapped. Some of the features of the plan are a huge storage lake in the Rocky Mountain Trench in British Columbia, Alberta, and Montana, a waterway extending eastward across Canada to the Great Lakes and linking up with the Mississippi through a Dakota Canal, a seaway to Hudson Bay. an Eastern Aqueduct from the Great Lakes to the east coast of the United States, and a Southwest Canal linking up with a California Aqueduct, a Sonora Aqueduct, a Chihuahua Aqueduct, a Rio Grande Aqueduct, and a Staked Plains Aqueduct. A less-ambitious and wholly domestic plan envisages transport of water from the Columbia and Snake rivers southwestward, possibly through the existing Colorado River System.

Nace (1967b, p. 19) speculated on some consequences of the NAWA PA plan—load-stresses caused by huge reservoirs in a structurally complex and potentially seismic area, thawing of vast permafrost areas by blanketing them with water, climatological effects occasioned by transport into warm areas of great volumes of cold water, and the possibly planetary effect of NAWAPA, together with an even larger proposal for Siberia, called the Davidoff Plan, for moving a great mass of water ($\sim$600 $\times$ 10^{11} metric tons/yr) from polar latitudes toward the equator. Hickman, (1966, p. 614) pointed out that the rivers that flowed into the Arctic Ocean warm it and themselves become colder and part of the southbound currents that carry cold water across the continental shelves and ocean bottom to the equator. If the water is brought south overland instead of being discharged into the Arctic Ocean, as contemplated in NAWAPA, it might be expected that the arctic would become colder, the tropics warmer, and North America warmer and snowier in the winter and cooler in the summer.

It is not difficult to conceive of myriad second-, third-, and fourth-order consequences that might result from changing the hydrology of an entire continent, but what about projects on a small scale that are already a reality or a near-reality? In Australia the Snowy Mountain-Tumut Project reversed the flow of three great east-flowing rivers, tunneled them westward through the range into dammed-up canyons in the rain shadow of the Snowy Mountains, and now the falling water is used for power generation and to irrigate what had been arid valleys. In the United States, Owens Valley water and Colorado River water has for years been diverted into Los Angeles, the Imperial Valley, and Mexico; now, through the California Water Project, water from the Feather River watershed in northern California will be brought south for 400+ mi to Los Angeles. One consequence of use of the Colorado River water has been a build-up in salt content to the point where it cannot be used beneficially for agriculture at the southwestern terminus in Mexico. Apparently no climatic effects of this water transport have been observed and in all probability the geologic consequences are so imperceptible as to remain unnoticed, particularly if no one is looking for them or trying to measure them. Denver brings water eastward across the mountains from the Colorado. According to Quinn (1968, p. 115), one out of every five people in the western states is served by a water supply system that transports water at least 100 mi and the total tonnage of water moved exceeds the total tonnage of freight carried by all of the railroads, trucks, and barges in the area. (See Figure 25.)

3. *Extraction of large volumes of subsurface water.* Extraction of subsurface water through wells to augment surface supplies for municipal and industrial use in a well watered region, such as is done in Houston, is not likely to result in environmental modifications unless, as is the case in Houston, withdrawal of the ground water causes settling of the surface. The principal problem here is damage to structures and creation of shallow, closed surface basins that, without drainage, can become swampy areas. On the other hand, withdrawal of large

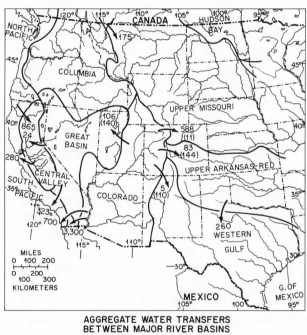

AGGREGATE WATER TRANSFERS
BETWEEN MAJOR RIVER BASINS

——▶ Direction of transfer
588 – Basin import in thousands of
     acre-feet per year
(140) – Additional transfer under
     construction

FIGURE 25. Aggregate water transfers between major river basins. (After *Geographical Review*, Vol. 58, 1968, copyrighted by the American Geographical Society of New York.)

volumes of ground water for irrigation in arid regions creates an oasis environment. Vegetation, apart from the cultivated crops, changes and the animal population changes. Over a period of continued irrigation, salts build up and alter the composition of the soil.

4. *Modification (dredging and straightening) of channels.* Shortening and deepening of natural river channels is a standard enginering solution to reduce flood dangers. In some places, dredges recover sand and gravel as a valuable by-product of dredging. The more efficient the channel, the more quickly large volumes of water can move through it. Increasing the rate of flow increases the capacity of the stream to transport sediment and therefore increases its erosive capacity. Channel engineering also affects aquatic life, particularly spawning grounds for fish, and may have unforeseen long-range effects. Straightening and dredging of the Rhine River over many years increased the rate of flow, as indeed it was supposed to do, but it thereby also increased erosion of the river bed, lowering the water level in the river. At Duisberg, Germany, a river port with 28 mi of wharfage for a great industrial complex, the river level has dropped 2 m since 1900 and it has been calculated that another 2-m drop will occur before the bed stabilizes. Faced with economic catastrophe, the city took advantage of a unique geologic situation. Duisberg is underlain by coal beds. Mining of this coal under carefully controlled conditions has permitted engineers to effect settling of the harbor area of the city to keep pace with the falling river level (Legget, 1968, p. 32).

5. *Construction of coastal fresh-water reservoirs by damming estuaries and sounds.* In 1966, R. D. Gerard suggested that construction of dams at both the east and west ends of Long Island Sound and conversion of the Sound to a fresh-water reservoir with a capacity of 42 million acre feet could solve New York City's water supply problem. The reservoir would receive the flow of the Connecticut and Housatonic rivers. He further suggested that many estuaries and other water bodies should be considered in terms of the coastal reservoir concept. Geologic consequences of such projects can be considered deductively. The coastal region, particularly the zone of tidal action, is a locus of some of the most powerful geological processes. The marine erosion and sediment transport systems, particularly the littoral drift, are capable of realizing great changes in relatively short spans of years. Apart from enormous biological changes, coastal reservoir projects may

be expected to cause considerable modifications in the coastline and require continuing and larger-scale engineering attention to deal with the secondary effects of the projects.

6. *Desalting facilities.* Desalting facilities, whether coastal or inland, produce essentially fresh water and a brine effluent or waste product. There is no problem now, but the growth of such facilities to meet municipal, industrial, and agricultural requirements for the future suggests that there will be a problem, one that will rank with the saltwater waste disposal problems of the oil industry. In the case of water, however, a low-value product, it is more difficult to include the cost of waste disposal in the price of the product. Coastal facilities will surely discharge the waste brine into the sea, locally increasing salinities, and giving rise to bottom-flowing currents of the denser saline water. Inland, the remedy will probably be subsurface injection of brines. The alternative is to process the brine so as to extract by-products such as sodium, potassium, and magnesium salts, sulfur, etc. However, if the forecast of 20 billion gallons per day desalting capacity by 1984 is correct (*Wall Street Journal,* April 29, 1965) potential production of minerals from the effluent brines would be well in excess of demand for such substances (Mero, 1965, pp. 46–47).

Coastal installations. Man's interference with coastal erosion and marine sediment transport systems has produced some of the most rapid and evident geologic consequences on record. Perhaps this record is more dramatic because reasonably accurate maps of coast lines have existed for a longer period of time than similar maps of other areas, or perhaps it is that the land–sea interface provides a better datum of reference than a meandering river channel. But no one will deny that powerful natural forces are constantly at work along the contact between sea and land (p. 52). A structure projecting from the land and intercepting the littoral drift or a dredge that destroys a profile of equilibrium can change a sand beach into a stony shingle in one season. The long-term effects of groins, jetties, breakwaters, sea walls, and dams have already been described (p. 56).

The ability of man to create new land from marshes and bays is well illustrated by San Francisco Bay. In 1850, the Bay encompassed an area of 680 sq mi; in 1968 the area had been reduced to about 400 sq mi. Although part of the Bay filling was the natural result of the sediment loads carried by the Sacramento and San Joaquin Rivers, placer gold mining operations supplied to these rivers great quantities of silt far above their normal loads. More directly, man has engaged in filling operations to create valuable real estate out of shallow marshes and tidelands. To protect the Bay and coordinate activities that would affect it, the California Legislature in 1965 created the San Francisco Bay Conservation and Development Commission (Feibusch, 1968). This commission published a detailed Bay Plan in January 1969. Of course, is must be remembered that the coastline is a locus of rapid geologic change with or without man's engineering projects. Along coasts characterized by barriers bars, bays, and lagoons, the natural geologic processes work to fill with sediment the bays and lagoons behind the bars. However, if man understands the forces at work he can attempt to use them beneficially or at least to design his structures to coexist economically with the natural systems in operation.

Agriculture. Agriculture is a mining-manufacturing process whereby plants are used to mine minerals, accumulated organic matter, and water from the earth and process them into substances from which human and animal digestive systems can extract nourishment. Continued harvesting of crops in one area rather quickly mines out such elements as nitrogen, potassium, and phosphorous; trace metals and other elements are depleted more slowly. Considering that some areas have been farmed more or less continually for millenia, it is clear that unless the depleted elements are restored to the soil, the crops produced will have a diminished nutritive value. Fertilizers have been in use for almost as long as man has cultivated the land. Early fertilizers were so-called natural fertilizers, principally animal wastes, that restored nitrogen and phosphorous to the soil. They were applied by turning animals into the fields or by collecting and spreading wastes from stables and barns and the "night soil" from human habitations. Long-term and intensive use of land as pasture is also a mining operation if the animal product does not die and rot on the land from which the mineral substances were extracted, or if pasture land is not fertilized.

In the industrialized countries with highly productive agriculture, the so-called commercial fertilizers have largely supplanted natural fertilizers. Commercial fertilizers restore nitrogen, phosphorous, and potassium. In areas of acid soils, ground limestone or lime is applied. In some commercial superphosphate fertilizers there are small amounts of uranium (which on decay produces radium 226, lead 210, and polonium 210) and fluorine. Although amounts are too small to be considered toxic over the short term, application of these fertilizers over several decades may well result in harmful concentrations (President's Science Advisory Committee, 1965, p. 83). With regard to trace elements, the problem is what to add and how much. Ten Eyck (1967, pp. 162–163) has suggested it will be necessary to return to soils some two to four million tons of metals per year and that future fertilizers should be fortified by as much as 3 percent of minor elements in order to maintain the nutritional value of produce. The problem is not simple, because metal deficiencies are not everywhere the same—one area is deficient in zinc, another in cobalt, a third in molybdenum. Moreover, the role of trace elements in nutrition is not fully understood.

In the last several years there have been more attempts at interdisciplinary exchanges between geologists, soil scientists, and nutritionists to explore mutual interests in the distribution of trace elements and their effects on the health of plants and animals. A symposium on the "Relation of Geology and Trace Elements to Nutrition" was held under the auspices of the Geological Society of America in New York in 1963; the proceedings were published as Geological Society of America Special Paper 90. The First Annual Conference on Trace Substances and Environmental Health, sponsored by the University of Missouri in 1967, was followed by a second conference in 1968. The Proceedings were published by the University of Missouri. It is clear from the papers presented in these symposia that a deficiency or an excess of certain elements in soils affect plant and animal physiology. Before corrective actions can be taken we need to know more about the composition of the earth's crust that we live on and from.

In addition to plant nutrients, in the practice of agriculture man adds other substances to the soil through use of pesticides, fungicides, and herbicides. The simple ecosystems of cultivated lands are highly vulnerable to invasion by unwanted plants, called weeds, and to attack by insects. Through sprays and dusts over a period of years there is built up in the soil concentrations of potentially poisonous metals such as arsenic, lead, copper, or mercury, or of chlorinated hydrocarbons such as DDT. Some concentrations reduce soil fertility but others simply turn up as concentrations in the crops harvested from the land. Animals that feed on, smoke, or otherwise ingest the vegetable material containing concentrations of heavy metals or chlorinated hydrocarbons build up concentrations of the same substances in various organs of the body. If the amounts reach the limit of tolerance for a particular substance the health of the organism suffers. Use of heavy-metal insecticides has been substantially reduced, but through years of application some soil is so enriched in the metals that concentrations continue to appear. An example is the concentration of lead in tobacco as a result of years of applications of lead arsenate to fields. DDT has spread so rapidly that animal populations the world over are contaminated with it. It concentrates in the fat bodies of carnivores. In a Long Island marsh with a 20-yr history of DDT spraying for mosquito control, the surface layer of mud contains 32 lb per acre of DDT (Erlich, 1968, p. 48).

From a geologic viewpoint, the practice of agriculture involves a continual mining and replenishment of minerals and elements in the thin upper surface layer. Minerals such as phosphate and potash are taken from the great natural concentrations of the world and widely dispersed. In attempts to nurture simple eco-systems that could not survive in natural competition, man poisons other plants, animals, and insects. This forces evolutionary changes in these organisms as they try to adapt to survive the poison.

Summary. This chapter has attempted to focus on some of the ways and on some of the areas in which human activities are producing significant geologic effects. Man's capabilities to cause changes of geological magnitude are increasing very rapidly because of (1) the increasing amounts of energy at his disposal and (2) the increase in his numbers. These two factors together, more people with more energy to spend, make man an increasingly powerful geological agent. Although his direct operations are presently limited to the outer 5 mi of the crust plus the atmosphere, he can indirectly perform work on the deep interior through use of shock waves and by shifting of mass on the surface (p. 174). If the planet earth were a sentient being, it would certainly regard man as the most virulent of geological agents. It has been suggested that when the human population reaches 12,000 million million people, or more than 2 people per square meter of the earth's surface, a severe heat problem will occur, and that above 60,000 million million (10^{16} to 10^{18}) the heat generated by human metabolic processes will completely overwhelm the normal heat budget of the earth (Fremlin, 1964, p. 287). This limit would mark man's finest hour as a geological agent.

REFERENCES

ABELSON, P. H. (1965a)   "Water for North America": *Science*, Vol. 147, no. 3654, p. 113.

ABELSON, P. H. (1965b)   "Air pollution": *Science*, Vol. 147, no. 3665, p. 1527.

Air Conservation Commission (1965)   *Air conservation: Report of the Air Conservation Commission:* American Association for the Advancement of Science, Washington, D. C., publication no. 80, 335 pp.

ALEXANDER, TOM (1967)   "Where will we put all that garbage?": *Fortune*, October 1967, pp. 148–151; 189–195.

AUTÚNEZ ECHAGARAY, FRANCISCO (1964)   *Monografía historica y minera sobre el distrito de Guanajuato:* Consejo de Recursos Naturales No Renovables, publicación 17E, Mexico, 588 pp.

BAILLY, PAUL A. (1966)   *Mineral exploration and mine developing problems related to use and management of other resources and to U. S. Public Land Laws:* Statement presented to the Public Lands Law Conference, University of Idaho, Boise, Idaho, October 10, 1966, updated to June 30, 1967, 44 pp.

BAUER, A. M. (1965)   *Simultaneous excavation of sand and gravel sites:* University of Illinois and National Sand and Gravel Association project no. 1, 60 pp.

BELTER, W. G. (1962)   "Radioactive effluent control in a future nuclear energy industry," in *Proceedings of the Fourth Inter-American Symposium on the peaceful application of nuclear energy:* Pan American Union, Washington, D. C., pp. 97–114.

BERGSTROM, R. E. (1968)   *Disposal of wastes: scientific and administrative considerations:* Illinois Geological Survey environmental geology notes, no. 20, January 1968, 12 pp.

BROOKS, D. B. (1966)   "Strip mine reclamation and analysis": *Natural Resources Journal*, Vol. 6, no. 1, pp. 13–44.

CARTER, L. J. (1968)   "Thermal pollution: A threat to Cayuga's waters?": *Science*, Vol. 162, no. 3854, pp. 649–650.

Chemical Week (1963)   "Bringing in concrete competition": *Chemical Week*, Vol. 93, no. 4, July 27, 1963, pp. 93–94.

Chemical Week (1965a)   "Technology newsletter": *Chemical Week*, Vol. 97, no. 16, October 16, 1965, p. 94.

Chemical Week (1965b)   "Drawing bead on lead": *Chemical Week*, Vol. 97, no. 18, October 30, 1965, pp. 24–25.

Chemical Week (1966*a*)   "Built to stay empty": *Chemical Week*, Vol. 99, no. 15, October 8, 1966, p. 95.

Chemical Week (1966*b*)   "Closing the nuclear fuel cycle": *Chemical Week*, Vol. 99, no. 18, October 29, 1966, pp. 85, 89–90.

Chemical Week (1967*a*)   "Big bill for low sulfur fuel": *Chemical Week*, Vol. 100, no. 25, June 24, 1967, p. 78.

Chemical Week (1967*b*)   "At sea about chemical wastes": *Chemical Week*, Vol. 101, no. 16, October 14, 1967, pp. 133–136.

Chemical Week (1967*c*)   "Technology newsletter": *Chemical Week*, Vol. 101, no. 24, December 9, 1967, p. 77.

Chemical Week (1968*a*)   "Will the voltmeter replace the gas gauge?": *Chemical Week*, Vol. 102, no. 8, February 24, 1968, p. 43.

Chemical Week (1968*b*)   "Bonus for clearing the air": *Chemical Week*, Vol. 102, no. 22, June 1, 1968, p. 20.

Chemical Week (1968*c*)   "Sulfur—from coal?": *Chemical Week*, Vol. 120, no. 22, June 1, 1968, p. 37.

Chemical Week (1968*d*)   "Burning for good riddance": *Chemical Week*, Vol. 102, no. 20, May 18, 1968, p. 59–60.

Committee on Pollution (1966)   *Waste management and control*: National Academy of Sciences-National Research Council publication 1400, 257 pp.

Conservation Foundation (1963)   *Implication of rising carbon dioxide content of the atmosphere*: The Conservation Foundation, 15 pp.

Department of the Interior (1967)   *Surface mining and our environment*: Washington D. C., 124 pp.

DYKES, D. R.; BRY, T. S.; KLINE, C. H. (1967)   "Water management": *Environmental Science and Technology*, Vol. 1, no. 10, October 1967, pp. 780–784.

Engineering and Mining Journal (1968)   "Mineral waste utilization symposium points out successes and failures": *Engineering and Mining Journal*, Vol. 169, no. 5, May, 1968, p. 110.

Engineering-Science, Inc., (1961)   *Effects of refuse dumps on groundwater quality*: California Resources Agency, California Water Pollution Control Board publication 24, Sacramento, California, 107 p.

Environmental Science and Technology (1967)   "Solid wastes": *Environmental Science and Technology*, Vol. 1, no. 3, March, 1967, pp.199–202.

ERLICH, P. R. (1968)   "Population, food and environment: Is the battle lost?": *Texas Quarterly*, Vol. XI, no. 2, pp. 43–54.

EVANS, D. M. (1966)   "Man-made earthquakes in Denver": *GeoTimes*, Vol. 10, no. 9, pp. 11–18.

FEIBUSCH, HANS A. (1968)   "Planning the future of San Francisco Bay":
Civil Engineering, Vol. 38, no. 1, January 1968, pp. 70–72.

FREMLIN, J. H. (1964)   "How many people can the world support?": New
Scientist, Vol. 24, no. 415, pp. 285–287.

GALLEY, JOHN E. (1968a)   "Economic and industrial potentials of geologic
basins and reservoir strata," in Subsurface disposal in geologic basins—
A study of reservoir strata: American Association of Petroleum Geologists,
memoir 10, pp. 1–10.

GALLEY, JOHN E., ed. (1968b)   Subsurface disposal in geologic basins—A
study of reservoir strata: American Association of Petroleum Geologists,
memoir 10, 253 pp.

GERARD, R. D. (1966)   "Potential freshwater reservoir in the New York
area": Science, Vol. 153, no. 3738, pp. 870–871.

GOLDSMITH, JOHN R., AND LANDLAW, STEPHEN A. (1968)   "Carbon Monoxide and Human Health": Science, Vol. 162, no. 3860, pp. 1352–1359.

HICKMAN, KENNETH (1966)   "Oasis for the future": Science, Vol. 154,
no. 3749, pp. 612–617.

HUBBERT, M. K. (1962)   Energy resources: National Academy of Sciences-
National Research Council, publication 1000-D, 141 pp.

HUBBERT, M. K. (1966)   "History of petroleum geology and its present
and future": Bulletin of American Association of Petroleum Geologists,
Vol. 50, no. 12, pp. 2504–2518.

HUBBERT, M. K. (1967)   "Degree of advancement of petroleum exploration in the United States": Bulletin of American Association of Petroleum Geologists, Vol. 51, no. 11, pp. 2207–2227.

HUGHES, G. M. (1967)   Selection of refuse disposal sites in Northeastern
Illinois: Illinois State Geological Survey environmental geology notes no.
17, 26 pp.

Interstate Oil Compact Commission (1968)   Subsurface disposal of industrial wastes, 109 pp.

JOHNSON, CRAIG (1966)   Practical operating procedures for progressive
rehabilitation of sand and gravel sites: University of Illinois and National
Sand and Gravel Association project no. 2, 75 pp.

JOHNSON, K. L.; DWORETZKY, L. H.; AND HELLER, A. N. (1968)   "Carbon
monoxide and air pollution from automobile emissions in New York
City": Science, Vol. 160, no. 3823, April 5, 1968, pp. 67–68.

KANE, J. W. (1967)   Monthly reservoir evaporation rates for Texas 1940
through 1965: Texas Water Development Board report no. 64, 111 pp.

KOELZER, B. A.; BAUER, W. J.; AND DALTON, A. E. (1968)   "The Chicagoland deep tunnel project": Paper presented at the Interstate Oil Compact Commission meeting, Miami, Florida, December 5, 1968.

Legget, R. F. (1968) "Consequences of man's alteration of natural systems": Texas Quarterly, Vol. XI, no. 2, pp. 24–35.

McGauhey, P. H. (1968) "Earth's tolerance for wastes": Texas Quarterly, Vol. XI, no. 2, pp. 36–42.

Magnuson, M. O., and Kimball, R. L. (1968) Revegetation studies at three strip-mine sites in north-central Pennsylvania: U. S. Bureau of Mines report of investigations 7075, 8 pp.

Mero, John C. (1965) The mineral resources of the sea: Elsevier Publishing Company, Amsterdam, 312 pp.

Mining Engineering (1967) "Surface mining continues to grow": Mining Engineering, Vol. 3, no. 10, October 1967, pp. 107–108.

Ministry of Housing and Local Government (1961) Pollution of water by tipped refuse—Report of the Technical Committee on Experimental Disposal of House Refuse in Wet and Dry Pits: Her Majesty's Stationery Office, London, 141 p.

Missouri Mineral Industry News (1968a) "Hazardous dams in Missouri —an editorial": Missouri Mineral Industry News, Vol. 8, no. 2, pp. 16–19.

Missouri Mineral Industry News (1968b) "More on hazardous dams in Missouri—an editorial": Missouri Mineral Industry News, Vol. 8, no. 4, pp. 43–44.

Montgomery, J. M., and Pomeroy, R. D. (1949) Report of Investigation for City of Long Beach regarding probable effects of proposed cut-and-cover trash disposal: Montgomery and Pomeroy, Engineers-Chemists, Pasadena, Calif., 25 pp.

National Academy of Sciences-National Research Council (1959) Radioactive waste disposal into Atlantic and Gulf coast waters: National Academy of Sciences-National Research Council publication 655, Washington, D. C., 37 pp.

Nace, R. L. (1967a) "Are we running out of water?": U. S. Geological Survey circular 536, 7 pp.

Nace, R. L. (1967b) "Water in flatland": GeoScience News, Vol. 1, no. 1, pp. 2–5, 18–22.

Oil and Gas Journal (1967a) "The nonleaded-gasoline tab: $4.2 billion": Oil and Gas Journal, Vol. 65, no. 21, May 22, 1967, pp. 74–75.

Oil and Gas Journal (1967b) "Panel asks ceiling on lead in gasoline": Oil and Gas Journal, Vol. 65, no. 43, October 23, 1967, p. 43.

Oil and Gas Journal (1967c) "Central waste-disposal unit set at Houston": Oil and Gas Journal, Vol. 65, no. 49, December 4, 1967, p. 41.

Oil and Gas Journal (1968) "API refining study spotlights wastes": Oil and Gas Journal, Vol. 66, no. 21, May 20, 1968, p. 59.

President's Science Advisory Committee (1965) "Restoring the quality of our environment": *Report of the Environmental Pollution Panel*, 317 pp.

QUINN, FRANK (1968) "Water transfers—must the American West be won again?": *Geographical Review*, Vol. 58, no. 1, pp. 108–132.

REINING, DON (1967) "Rock, sand and gravel resources—strong but challenged": Preprint of paper delivered to American Institute of Mining and Metallurgical Engineers, Los Angeles, California, Feb. 19–23, 1967.

RICH, T. A. (1967) "Air pollution studies aided by overall air pollution index": *Environmental Science and Technology*, Vol. 1, no. 10, pp. 796–800.

RISSER, H. E., AND MAJOR, R. L. (1967) "Urban expansion—an opportunity and a challenge to industrial mineral producers": Illinois Geological Survey environmental geology notes no. 16, 19 pp.

SCHELLIE, K. L., AND ROGIER, D. A. (1963) *Site utilization and rehabilitation practices for sand and gravel operations*: National Sand and Gravel Association, 80 pp.

SHERLOCK, R. L. (1922) *Man as a geological agent*: H. F. & G. Witherby, London, 372 pp.

TEN EYCK, H. S. (1967) "The multiple problems facing the fertilizer industry": *Mining Engineering*, Vol. 19, no. 7, July 1967, pp. 161–164.

TRUAX, C. N., JR. (1965) "Water storage potential of surface mines of coal lands": *Mining Congress Journal*, Vol. 51, no. 11, November 1965, pp. 40–41, 45–46.

U. S. Bureau of Mines (1965a) *Mineral facts and problems*: U. S. Bureau of Mines bulletin 630, 1118 pp.

U. S. Bureau of Mines (1965b) *Minerals yearbook, Vol. I, Metals and minerals (except fuels)*, 1095 pp.

U. S. Bureau of Mines (1968) *Wealth out of waste*, 28 pp.

WARNER, D. L. (1967) *Deep wells for industrial waste injection in the United States—Summary of data*: Federal Water Pollution Control Administration, Water Pollution Control Research Series, publication no. WP-20-10, 45 pp.

CONSERVATION AND MANAGEMENT

6

General statement. The conservation movement has grown enormously in strength and breadth in the 1960s as a result of widespread concern about natural resources and the quality of the environment. President Kennedy's interest in conservation and his choice of Stewart Udall as secretary of the interior provided Federal leadership and authority in support of conservation, which was carried over into the Johnson administration through the continued efforts of the secretary of the interior and the strong personal efforts of Mrs. Lyndon B. Johnson. The Federal leadership broadened the definition of conservation to "applied ecology" (*Department of the Interior 1964 Conservation Yearbook*, p. 9) and thereby put a meaning into the word that went far beyond its original sense. Conservation as now defined includes all of the physical, social, and legal problems attendant on the use of the land, or, as Beazley (1967, p. 345) defined it in a more cultural sense, "Conservation

. . . is the establishment and observation of economically, socially, and politically acceptable norms, standards, patterns, or models of behavior in the use of natural resources by a given society."

The inclusion of a wide variety of environmental problems under the umbrella of "conservation" caused a great deal of pushing and shoving of traditional conservationists to make way for the new "environment-alists." Federal Government concern with environmental abuses such as air pollution, water pollution, strip mining, and urban deterioration, which directly affect large numbers of people, has left some of the old conservationists on the outside looking in. The conservation movement is in the uncomfortable position of the small snake that has swallowed a very large and active elephant. Although the traditional conservation-ists are articulate in defending the need to preserve a parcel of natural habitat or species of wild creature, their concern is not directly of consequence to the average city dweller who is breathing bad air, who wants to take his family fishing somewhere within a day's drive of the city, and who has only academic interest in the survival of the whooping crane.

Broadening of the conservation movement to a total environment movement has brought a lot of new people into it—scientists, engineers, economists, geographers, and ecologists—people who are professionally concerned with the environment on a working-day basis. In Washington they have taken the leadership from the naturalists who dominated the movement in the past. However, on the local level, the part-time conservationists—organized into garden clubs, sportsmen's clubs, boating clubs, heritage and historical societies—retain the leadership. In some areas, smaller groups with special interests have combined with others to form conservation federations or congresses. There is thus a dichotomy between the Federal leadership that is influenced by scientific, engineering, and economic realities (the need to fix priorities, the need to consider the urgent problems confronting the largest numbers of people, and the need to resolve conflicts between users of the land in an informed manner) and the local groups with a fervor to preserve and protect some natural scene or species at any cost. The local groups are becoming more sophisticated through the act of banding together for political strength. When bird watchers and bird hunters sit down together in the same federation of congress, united by their desire to protect and preserve the nesting and breeding grounds of waterfowl, it surely paves the way for better communication between other naturally antagonistic groups such as quarry operators and the protectors of woodland glades, and between Main Street and Washington.

In their report *Alternatives in Water Management* the National Academy of Sciences-National Research Council Committee on Water of the Division of Earth Sciences remarked that (1966, p. 26):

The change in concept for the natural environment from that of a workshop to that of a temple and the conflicting existence of both concepts presents the resource planner with his most sensitive task: drawing a line between workshop and temple, or attempting to merge them.

It is important for anyone professionally involved with the land to understand the spirit and direction of the new conservation movement. The environmental geologist can contribute substantially to the movement. The land-use planner and the engineer will find conservationists a powerful friend or an effective enemy.

As public concern over environmental problems has mounted and various citizen groups have organized to force action, there has been a predictable governmental response. One of the first signs of the environmental crisis was increasing frequency of phone calls between legislators and government agencies responsible for natural resource conservation and public health. The lack of hard information on the environment prompted a series of studies. The results of studies plus continued pressure produced hearings. Environmental protection legislation was enacted. Administrators found sympathy for budget requests in the area of environmental problems. Now, a vast host of government employees are in the "environment business."

In the Department of the Interior old-line organizations such as the Geological Survey, Bureau of Mines, Bureau of Reclamation, and Fish and Wildlife Service began new programs to produce information on water resources, air and water pollution, mined-land reclamation, earthquakes and landslides. Newcomers like the Office of Saline Water (1952) and Office of Water Resources Research (1964) began operations. The Federal Water Pollution Control Administration was transferred from the Department of Health, Education, and Welfare to the Department of the Interior in 1966. The Department of Commerce reorganized the Weather Bureau and Coast and Geodetic Survey into the Environmental Sciences Services Administration. In agriculture, the Soil Conservation Service broadened its service to farmers to include developing soil and water information for small communities and planning groups. The National Forest Service increased ecological studies. The Department of Health, Education, and Welfare began extensive studies of air and water pollution. Even the U. S. Army Corps of Engineers included studies of ecology in their water projects. The President's Science Advisory Panel undertook environmental studies; the National Academy of Sciences–National Research Council undertook environmental studies. The Atomic Energy Commission expanded programs in radioactive waste disposal. The National Aeronautics and Space Administration undertook studies of environmental phenomena by remote sensing. Independent units like the Tennessee Valley Authority became concerned with air and water pollution. The Appalachian Regional Commission concerned itself with mined-land reclamation. The Public Land Law Review Commission considered environmental protection in their review of the nation's public land laws. Along with the new boards, commissions, administrations, councils, and compacts came more environmental legislation.

As agency after agency undertook programs in environmental science and engineering their investigators began to run into each other, particularly in the field of water. The establishment came under scrutiny from watchdog agencies in goverment like the Bureau of the Budget, as well as outside agencies, asking, "Can duplication of programs be avoided? Can the federal organization as constituted deal effectively with environmental problems?" Bills to reorganize the Department of the Interior (with agencies from the Departments of Commerce and Agriculture) into a Department of Natural Resources were introduced. Executive Order 11472, issued June 3, 1969, established the Environmental Quality Council and the Citizens' Advisory Council on Environmental Quality. The council consists of the vice-president and the secretaries of agriculture, commerce, health, education, and welfare, housing and urban development, the interior, and transportation. The president presides over meetings of the council, and the science advisor serves as executive secretary. The director of the Bureau of the Budget, the chairman of the Council of Economic Advisers, and the executive secretary of the Council for Urban Affairs may participate in the deliberations of the council as observers.

Functions of the council include (1) reviewing the adequacy of existing systems for monitoring and predicting environmental changes,

(2) seeking advancement of scientific knowledge of changes in the environment and encouraging development of technology to prevent or minimize adverse effects on man's well-being, and (3) assuring assessment of new and changing technologies for their potential effects on the environment. The Office of Science and Technology provides or arranges for necessary staff services and facilities, and each department or agency represented on the council provides information and assistance as available. The Citizens' Advisory Committee consists of a chairman and not more than 14 other members appointed by the president.

The near future will probably see major reorganizations in the federal structure to improve the government's capability to deal with the total environment and eliminate the interagency jealousies which cost the taxpayers so much unnecessary expense in duplication. In fact, environmental problems are forcing reorganization of government at all levels because existing structure does not seem to be able to deal with the problems effectively.

MANAGEMENT OF THE ENVIRONMENT

The new conservationists and particularly the Federal conservationists commonly include "stewardship" of the land in the general mission of conservation. There is thereby added to the broad definition of "applied ecology" the responsibility of management. Management involves planning and decision-making; both of these require data. Thus in this comprehensive view, conservation is an enterprise that includes collection and collation of data, analysis of problems, planning for desirable objectives, consideration of alternative procedures, and decision-making. Alternatives in decision-making are discussed on p. 196. It is also beneficial to consider the problems of management after plans have been formulated and decisions have been made. These are problems of implementation. The principal difficulty in managing the environment is managing the people in it.

Management of the land and its resources requires consideration of three systems—the physical (geological-meteorological) system of earth and atmosphere, the biological system that is sustained more or less at the earth-atmosphere interface, and the cutural system of the dominant species, man (Figure 26).

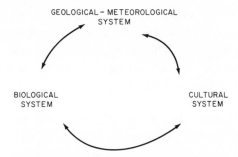

FIGURE 26. Three major environmental elements that must be considered
in management.

The physical system. Management of the geological sector of the physical system depends to a great extent on the ancient and honorable
field of civil engineering. The engineer, using geological, hydrological,
and meteorological data, designs his structures to achieve objectives
formulated as a result of business or governmental decisions made within
an economic framework. In this sector engineering capabilities for implementing management goals are relatively advanced, or so they seem
now. Perhaps the most serious criticism that can be made is that action
is commonly taken to control, modify, or utilize one environmental
component and no consideration is given to the second- and third-order
effects of the management decision. This is the fault of entrusting
management agencies and bureaus with a single mission, for example,
flood control or navigation. Lamentably (or happily, depending on your
point of view) capabilities to manage the atmospheric sector are not
well developed. There are no meteorological engineers. The science of
meterology is only now on the threshold of finding out enough about
the system to permit development of meteorological or atmospheric
engineers. The atmosphere certainly ranks with water as an essential
resource to sustain life, both directly in providing oxygen to the living
organisms and indirectly in distributing water over the land. As a
transportation resource it ranks with the seas, and its use to support
both cargo and passenger vehicles is rising exponentially. Only in recent
years have there been experiments designed to precipitate moisture from
the atmosphere to produce rain and to dissipate fog around airports;
plans to deenergize large storms before they result in damage are being

considered. In 1967 Soviet scientists announced a successful hail-suppression experiment over about 1.25 million acres (*Science*, June 23, 1967, Vol. 156, p. 1580). Thus it appears we are standing upon the threshold of atmospheric engineering, for clearly management is not possible without engineering capability.

The biological system. The biological system—the living resources of the planet—was the first management concern of the human culture. The earliest attempts were directed at management of food and fiber supply in organized agriculture and animal husbandry. Although industrial nations have developed relatively sophisticated farm and ranch management techniques, fishing for the most part remains a gathering of a natural crop that does not yet yield itself to management in the sense of planned production. In modern agriculture pesticides and herbicides are used without much consideration of their second and third order environmental effects. Public health and sanitary engineering are other areas in which management capabilities are well advanced. Forest management is successfully practiced in most of the advanced nations of the world. But here again, mission-oriented government management agencies tend to view their piece of the resource as a closed system and do not effectively participate in an overall environment management program. For example, in the western national forests of the United States, a zealous Forest Service obstructs legitimate development of mineral properties, apparently unaware or unappreciative of the role of minerals in maintaining modern culture.

The oceans. Oceanic engineering has in the past been concerned mainly with physical systems rather than biological systems, with surface and subsurface transport and design and construction of engineering works in the zone where the sea impinges on the land. Working for the most part empirically, engineers have had reasonable but not complete success in their attempts to build and operate harbor installations, maintain open channels, and control beach erosion. Recently, engineering efforts have been directed toward design and construction of systems to explore and produce minerals from the sea floor and below. Stationary and floating marine platforms, varieties of submersibles, and improved individual diving equipment have been produced. However, oceanic engineering is in its infancy. Little or no progress has been made beyond the collecting of scientific data on water movement and sediment transport. Marine biology has received a great deal of impetus from impending world famine but marine "agricultural engineering" is not yet a reality. So, without adequate knowledge of the sea, and without the engineering capability to manage it, our marine environmental "programs" continue as they have over the past decades—fishing fleets and garbage barges put merrily out to sea; the fishermen gather and the garbage men dump.

The cultural system. The cultural system wherein the problem is management of people presents the most formidable challenge. If the physical and biological systems in the environment are to be managed to assure to man a supply of resources adequate to supply his physical and aesthetic needs, then man must create within his political, legal, and social system an appropriate mechanism for management, and if effective management is not possible within the political, legal, and social framework that prevails, he must change the framework. The alternative is, ultimately, an environment that will not support the human culture as it has developed.

The first problem is that environmental management decisions pertaining to natural earth processes and resources commonly transcend the boundaries of political units. Management of water resources where a major river flows through a number of states or nations is a case in point. If a state line runs through an irrigation district, some arrangement must be made to manage the district as a whole; half a reservoir cannot be managed. Decisions over the long term may be locally unpopular. Management responsibility must carry with it the authority to allocate resources, to move communities from areas of hazard to areas of safety and from areas of scarcity to areas of plenty. Decisions to ban a large-volume water use such as irrigation in favor of long-term municipal and industrial development will be strongly or violently opposed by farming communities. Management of the atmosphere, a dynamic envelop of gases, can only be effective on a continental or global basis because the management decisions made at one particular longitude will ultimately affect the areas to the east or west. A political entity that precipitates a large part of the moisture in its air to improve its own agricultural yield and water resource position may expect strong protests or military action from a downwind neighbor faced with prospects of becoming a desert. Thus, although local environmental problems largely in closed systems can be managed on a local level, the pressing problem of water resources and air pollution are, on the smallest scale, regional problems and management must rest in regional or national authorities.

Another problem in countries where land is held in private ownership is that the authority to manage the environment conflicts with the right of the individual to manage his own property. Regional environmental management is not possible within the traditional legal framework. Nationalization of the land, a system extant in some socialistic and communistic societies, commonly requires strong oppressive measures by the authority because it runs counter to one of the basic instincts of man, the so-called territorial instinct (Ardrey, 1966, pp. 111–117). Although repression may be successful over the short term, it sets in motion strong currents of reaction that ultimately threaten governmental stability. After all, through history the great social upheavals have been a result of the individual desire for land. Here then appears a fundamental conflict—the individual's strong desires for ownership of land or a territory wherein he can protect his privacy and engage in a productive pursuit, and the equally strong need of society to manage the land in a manner insuring supplies of clean air, clean water, adequate food, adequate energy, and adequate materials. Drastic political, legal, and social changes will be required before these two needs can be satisfied in the same place and at the same time. Ardrey (1966, pp. 115–117) said:

From the days of Stalin's enforced collectivization of the land, the peasant has been permitted to retain a tiny private plot for family cultivation. It is the last bedraggled remnant of the pair territory in the Soviet Union, and in times of political crisis and idealogical pressure its size has been reduced. Today the private plot averages half an acre in size, but there is little likelihood of further reduction. Without it, Russia would starve.

Private plots occupy about 3 percent of all Russian cultivated land, yet they produce almost half of all the vegetables consumed, almost half the milk and meat, three-quarters of all eggs, and two-thirds of that staff of Russian life, potatoes. After almost half a century the experiment with scientific socialism, despite all threats and despite all massacres, despite education, propaganda and appeals to patriotism, despite a police power and a political power ample, one would presume, to effect the total social conditioning of any being within its grasp, finds itself today at the mercy of an evolutionary fact of life: that man is a territorial animal.

The territorial nature of man is genetic and ineradicable. We shall see, farther along in our inquiry, a larger and older demonstration of its powers in our devotion to country above even home. But as we watch the farmer going out to his barn with the sun not risen above the wood lot's fringe, we witness the answer to civilization's central problem which is none but our evolutionary nature could provide. Here is man, like any other territorial animal, acting against his own interest; in the city he would still be sleeping, and making more money too. What force other than territory's innate morality could so contain his dedications? But here is also the biological reward, that mysterious enhancement of energy and resolution—territory's prime law and prime enigma—which invests the proprietor on his own vested acres. We did not invent it. We cannot command it. Nor can we, not with all our policemen, permanently deny it.

He who has will probably hold. We do not know why; it is simply so. It is a law that rings harshly in the contemporary ear, but this is a defect of the ear, not the law. I believe that we shall see, as this inquiry develops, that, harsh though the law may be, in this territorial species of which you and I are members it has been the source of all freedom, the curse on the despot, and the last desperate roadblock in the path of aggression.

Perhaps Ardrey's "territorial imperative" is one of the driving causes behind the high incidence of social instability in urban areas; perhaps over generations of urban living man will through selective breeding subdue the territorial imperative and convert himself into a colonial animal. But it will not be without social pain.

It appears clear that before man can attempt a coordinated and comprehensive program of management of the physical and biological sectors of the environment he must develop a satisfactory method of managing the cultural sector—that is to say, a method of managing people. The culture is made up of political, economic, social, legal and, religious institutions. Robert Hargrove Montgomery, Professor Emeritus of Economics at The University of Texas, advanced the thesis that technological change requires an equal amount of cultural change and that as technological change accelerates, cultural change accelerates, or, put more simply, as man changes his tools, he must also change his society. He suggested that this "cultural equation," which equates technological change with cultural change (defined in terms of politics, law, economics, business, and religion) is every bit as significant to man as the Einstein equation relating energy and mass. In this context, the need to manage the environment has been brought about by the ever-increasing effects that man's activities have on his environment; the increasing effects are the product of man's increased capability to change his environment; the increased capability to change is the child of advancing technology.

Management of people is a phrase that evokes to the rugged individualist unpleasant pictures of barbed-wire stockades, of mindless masses of humanity prodded here and there by Big Brother in an Orwellian world, of thought control and brainwashing. Yet, in a kinder sense the elementary function of government is management of people, politics is the administration of government operations, and political science deals with the form and principles of management. From ancient times religion has been an instrument of people management. More recently a new discipline, or, more properly, an old discipline with a new name, social psychology, devotes itself to aspects of the problems of managing people. Commonly in modern society, a group trying to persuade an electorate, (or even a people without the franchise) that a particular course of action is desirable and should be accepted, speaks in terms of "informing and educating" the people. Massive propaganda offensives utilizing news media, both subtle and obvious, are capable of changing attitudes in a remarkably short time, even in a sophisticated and cynical population. Even governments with absolute authority have found it necessary to win general acceptance of major policies and voluntary compliance to avoid harsh methods of enforcement.

ALTERNATIVES IN MANAGING THE ENVIRONMENT

The problem before society is not whether conservation is good or bad, whether to conserve or not to conserve, whether to make use of the environment or not to make use of it, but the problem of alternatives. The decisions to be made are management decisions. How can we best manage the complicated and interrelated earth—people system to the maximum benefit of society now and in the future. In order to weigh alternatives some method must be developed for assigning values to the various factors that make up an alternative. For example, what part of the nation's resource of money and manpower should be budgeted to preserve near-extinct species of wildlife such as the whooping crane? The problem raises the question, What is the value of the whooping crane to society? How can it be measured? Will the answer be the same in a fat society as in a lean society? In the 1970s the whooping crane might be judged more valuable to society than it was in 1938, or, saying it another way, we might be able to afford to spend more on whooping cranes now than we could in 1938. By 1967 the status of whooping cranes had increased to the point where their return to traditional nesting grounds in the Aransas Wildlife Refuge shut down exploration and development of a new gas field in adjacent San Antonio bay. Department of Interior officials persuaded Sunray DX Oil Company to halt drilling operations and move the rig until the whoopers undertook their spring migration to the north. (*Oil and Gas Journal*, 1967). Rich countries can invest more in the care of wildlife than poor countries, which obviously must rank certain social services such as education and welfare over wildlife. But even in the United States today a large segment of the population, given the choice, would transfer the whooping crane budget item into social programs for improving the quality of education for migrant workers. Historically, in times of national crises such as war, conservation programs are cut back or suspended, a clear indication that they are judged as nonessential; in the war years whooping cranes did not make headlines. By any objective criteria the value of the whooping crane has not changed—society has changed the standards by which values are assigned and has selected an alternative within the existing economic framework.

Thus when resources are limited, and they always are, priorities must be assigned. How are they to be assigned? Ideally, if every member of an electorate were fully informed on all aspects of the management problem and were able to express himself on all problems, the whooping crane matter could be decided by popular vote. As a matter of fact, each member of the electorate is not fully informed and every decision cannot and should not be put to a vote. The electorate vests the overall management of the system in an administration, the administration chooses the heads of the major divisions of government and sets a broad budget policy, the heads of divisions make subordinate policy, and professional managers within the departments make recommendations on the advice of specialists in various disciplines. The specialists determine how to help the whooping crane and how much it will cost; various managers review the whooping crane program within the framework of their own budgets; the head of the department usually receives a recommended budget larger than his instructions permit. Then, based on his judgment of the importance of whooping cranes as against, for example, fish surveys, he cuts whooping cranes or he cuts something else. The question, Do we really need the whooping crane program? is not asked by budget officers up and down the line. They ask, Can we afford this whooping crane program? This is not the same question. The budget officer does not try to put a value on the program in terms of its value to society, he puts a value on it in terms of available money. But if he includes a whooping crane item in the budget he has to justify it in terms of social benefit as against cost because he knows someone else will be critically examining his budget. This is the way it works.

There are a large number of conservation programs that are desirable and that contribute to the long-term public good. On the basis or value to society, assuming it can be measured, a program in the Department of the Interior might be more valuable than a program in the Department of Agriculture. As a practical matter, the Department of Agriculture program might very well be implemented because it can be afforded while the Department of the Interior program is eliminated because it cannot be afforded. This is a consequence of assigning priorities on the basis of departmental budgets instead of by program merit. (Indirectly, of course, this means politics.) It would be most interesting to have an independent panel compare the programs of the U. S. Geological Survey in the Department of the Interior with those of the Soil Conservation Service of the Department of Agriculture in terms of contribution to the problem of managing the earth–people system.

This problem of *selection of alternatives* in a society which every day grows larger in terms of numbers of people, more demanding in terms of the intensity of its use of the earth, and more complex in terms of the multiplicity and variety of the ways in which it interacts with the environment, presents a democratic form of government with what is perhaps its most rigorous test as a politically viable system. Science and technology can provide answers to environmental problems. Usually the solutions are simple but hard; that is to say, scientific and economic analysis of the problem provide the answer to the problem, but the corrective measures necessary to its solution may very well be difficult or impossible to put into action in a democratic society. For example, the clear answer to a severe pollution problem in a local area might be to move industrial facilities and a large number of people to another area; the most reasonable answer to a threatened water shortage might require a shift of population; the most rational solution to a national problem might necessitate reduction in population increase to, say, .75 percent per year. Implementation of these solutions would be difficult in a society where absolute power is concentrated in a central government; in a democratic society such technocratic decisions cannot be put into effect at all, or at least not until the problem has reached the point of catastrophe, whereupon the logical solution is dictated by an implacable environment.

The Boca Ciega Bay (Florida) case illustrates the intensity of current conflicts over land use and the challenges it brings to the traditional roles of state, federal, and local agencies. The following account is from the *Conservation Foundation Letter* of April 22, 1968:

The Fight over Boca Ciega Bay

The story of the court test began more than 10 years ago on the west coast of Florida, just outside St. Petersburg.

Two developers—Alfred G. Zabel and David H. Russell—owned a prosperous trailer park on one of the many inlets of Boca Ciega Bay. They bought 11 acres of submerged land from the state, then sought permission to dredge and fill in the area for more trailers.

From the beginning there was adamant opposition, most notably from local citizens and conservationists. For one thing, the submerged land is a prime estuarine habitat. "The preservation of nursery grounds is the main interest," says A. R. Marshall, Florida field supervisor of Interior's Bureau of Sport Fisheries and Wildlife. He noted that biologists have taken samples of 40 species of young fin fish in the Zabel-Russell area. Such scientific findings greatly strengthened the conservationists' cause.

Secondly, it was considered the last straw. As Colonel R. P. Tabb, district engineer for the Corps, later wrote in his ruling: "During the past 15 years the surface area of Boca Ciega Bay has been substantially reduced (by 20%) by literally dozens of large-scale real estate fills . . . [which] have changed the Bay from an attractive natural body of water into an artificial area with little to recommend itself from an esthetic viewpoint."

Developers in Florida are required to get three permits before they can fill—county (or city), state and federal (Corps). "In the past," says James E. Sykes, of the Bureau of Commercial Fisheries Biological Laboratory at St. Petersburg, "these regulatory measures have been more a formality than an obstacle to land developers."

But this time conservation agencies and an aroused public battled the Zabel-Russell proposal in a running series of legal skirmishes—from Pinellas

County up through two intermediate courts to the Florida Supreme Court, back down, and up again. Finally, the state high court ruled for the developers, and the county was forced to issue a fill permit. A permit from the state came easily, but then the developers were stymied again—by the corps. It held a five-hour hearing in November 1966 which featured voluminous testimony against the permit, and on March 6, 1967, the Corps denied the Zabel-Russell application.

The Corps did not rely solely on its jurisdiction under the Rivers and Harbors Act. Indeed, it said the dredge and fill "would have no material adverse effect on navigation." Instead, it based its denial on the Coordination Act, since the Fish and Wildlife Service objected to the proposal and "the evidence . . . clearly indicates that the work would have a distinctly harmful effect on the fish and wildlife resources in Boca Ciega Bay."

Zabel and Russell filed suit in the Tampa District Court, challenging the authority of the Corps to deny a permit on grounds of damage to natural resources. Since that was essentially the only reason for the denial, the case became a test of Corps power under the Coordination Act—with not just Boca Ciega Bay but all wetlands and estuaries in the nation at stake.

The Corps, through the Justice Department, filed a motion to dismiss the complaint. In vain, it cited the legislative history of the Coordination Act and the intent of Congress in enacting it. Judge Krentzman agreed that Congress may have *meant* to give the Corps authority to consider natural resources, but said the language of the law failed to actually *accomplish* this. It must be very clear, Krentzman said, denying the motion.

Multiple working hypotheses. The complex nature of conservation problems requires that the approach to them be at the same time quantitative and qualitative. It is necessary to consider together scientific, engineering, economic, political, sociological, and legal data. The engineer who solves his problems with numbers and is conditioned to believe that there is only *one* correct answer is particularly frustrated with the qualitative analysis made necessary by the kinds of data that must be considered in other disciplines. Geologists have for many years been forced to qualitative analysis because the extreme complexity of natural earth systems makes it impossible to deal with them only in terms of measured quantities. They have in fact, been overapologetic about their tardiness in quantifying their analyses and geology has been regarded as less of a science than physics, for example, by some scientific sycophants because the answer to geological problems could not always be given absolutely in numbers. Lovering (1966, pp. 8–9) addressed himself to this point:

Many scientists believe that only quantitative data should be admitted as scientific evidence, that qualitative data are wholly subjective and must, therefore, be rigorously excluded from consideration, but as Birch (1951) remarked, "No one ever discovered a quality apart from a quantity nor a quantity apart from a quality. Why, then, are we so anxious to adopt the weird hypothesis that the quantitative is objective and real but the qualitative only subjective?" There is at the present time a strong tendency on the part of many geologists to feel that the use of numbers and mathematics gives an odor of sanctity to their work, but there are others who question whether the odor is that of sanctity. The method of solving problems used in this seemingly rigorous approach is essentially an empirical one and depends on gathering quantitative data throughout the investigation. These data are then fitted into a simplified or complex theory depending on whether or not a data-processing machine is available, and the investigation is terminated with a quantitative answer. Inductive and deductive reasoning are minimized and the data accumulated are rarely subjected to critical analysis; instead there is rather a child-like trust in the power of a statistically safe number of samples—always assumed to have been obtained—to justify results of mathematical manipulations. The distinction between cause and effect may be lost entirely, and although in engineering practice such methods may be logical and successful, their application to problems in geology often is naive.

As for myself, I believe that it is more rational and more fun to depend on the interplay of observation and reasoning, the critical selection of the best and least ambiguous data, the seeking out of several explanations as working hypotheses to be followed by testing and analysis and the search for verification or rejection. It is of the utmost importance that the investigator gathering evidence discriminate between interesting trivia and essential minutia and that he discipline himself to ignore the former and pursue the latter doggedly as far as required to solve the problem. Quite commonly the investigator must first seek the answer in qualitative terms—must seek to express the answer as lying between limits and proceed to a more and more quantitative approach only when it is obvious that the quantitative data are understood and that the answer as provided by the quantitative approach has validity.

The classical geological approach to complex earth problems—known as the *method of multiple working hypotheses*—was stated in 1890 by T. C. Chamberlin, a distinguished geologist and president of the University of Wisconsin. Chamberlin's essay deserves the close attention of planners and conservationists because planning and the solution of conservation problems involves consideration of a variety of approaches together with projections of the second-, third-, fourth-, and fifth-order derivative of whatever initial actions are taken. Certainly planning is an intellectual exercise that demands consideration of alternative solutions and this is the method of multiple working hypotheses. Parts of Chamberlin's essay (Chamberlin, 1890 as reprinted in *Science*, Vol. 148, May 7, 1965, pp. 754–759) follow:

As methods of study constitute the leading theme of our session, I have chosen as a subject in measurable consonance the method of multiple working hypotheses in its application to investigation, instruction, and citizenship.

There are two fundamental classes of study. The one consists in attempting to follow by close imitation the processes of previous thinkers, or to acquire by memorizing the results of their investigations. It is merely secondary, imitative, or acquisitive study. The other class is primary or creative study. In it the effort is to think independently, or at least individually, in the endeavor to discover new truth, or to make new combinations of truth, or at least to develop an individualized aggregation of truth. The endeavor is to think for one's self, whether the thinking lies wholly in the fields of previous thought or not. It is not necessary to this habit of study that the subject-material should be new; but the process of thought and its results must be individual and independent, not the mere following of previous lines of thought ending in predetermined results. The demonstration of a problem in Euclid precisely as laid down is an illustration of the former; the demonstration of the same proposition by a method of one's own or in a manner distinctively individual is an illustration of the latter; both lying entirely within the realm of the known and the old.

Creative study, however, finds its largest application in those subjects in which, while much is known, more remains to be known. Such are the fields which we, as naturalists, cultivate; and we are gathered for the purpose of developing improved methods lying largely in the creative phase of study, though not wholly so.

Intellectual methods have taken three phases in the history of progress thus far. What may be the evolutions of the future it may not be prudent to forecast. Naturally the methods we now urge seem the highest attainable. These three methods may be designated, first, the method of the ruling theory; second, the method of the working hypothesis; and, third, the method of multiple working hypotheses. . . .

Conscientiously followed, the method of the working hypothesis is a marked improvement upon the method of the ruling theory; but it has its defects—defects which are perhaps best expressed by the ease with which the hypothesis becomes a controlling idea. To guard against this, the method of multiple working hypotheses is urged. It differs from the former method in the multiple character of its genetic conceptions and of its tentative interpretations. It is directed against the radical defect of the two other methods; namely, the partiality of intellectual parentage. The effort is to bring up into view every rational explanation of new phenomena, and to develop every tenable hypothesis respecting their cause and history. The investigator thus becomes the parent of a family of hypotheses; and, by his parental relation to all, he is forbidden to hasten his affections unduly upon any one. In the nature of the case, the danger that springs from affection is counteracted, and therein is a radical difference between this method and the two preceding. The investigator at the outset puts himself in cordial sympathy and in parental relations (of adoption, if not of authorship) with every hypothesis that is at all applicable to the case under investigation. Having thus neutralized the partialities of his emotional nature, he proceeds with a certain natural and enforced erectness of mental attitude to the investigation, knowing well that some of his intellectual children will die before maturity, yet feeling that several of them may survive the results of final investigation, since it is often the outcome of inquiry that several causes are found to be involved instead of a single one. In following a single hypothesis, the mind is presumably led to a single explanatory conception. But an adequate explanation often involves the co-ordination of several agencies, which enter into the combined result in varying proportions. The true explanation is therefore necessarily complex. Such complex explanations of phenomena are specially encouraged by the method of multiple hypotheses, and constitute one of its chief merits. We are so prone to attribute a phenomenon to a single cause, when we find an agency present, we are liable to rest satisfied therewith, and fail to recognize that it is but one factor, and perchance a minor factor, in the accomplishment of the total result. . . .

A special merit of the method is, that by its very nature it promotes thoroughness. The value of a working hypothesis lies largely in its suggestiveness of lines of inquiry that might otherwise be overlooked. Facts that are trivial in themselves are brought into significance by their bearings upon the hypothesis, and by their causal indications. As an illustration, it is only necessary to cite the phenomenal influence which the Darwinian hypothesis has exerted upon the investigations of the past two decades. But a single working hypothesis may lead investigation along a given line to the neglect of others equally important; and thus, while inquiry is promoted in certain quarters, the investigation lacks in completeness. But if all rational hypotheses relating to a subject are worked co-equally, thoroughness is the presumptive result, in the very nature of the case.

In the use of the multiple method, the re-action of one hypothesis upon another tends to amplify the recognized scope of each, and their mutual conflicts whet the discriminative edge of each. The analytic process, the development and demonstration of criteria, and the sharpening of discrimination, receive powerful impulse from the co-ordinate working of several hypotheses.

Fertility in processes is also the natural outcome of the method. Each hypothesis suggests its own criteria, its own means of proof, its own methods of developing the truth; and if a group of hypotheses encompass the subject on all sides, the total outcome of means and of methods is full and rich.

The use of the method leads to certain peculiar habits of mind which deserve passing notice, since as a factor of education its disciplinary value is one of importance. When faithfully pursued for a period of years, it develops a habit of thought analogous to the method itself, which may be designated a habit of parallel or complex thought. Instead of a simple succession of thoughts in linear order, the procedure is complex, and the mind appears to become possessed of the power of simultaneous vision from different standpoints. Phenomena appear to become capable of being viewed analytically and synthetically at once. It is not altogether unlike the study of a landscape, from which there comes into the mind myriads of lines of intelligence, which are received and co-ordinated simultaneously, producing a complex impression which is recorded and studied directly in its complexity. My description of this process is confessedly inadequate, and the affirmation of it as a fact would doubtless challenge dispute at the hands of psychologists of the old school; but I address myself to naturalists who I think can respond to its verity from their own experience.

It has not been our custom to think of the method of working hypotheses as applicable to instruction or to the practical affairs of life. We have usually regarded it as but a method of science. But I believe its application to practical affairs of life has a value coordinate with the importance of the affairs themselves. I refer especially to those inquiries and inspections that precede the coming-out of an enterprise rather than to its actual execution. The methods that are superior in scientific investigation should likewise be superior in those investigations that are the necessary antecedents to an intelligent conduct of affairs. But I can dwell only briefly on this phase of the subject. . . .

The application of the method of multiple hypotheses to the varied affairs of life is almost as protean as the phases of that life itself, but certain general aspects may be taken as typical of the whole. What I have just said respecting the application of the method to instruction may apply, with a simple change of terms, to almost any other endeavor which we are called upon to undertake. We enter upon an enterprise in most cases without full knowledge of all the factors that will enter into it, or all of the possible phases which it may develop. It is therefore of the utmost importance to be prepared to rightly comprehend the nature, bearings, and influence of such unforeseen elements when they shall definitely present themselves as actualities. If our vision is narrowed by a preconceived theory as to what will happen, we are almost certain to misinterpret the facts and to misjudge the issue. If, on the other hand, we have in mind hypothetical forecasts of the various contingencies that may arise, we shall be the more likely to recognize the true facts when they do present themselves. Instead of being biased by the anticipation of a given phase, the mind is rendered open and alert by the anticipation of any one of many phases, and is free not only, but is predisposed, to recognize correctly the one which does appear. The method has a further good effect. The mind, having anticipated the possible phases which may arise, has prepared itself for action under any one that may come up, and it is therefore ready-armed, and is predisposed to act in the line appropriate to the event. It has not set itself rigidly in a fixed purpose, which it is predisposed to follow without regard to contingencies. It has not nailed down the helm and predetermined to run a specific course, whether rocks lie in the path or not; but, with the helm in hand, it is ready to veer the ship according as danger or advantage discovers itself. . . .

The method of multiple hypotheses assumes broadly that the acts of a fellow-being may be diverse in their nature, their moves, their purposes, and hence in their whole moral character; that they may be good though the dominant character be bad; that they may be bad though the dominant character be good; that they may be partly good and partly bad, as is the fact in the greater number of the complex activities of a human being. Under the method of multiple hypotheses, it is the first effort of the mind to see truly what the act is, unbeclouded by the presumption that this or that has been done because it accords with our ruling theory or our working hypothesis. Assuming that acts of similar general aspect may readily take any one of several different phases, the mind is freer to see accurately what has actually been done. So, again in our interpretation of motives and purposes, the method assumes that these may have been any one of many, and the first duty is to ascertain which of possible motives and purposes actually prompted this individual action. Going with this effort there is a predisposition to balance all evidence fairly, and to accept that interpretation to which the weight of evidence inclines, not that which simply fits our working hypothesis or our dominant theory. The outcome, therefore, is better and truer observation and juster and more righteous interpretation.

There is a third result of great importance. The imperfections of our knowledge are more likely to be detected, for there will be less confidence in its completeness in proportion as there is a broad comprehension of the possibilities of varied action, under similar circumstances and with similar appearances. So, also, the imperfections of evidence as to the motives and purposes inspiring the action will become more discernible in proportion to the fullness of our conception of what the evidence should be to distinguish between action from the one or the other of possible motives. The necessary result will be a less disposition to reach conclusions upon imperfect grounds. So, also, there will be a less inclination to misapply evidence; for, several constructions being definitely in mind, the indices of the one motive are less liable to be mistaken for the indices of another.

The total outcome is greater care in ascertaining the facts, and greater discrimination and caution in drawing conclusions. I am confident, therefore, that the general application of this method to the affairs of social and civic life would go far to remove those misunderstandings, misjudgments, and misrepresentations which constitute so pervasive an evil in our social and our political atmospheres, the source of immeasurable suffering to the best and most sensitive souls. The misobservations, the misstatements, the misinterpretations, of life may cause less gross suffering than some other evils; but they, being more universal and more subtle, pain. The remedy lies, indeed, partly in charity, but more largely in correct intellectual habits, in a predominant, ever-present disposition to see things as they are, and to judge them in the full light of an unbiased weighing of evidence applied to all possible constructions, accompanied by a withholding of judgment when the evidence is insufficient to justify conclusions.

I believe that one of the greatest moral reforms that lies immediately before us consists in the general introduction into social and civic life of that habit of mental procedure which is known in investigation as the method of multiple working hypotheses.

Benefit-cost analysis. A method in vogue in United States governmental circles which is supposed to permit an administrator to evaluate the desirability of a project, justify its cost, and assign it a priority, but which all too often is used to persuade other groups that a project championed by the administrative agency should indeed be funded, is called benefit-cost analysis. The analysis is made to show that benefits accruing from a particular action exceed the cost of the action. The process has been examined by Hammond (1966), who traced the history of benefit-cost analysis from the River and Harbor Act of 1902 and exposed some of the absurdities in its applications. According to Hammond (1966, p. 195):

The computation of benefit-cost ratios was intended to serve two purposes which in essence are separate. It establishes which public projects are prima facie likely to yield economic benefits and hence are worthy to be submitted for congressional approval; and it furnishes a basis for the apportionment of the cost of such projects between the federal government and others.

He pointed out (p. 197):

The point in time at which the benefit-cost ratio began to get out of hand, so to speak, can be dated with sufficient accuracy as the early years of the New Deal, when massive public works became the vogue as a way of diminishing unemployment, and when a narrowly financial estimate of benefits and costs appeared to underestimate the advantages of creatively employing "labor which otherwise might have to be provided subsistence when idle." . . .

The Bureau of Reclamation in particular began to make play with "secondary" or "indirect" benefits, evaluating such things as the increased attendance to be expected at motion picture theaters in an area affected by a reclamation project (at a figure amounting to thirty-nine per cent of the expected admission fees); a process which, carried to its logical conclusion throughout the life of, say, a dam designed to last half a century or more, has implications at which the mind boggles.

Hammond concluded (pp. 221–222):

. . . Benefit-cost analysis should be recognized for what it is—a useful way of roughly assessing the promise of a particular project or comparing ways of carrying out a project—and not taken for what it is not, nor can never be —a precision tool for attaining general economic efficiency. Speculative calculations of wide scope, concerning such concepts as "social costs" and "general economic welfare," are inherently inconclusive and in any case have no place in day-to-day decisions. "Intangibles" as Senate Document 97 commendably lays down, should be left to "informed judgement."

That phrase goes to the root of the matter. In the last analysis, the responsibility for decision must not, because it properly cannot, be shifted from the administrator dealing with the individual case to a departmental economist operating a prescribed formula. In a country where mistrust of government is ripe, the temptation to substitute supposedly impersonal calculation for personal, responsible decision and to rely on the expert rather than size up the situation by oneself, cannot but be exceedingly strong; in a country where experts abound, there will always be plenty who will advocate that course. This essay will have served its purpose if it does something to redress the balance, if it encourages contumacious and skeptical tendencies in decision-makers confronted with economic-analytical findings.

208 ENVIRONMENTAL GEOLOGY

One must never forget that though pure economics is a matter of logic, applied economics is a matter of informed common sense.

Hammond's salty essay should be required reading for all conservationists. The perspicacious reader will see a clear relationship between aspects of benefit-cost analysis and the method of multiple working hypotheses put forward so many years ago by Chamberlin (p. 201), particularly in the use of benefit-cost procedures to compare ways of carrying out a project. He will also note strong similarities between Lovering's argument in defense of the qualitative (p. 200) and Hammond's objections to benefit-cost analysis as a "precision tool" and to decision-making by formula-operating economists.

Kollmorgen(1953), in a paper with the interesting title "Settlement Control Beats Flood Control," reviewed some of the planning alternatives in the Kansas River basin, pointing out the desirability of retaining floodplain agricultural lands in production and noting the natural improvement and enrichment of soils that result from periodic flooding. He strongly criticized the cost-benefit ratios used to justify an elaborate series of dams and reservoirs as "a weird structure of fairy land economics." He concluded that "land and soil destroyed by flooding is largely a myth and, therefore, does not justify flooding out one set of farmers behind dams to save another set of farmers below dams." He pointed out that urban and industrial losses could be eliminated with levees and zoning, that farm improvements could be zoned to flood-free elevations, that crop losses could be largely eliminated by damming narrow tributaries, and that water navigation on the Missouri River is "a total myth and justifies no expenditure whatsoever."

The plain and simple truth is that complex natural problems do not lend themselves to rigorous quantitative treatment at the current stage of our competence. Geologists learned this a long time ago. Complex social problems are no different. Problems involving both physical and biological natural phenomena and social factors cannot yet be solved by formulas. Everyone will recognize that it is frustrating to deal with problems in which some parameters can be measured and assigned numbers and others either cannot be measured, or cannot be measured in the same kinds of units. For example, costs of a dam can be calculated, the amount of water and silt that will be impounded can be figured within limits if there are adequate data on the drainage basin;

a number can be placed on the value of the water in the reservoir in terms of its direct use in agriculture or for municipal and industrial purposes; the value of valley land removed from productive agriculture can be estimated; the value of the electric power generated can likewise be expressed numerically. Less secure is the dollar value of the structure for flood control, although this can be approximated through historical data on extent of periodic flood damage over a term of many years. The social benefits are not so easily measured. What is the value of a recreational facility? Certainly it is more than the gross receipts of the recreation-based facilities associated with it or the number of users multiplied by a dollar factor. The beneficial secondary and tertiary effects of a lake are apparent to anyone who considers them, but how to quantify them? Can a formula even produce figures with the right order of magnitude? Are the figures reproducible by independent analysts? Such figures are subject to "bending" by enthusiasts dedicated to a mission. One approach is to equate the benefit to the cost the user is willing to incur to visit the reservoir. Grubb and Goodwin (1968), in an evaluation of recreation benefits that would be generated through construction of new reservoirs under the Texas Water Plan, considered the user's cost as the direct travel cost (not including automobile depreciation, insurance, taxes) he is prepared to incur to visit the reservoir. This figure was derived from sampling to determine number of visitors and distance traveled in a survey of eight existing reservoirs. Grubb and Goodwin (1968, p. 1) concluded that the present worth in 1970 of recreation benefits in 54 proposed reservoirs is more than $550 million. If this sum were used in an accounting sense, and unfortunately such figures commonly are used in this way as real numbers, it would constitute about 15 or 20 percent of the cost of the projects contemplated in the first Texas Water Plan.

But these recreation benefits are not income from the facility in the same way as income derived from sale of electric power or irrigation water, nor are they in the same category as flood damage averted through existence of the dam and water storage capability. Indeed, that they constitute a real addition to general (as against local) prosperity by putting money into circulation through travel is moot. It could be argued that if the reservoir did not exist the user might well occupy the same period of leisure time by going somewhere else and generating the same travel cost, or by going to a movie or sporting event. Moreover, a recreation benefit is a dependent benefit, depending on a generally prosperous economy. The user would visit the reservoir only if he had surplus money and leisure time. Either or both may be diminished by changes in the economy. Of course, this same argument could be used with regard to other reservoir-generated income, as for example, sale of electric power. In an economic depression, both re- creation visits and power sales would be expected to diminish. However, recreation would certainly be more sensitive to a depression trend.

This is not an argument against construction of reservoirs or that they do not have value as recreation centers. The proof is that people visit them for recreation. It is, however, a caution against using dollar values for recreation benefits as real numbers, in an accounting sense, to balance construction costs.

What about other environmental effects of the dam? What values, positive or negative, should be assigned to the changes induced in wild- life communities that are affected by the environmental modifications brought about through interruption of the river's regimen? What is the worth of a historic house that was condemned and flooded? Will there be significant microclimatic changes induced by the large body of water? Will valuable mineral deposits be inundated? If already known to exist, these can be evaluated—clays, sand and gravel, stone, for example—but if not known to exist, what is the potential for discovery of mineral deposits in the area to be inundated? In the final analysis, the decision on such a project should not be made by an accountant or by an administrator who leans on the kind of shaky balance sheet that can be derived from application of formulas to a body of data that must in large part be qualitatively evaluated. Brooks (1966, pp. 30–44) has discussed the application of benefit-cost analysis to strip mine reclama- tion. He said (p. 31):

What are the benefits, and what are the costs of strip mine reclamation? As emphasized . . . , the benefits of both regulation and post-mining reclama- tion are represented by external costs avoided. When corrosion of boats or silting of ponds and streams can be reduced, this is a benefit. In addition there are benefits from making the land productive. Represented by profits from grazing or tree harvesting, and in recent years, from orchards, homesite construction, or recreation fees, these benefits have often been captured by private owners. Other productive uses are likely to lie within the public sector. Use of strip pits for sanitary dumps is among these. Also with the public sector are certain recreational uses and the production of fish and wildlife, particularly when they are treated as primary products of reclamation, rather than by-products. It has been suggested that the strip pits themselves be used as tourist attractions.

The costs of strip mine reclamation appear in two stages. Some are incurred after mining is completed and are clearly associated with the reclamation program. When abandoned pits are being reclaimed, all costs are of this type. But operating pits also incur costs because of strip mine regulations and anticipated reclamation activities. Such hidden, but, nevertheless, additional costs must also be counted against the benefits of strip mine reclamation.

The problem in the benefit-cost analysis of strip mine reclamation is converting in a convincing way the benefits into a measurable quantity. If costs are in dollars, then benefits must be couched in terms of dollars. Brooks said (p. 32):

It has been implicitly assumed that by evaluating social benefits and social costs in terms of dollars, the social value of proposed actions may be approximated.

It is this assumption that must be critically evaluated in every application of benefit-cost analysis and particularly where the formula appears to give an answer contrary to common sense.

Kneese (1965, pp. 238, 241-244) stressed the contributions made by economic theory to the problems of decision-making:

Economic theory has provided an operational normative model for water resources planners. . . . Through the use of this model it has been possible to be rather specific about decision criteria in the planning of projects and systems. Furthermore, it has been possible to formulate workable empirical approaches to estimation of the benefits and costs that the model instructs us to compare.

Nevertheless, he pointed out some weaknesses in current practices in the area of recreation benefit estimate. Federal agencies have allocated large costs to recreation benefits in budgets for reservoirs—for example, $40 million in the case of the Auburn Reservoir on the American River in California (Bureau of Reclamation) and $140 million in the case of the Potomac River Project (Corps of Engineers). Figures are based on a standard figure per visitor day. Kneese (p. 242) said the following.

I am in no way attempting to dispute the legitimacy of the importance of recreation benefits, but I am asserting that present modes of calculating them amount to little more than multiplication of two arbitrary numbers.

The National Academy of Sciences-National Research Council on Water observed as follows (1966, p. 31):

Lake Tahoe will turn from blue to green unless costs are borne to stop sewage from being dumped into it. Let us find out how great the costs are before prejudging that it is or is not worth letting the lake turn color. If it will cost $5.00 per hour of viewing time for anyone who will ever see the lake to keep it blue, one may conclude that there are better alternatives for these expenditures. But if the cost would amount to only a fraction of a cent per person visiting the lake and if the cost of alternative means of disposal of the sewage would raise the cost of living of the polluters only slightly, one might rationally conclude that it would be a wise action to keep the lake blue.

There are two unknowns. The cost of alternative methods of sewage disposal can perhaps be calculated with some confidence. But how many people will see the lake over what span of years? If the expense is to be justified by this figure, an analyst who likes blue lakes might easily make some rather unlikely assumptions as to the numbers of people who will view the lake over the next 20 years and if this will not yield a favorable figure, why not consider a term of 30 or 50 years?

For the July 4, 1967, Independence Day celebration the Department of Housing and Urban Affairs listed some of the Revolutionary War historical landmarks preserved or restored through federal grants:

Concord, Mass.—The Concord Conservation Commission received $71,-225 to help purchase about 72 acres near the Minute Man National Park connected with the opening days of the Revolutionary War.

Milton, Mass.—A grant of $10,650 to help acquire and preserve a section of the roadbed and terminal of a horse-drawn railroad built in 1826 to carry granite blocks for the construction of the Bunker Hill Monument.

Annapolis, Md.—A $30,952 grant for work that includes the house of Gov. William Paca, who signed the Declaration of Independence.

Philadelphia—A $40,698 grant to help acquire the site of the birthplace of Dr. Benjamin Rush, also a signer of the Declaration of Independence.

York, Pa.—A $46,700 grant to acquire the headquarters of Gen. Horatio Gates and an adjoining tavern dating from pre-Revolutionary times.

Under open space grants the point near Trenton, N.J., where Gen. George

Washington crossed the Delaware has been preserved, and so has Washington's campsite on a bluff near Endicott, N.Y., after the battle of Long Island.

An open space grant of $800,000 also helped New Jersey acquire 49.3 acres of waterfront land for a park overlooking the island on which the Statue of Liberty stands.

A study of the process by which money values were placed on the irreplaceable historical values represented by these landmarks would provide a very interesting example of the problem under discussion.

On the other side of the coin, even though it is difficult to put precise numbers on some kinds of benefits—such as the recreation value of a lake or park—and rigorous application of formulas to economic analysis in such cases is a delusion, it is, nonetheless, necessary and profitable to consider economic measures of benefits and cost under various hypotheses or alternatives. It is useful to make an economic analysis using various assumed values to test an hypothesis and to determine correct orders of magnitude for comparative purposes. The sin in applied economics is to be beguiled by one's own numbers. This might be called the delusion of the decimal point. Davis (1963), in discussing recreation planning, made the following points (p. 241):

It is commonly charged that recreation values are "priceless," that recreation is an esthetic pursuit having unique personal and spiritual values, that economic worth implies commercialization, and that economic processes serve only mass tastes . . . . No goods are priceless in the sense of having an infinite price. There is a limit individually and collectively to how much real and personal wealth we would sacrifice to obtain any recreational experience or preserve any scenic resource. This limit is defined by the incremental social gain to be realized from a unit of expenditure on recreation and from other alternatives. It would be illogical to continue pumping expenditures into recreation development if the funds could produce greater satisfaction in another purpose.

The dichotomy between economic and esthetic pursuits is a false dichotomy if the esthetic pursuits are pursued rationally, i. e., for the purpose of attaining the best state of satisfaction available to the pursuer. All rational behavior can be worked over with the tools of economics. . . .

Economic evaluation of recreation is not equivalent with commercialization of recreation. To value a good by money measure does not mean that its value should be captured in the private economy. Economic values can serve as guides to social choice even though they are not registered in the commerce of the nation. If recreational use of a given bundle of resources has social value superior to its commercial alternatives, it is possible to demonstrate this by economic measures.

To sum up these several comments by Hammond, Brooks, Kneese and Davis, it would seem that:

1. To properly analyze benefits and costs and select the most rewarding alternative it is necessary to attempt to assign economic (money) values to the various units that make up the problem.
2. It is very difficult, if not impossible, to measure some units under consideration (recreation value, aesthetic value, historical value, cultural value, education value) by standards which permit objective and reproducible evaluations. Under different assumptions, these quantities range widely in value.
3. For this reason, precise formula analysis is misleading.
4. Nevertheless, economic analysis can be helpful in selecting an alternative if the analysis is made with clear recognition of its limitations and judgment is applied in allocation of money values. What this all comes down to is embodied in Hammonds' comment that applied economics is common sense. Perhaps this seems so obvious that one wonders why it is necessary to labor the point. The reason is that the conclusions emanating from an economic analysis are commonly presented to decision-makers who are not familiar with the process used to reach the conclusions or who do not have the time to scrutinize every assumption. The columns of neat figures printed out by a computer have an air of authenticity and do not betray the uncertainties in the original data. They do not reflect the assumptions, whether they be sound or dubious, on which the conclusions stand, or, in the terms of Gilbert and Sullivan, they lend an air of verisimilitude to an otherwise bald and unconvincing narrative.

The role of the environmental geologist in conservation. Because of employment associations, geologists are identified in the mind of the public with the extractive mineral industries, oil and mining companies, or perhaps an inspiring professor of freshman geology is still remembered by a former student as he drives through a spectacular road cut. Few are aware of the geologists employed as professional scientists with various federal and state agencies such as the Geological Survey, Bureau of Mines, Bureau of Reclamation, Soil Conservation Service, Park Service, state geological surveys, conservation departments, water commissions, and highways departments, as teachers in the school systems, or as geologists employed by engineering and construction firms. In 1966, employment of some 20,000 earth scientists in the United States was distributed as follows (Henderson, 1967, p. 18):

Employer	Percent
Industry	44.4
Federal government	14.4
Schools	25.3
Self-employed	8.2
Other government	4.8
Other (not employed or no report)	2.9
	100.0

Notwithstanding the substantial number of geologists directly engaged in conservation work or indirectly developing earth data for use in conservation programs, and notwithstanding the prominence of geologists in the early conservation movement (John Wesley Powell, John Muir, C. R. Van Hise, C. K. Leith), geologists are commonly regarded as suspect by modern conservationists. Such an image is detrimental to the science and the profession and it should be redrawn (Flawn, 1966).

According to the comprehensive definition of conservation, any geologist engaged in developing new information about the earth environment is a conservationist, but it would seem more appropriate to restrict the honor of the term to those engaged in applying geological data to the study and solution of problems arising from man's use of the earth.

Conservation is an area where a socially minded geologist can make an important contribution, either through professional employment with a public agency or as a knowledgeable citizen working voluntarily in civic affairs. Simply stated, his contribution is made through his ability to evaluate conservation problems and programs with knowledge of the realities of resource occurrence and earth processes. There are too many people making decisions about the land who do not understand its fundamental geologic character—many politicans without sufficient knowledge of either geological processes or resources are writing laws to control geological processes and create resources; many economists are proposing answers to resource problems without knowing the facts of mineral occurrence; many planners are deciding how the land should be used without knowledge of its fundamental composition and structure and the natural processes in operation; many soil scientists are making geologic interpretations on the basis of incomplete knowledge; and many civil engineers know just enough geology to persuade themselves that they do not need geological counsel. The geologists must share the blame for this unfortunate situation, because in general their curricula have not prepared earth scientists to apply their science to environmental problems.

REFERENCES

ARDREY, ROBERT (1966) *The territorial imperative:* Atheneum Publishers, New York, 390 pp.

BEAZLEY, RONALD (1967) "Conservation decision-making: A rationalization": *Natural Resources Journal,* Vol. 7, no. 3, pp. 345–360.

BROOKS, D. B. (1966) "Strip mine reclamation and economic analysis": *Natural Resources Journal,* Vol. 6, no. 1, pp. 13–44.

CHAMBERLIN, T. C. (1890) "The method of multiple working hypotheses": originally printed in *Science,* Vol. 15, no. 92; reprinted in *Science,* Vol. 148, May 7, 1965, pp. 754–759.

Committee on Water, National Academy of Sciences-National Research Council (1966) *Alternatives in water management:* National Academy of Sciences-National Research Council publication 1408, 52 pp.

DAVIS, R. K. (1963) "Recreation planning as an economic problem": *Natural Resources Journal,* Vol. 3, no. 2, pp. 239–249.

FLAWN, P. T. (1966) "Geology and the new conservation movement": *Science,* Vol. 151, no. 3709, pp. 409–412.

GRUBB, H. W., AND GOODWIN J. T. (1968) *Economic evaluation of water-oriented recreation in the preliminary Texas Water Plan:* Texas Water Development Board report no. 84, 28 pp.

HAMMOND, R. J. (1966) "Convention and limitation in benefit-cost analysis": *Natural Resources Journal,* Vol. 6, no. 2, pp. 195–222.

HENDERSON, BONNIE C. (1967) "Earth science manpower": *GeoTimes,* Vol. 12, no. 1, January 1967, pp. 16–18.

KNEESE, A. V. (1965) "Economic and related problems in contemporary water resources management": *Natural Resources Journal,* Vol. 5, no. 2, pp. 236–258.

KOLLMORGEN, W. M. (1953) "Settlement control beats flood control": *Economic Geography*, Vol. 29, no. 3, 208–215.

LOVERING, T. S. (1966) "Some cultural contributions of the geological arts and sciences": *New Mexico Academy of Sciences Bulletin*, Vol. 7, no. 1, pp. 1–9.

Oil and Gas Journal (1967) "Sunray's gas whopper muzzled by whoopers": *Oil and Gas Journal*, Vol. 65, no. 48, November 27, 1967, p. 55.

APPLICATION OF ENVIRONMENTAL GEOLOGIC DATA

7

General statement. Knowledge about earth processes, earth resources, and behavior of earth materials benefits few people unless it is put to work. After the planner understands potential geologic hazards in the planning area, after he has located and evaluated earth resources of the area, and following his analysis of the economic benefits to be derived through informed engineering, he faces a formidable problem in converting information into action.

The state geologist of California recently reported on the frustration commonly encountered in putting geologic data to work for society (Campbell, 1966, p. 7):

A few years ago, the Division [California Division of Mines and Geology] undertook "urban geologic mapping" in the area of San Clemente, a rapidly growing community on the southern California coast. The geologist in charge, within his first few days in the field, noted that a new-building civic center was situated in an area of questionable landslide and brought the circumstances to the attention of the city engineer who, however, apparently took no action on the information. The map, depicting this and many related situations in and around the community, was placed on open file a few weeks ago. Almost coincident with this come reports of cracks that are developing in the new City Hall!

Clearly, when an environmental geologic report has been prepared it must be "sold." It must be sold to planning agencies and engineering departments. Circulation of reports by mail to the heads of agencies is not enough. The writer admits to differences of opinion on this point. Does a scientific and engineering fact-finding department really have a "selling" mission? Does not their job stop after the data are developed and turned over to authorities responsible for planning and policy? Perhaps if the data were nontechnical, and their implications readily apparent to nontechnical people, it would be enough to develop the information and distribute it. However, considering the nature of the information, the very least the data-producing agency can do is to explain the report in conference with appropriate government officials charged with responsibility for planning, engineering, and management. The environmental geology group of the Illinois Geological Survey maintains continuous liaison with planners during preparation of reports.

It is difficult for the geologist who is employed by a public agency to take action individually beyond that sanctioned by his department head. Such action only results in trouble for the department and a sudden change in employment for the crusader. He can, however, take action through a professional association when it becomes clear that dangerous and costly mistakes are being made in the face of sound and documented conclusions in a professional report. After investigation, the association can send a representative to stand up in a city council meeting and publicly fix the responsibility for ignoring the report. A public statement from a professional man in good standing with facts to support his position carries weight with politicians, at least on the local level—few, if any, would be willing to grant a permit for a subdivision in an area subject to potential flooding if a geologist with the data on run-off, flood frequency, and maps showing areas of hazard were to make a public protest. Responsibility for the possible death by drowning of a young child is then put into the record. When a planning agency has prepared a sound plan using geologic data, it is the duty of the geological agency and individuals who worked to develop the information on a professional basis to defend and support the plan.

The most vigorous opposition to land-use plans and recommendations commonly comes from landowners, individually or in real estate associations, whose right to use their land as they see fit is abridged by the plan or who believe the value of their property has been damaged by geologic appraisal of their property as unsuited for certain uses or certain kinds of construction. In the past, federal and state geological surveys have been attacked politically because they incurred the wrath of property owners by appraising their land as hazardous for residential or commercial development. As a result, they have been careful not to condemn property for particular uses, but simply to present the data, which should indicate to engineers that construction in the area will require special engineering design to survive the hazard or that the area of potential flood hazard is below such and such a contour with a frequency of once every 10 years. All too often these reports receive little attention, and all too often the agency that developed the information seems to be glad to be overlooked.

Anchorage, Alaska, in a case in point (p. 26). In 1959, 5 years before the damaging Good Friday earthquake of March 27, 1964, a U. S. Geological Survey bulletin (Miller and Dobrovolny, 1959, pp. 37, 102–107) pointed out that the Bootlegger Clay which underlies a large area of Anchorage is an unstable material that when wet can be dislodged by some triggering action. They said that the relatively low cohesive strength of the formation should be taken into consideration in the design of large structures that are to have footings in the Bootlegger Clay. They published the engineering properties of the clay. They said that shocks such as those associated with earthquakes set into motion material that is stable under most conditions. They pointed out that Anchorage is in an earthquake region. They documented a number of previous slumps and slides within the Bootlegger Clay. Nowhere in the report, however, did the authors condemn the Bootlegger Clay as material that provided an unsafe foundation for structures. The report apparently passed unnoticed and unappreciated by city authorities. The sponsoring agency, the U. S. Geological Survey, did not consider it its responsibility to "sound the alarm."

Following the Good Friday earthquake an evaluation team made a thorough study of the damage and causes thereof, which was summarized in a U. S. Geological Survey professional paper (Hansen, 1965). The author said (p. A12):

The Bootlegger Cove Clay has become renowned, since the March 27 earthquake, for its part in the devastation. Most of the severe damage in the Anchorage area is traceable to failure within this formation, and an understanding of the mechanisms of landsliding in the Anchorage area requires some knowledge of its character and physical properties. Because of its critical relationships to landsliding, it has been studied intensively since the earthquake, by the Corps of Engineers and by consultants to the Corps.

This scientific postmortem report did not make any recommendations about future land use in the area based on its findings; nevertheless, it is written clearly enough for city authorities to be completely informed on the realities of geologic processes and foundation materials in and around Anchorage. The city's responsibilities to the public are clear, the data are available, and any deviations from geological and engineering recommendations must be made advisedly, with foreknowledge of inherent risks.

MECHANISMS FOR ACTION

Codes and ordinances. Once convinced of the desirability of protecting its resources, of taking advantage of geological conditions in municipal engineering projects, and of taking steps to protect lives and property against geologic hazards, the authorities have a number of effective means of implementing plans.

City and county zoning ordinances are a traditional and practical method of controlling land use, and building codes are documents that set standards and specifications for construction. However, ordinances and codes must be backed up by a firm refusal to grant exceptions or deviations that violate geological and engineering recommendations. That is not to say that decisions on land use spelled out in zoning ordinances should be inflexible. They can and must change as the city grows and changes. However, throughout the history of the city, zoning should be guided by geological knowledge about processes, resources, and behavior of rocks and soils. Building codes likewise are subject to revision as new engineering techniques and new materials are developed. Some might argue that a person should be able to build on his own property as he sees fit, and that damage to the structure resulting from improper design or materials is his own risk and his own business. However, in urban areas where building sites are small damage is commonly not confined to the property of the culpable. Neighbors are endangered and damaged by the irresponsibility of one property owner. As long as governments are charged by the people with responsibility for public health, safety, and general welfare, they must exercise this responsibility through planning, subdivision, grading, excavation, and building codes and ordinances.

It is profitable to examine the experience of the various political divisions of southern California in attempting to set up and administer mechanisms for implementing geological and engineering recommendations. Because of the urgency of land-use problems in southern California these political divisions have moved further than other urban regions in applying scientific knowledge of the terrain. The urgency is due to a combination of factors: (1) population, growing at a tremendous rate, has resulted in extensive development of steep hillside building sites; (2) on many hillsides, the composition and structure of the rocks makes them readily subject to landslides if slopes are steepened or drainage is obstructed; (3) the area is subject to heavy, cloudburst rainstorms and earthquakes, either of which can trigger landslides even if natural equilibria have not been destroyed by works of man—a number of ancient landslides have been mapped by geologists in this area. The following summary of experience in southern California is from Scullin (1966).

After World War II, development of foothill and mountainside building sites accelerated. Cities and counties did not make much effort to control this development, and over a period of some years of infrequent rains landslides were few; thus the public remained unaware of the consequences of excavation practices resulting in oversteepened cut slopes, loose fills pushed into canyons or allowed to spill over slopes, and natural drainages blocked or obstructed by changes in hillside contours. In 1951–1952, however, heavy rains tested the newly sculptured terrain and the City of Los Angeles was faced with a $7.5-million bill for damage to public and private property. From this came the Los Angeles Grading Ordinance of 1952. In the succeeding 10 years a number of neighboring cities and counties passed similar grading ordinances. Los Angeles created a grading section within the Department of Building and Safety; permits, inspections, and certifications were required. The system was successful in reducing failures of fills and slopes but was not entirely satisfactory. Geological appraisals were left to engineering discretion and geological data were not developed and used properly. In 1956, Los Angeles established a Geological Hazards Committee. From 1956 to 1960 the city required a geological report before issuing a grading permit, but the reports were preliminary in nature and communication between geologist, engineer, and subdivider was such that the reports for the most part were not interpreted correctly. In 1960 the form of future geological reports was defined by the Los Angeles City Geologic Qualifications Board. Qualifications were established for engineering geologists. But there was still no effective teamwork between geologists, soils engineers, and civil engineers. In 1962, after another period of heavy rains, Glendale, California, initiated combined soils engineering and engineering geological investigations which required full-time inspection by soils engineers, weekly geological inspections, and final certification by civil engineers. The system of continuing integrated professional supervision was adopted by other cities and counties over the next few years, with Los Angeles endorsing the procedure in 1963. The success of professionally supervised grading in eliminating failures cannot be evaluated in the short time that has elapsed since it was instituted as a general practice, but according to Scullin (1966, p. 230) the record to 1966 was good (see chart on page 224). He pointed out that the best of professional site design and engineering is futile if uninformed landowners subsequently undertake to modify the design. Principal abuses are (1) failure to maintain drains, (2) changing or diverting drainage, (3) cutting out or unloading toes of slopes to create larger flat areas, (4) introduction of excessive water in slopes through watering of lawns and gardens, overflowing pools, poor placement of septic tank laterals, etc.

The town of Portola Valley, California, at a meeting of the Council on February 12, 1968, heard recommendations from their Geologic Hazards Committee to the effect that the town retain an engineering geologist, compile a geologic hazards map, and require geologic reports for consideration of use permits involving public assembly (Minutes of the Council of the Town of Portola Valley, California, February 12, 1968).

Slosson (1969) discussed the use of geology in planning a number of residential developments in California, including the Palisade Hills

Private construction in Orange county from November 1, 1962,
through March 31, 1966

Grading permits issued   1,077
Total cubic yards of earth moved   49,000,000
Building permits issued   19,657
Number of structural failures due to
   geological failures (landslides, etc.)   None

Private construction in Los Angeles County from July 1, 1960,
to May 1, 1966

Grading permits issued   4,000
Total cubic yards of earth moved   133,300,000
Building permits issued   227,000[a]
Number of homes approved under present
   procedures damaged as a result of
   undetected geologic hazards   1

Private construction in the city of Los Angeles from April 23, 1963,
to April 30, 1966

Grading permits issued   7,000
total cubic yards of earth moved   40,000,000
Building permits issued   12,000
Structures damaged due to geologic hazards
   under present procedures   None

[a] Includes 30 cities plus unincorporated county. Estimated 75,000
structures on sites graded under 4000 grading permits.

subdivision in the Santa Monica Mountains, the Diamond Bar Ranch
subdivision near Brea Canyon, and the Porter Ranch subdivision in
the north section of the West San Fernando Valley on the flank of
the Santa Susana Mountains. He also described in detail the geological
design of a proposed refuse disposal site near the Palos Verdes Hills
area of metropolitan Los Angeles. The plan called for the installation
of a 15-ft clay seal to prevent leacheate from the land fill from penetrating an underlying aquifer.

As a result of the knowledge and experience developed in southern
California, the International Conference of Building Officials accepted
a chapter on excavation and grading for the Uniform Building Code
of 1964. This chapter, Chapter 70 (see Appendix I), provides for
the use of professional consultants on earthwork by allowing the

building official to require investigations by soils engineers and engineering geologists. He can require developers to retain these professional consultants during construction and to certify site stability. Scullin (1966, p. 232) called Chapter 70 the best performance document of its kind written to date. He said:

Each provision and standard of Chapter 70 was tested to conform to five basic principles before being included:
1. It established safe minimum standards for the protection of public health, safety, and welfare without imposing excessive control or causing hardship where control is unnecessary or only limited regulation is required.
2. It may be uniformly applied anywhere that the necessity of controlling excavation and grading is recognized.
3. It conforms to the pattern and intent of the Uniform Building Code. It should not conflict with or restate provisions already included in the code.
4. It is easy to use and enforce.
5. It encourages utilization of qualified experts for the purpose of investigating, evaluating, and recommending safe minimum standards where unfavorable or hazardous conditions might exist.

Any change or modification of Chapter 70 should meet the above five basic principles. Any change or modification of Chapter 70 should retain basic conformance with the intent and scope of this code.

Direct public action. In California, awareness of geologic hazards was brought about through catastrophe, extensive property damage, and danger to life. Corrective action was taken out of necessity. Urban pressures are also building up in areas not subject to such violent movements of the land. Although in many large American cities spectacular land failures of the kind that alarm the public do not occur, failure to apply scientific knowledge about the environment commonly results in a steady and unnecessary drain on the communities' resources. Design without knowledge and continuing high maintenance costs produces extraordinary capital costs for large public works, not to mention vexing perennial repairs to small structures.

How can a small group of scientists and engineers overcome the inertia of municipal engineering departments wedded to traditional empirical methods? Voluntary consultants are seldom appreciated. Responsibility is a burden that comes with knowledge and education.

The geologist driving to work who sees a contractor using a montmor-illonite clay as a stable fill material is professionally obligated to do more than shake his head in dismay. Professional men who have observed poor engineering practices in their communities or who can evaluate the causes of engineering failures reported in the local news have an opportunity to initiate corrective action through a local professional organization. An organization convinced that improvement is desirable can set up a committee to study the situation, ascertain the facts, and prepare a report. If they are rebuffed by public adminis-trators unwilling to face changes, the more eloquent professional men can take their case to the city council and to the civic clubs. Press coverage focuses community attention on the matter. At the very least, such action forces municipal departments to scrutinize their own procedures to prepare a defense. At the best, their efforts result in revisions of out-of-date codes and ordinances.

REFERENCES

CAMPBELL, IAN (1966) "California": *The State Geologists Journal*, Vol. XVIII, no. 2, pp. 6–8.

HANSEN, W. R. (1965) *Effects of the earthquake of March 27, 1964, at Anchorage, Alaska*: U. S. Geological Survey professional paper 542 A, 68 pp.

MILLER, R. D., AND DOBROVOLNY, EARNEST (1959) *Surficial geology of Anchorage, Alaska, and vicinity, Alaska*: U. S. Geological Survey bulletin 1093, 128 pp.

SCULLIN, C. M. (1966) "History, development and administration of excavation and grading codes," in *Engineering geology in southern Cali-fornia*: Association of Engineering Geologists special publication, pp. 227–236.

SLOSSON, JAMES E. (1969) *Engineering geology—Its importance in land development*: The Urban Land Institute technical bulletin 63, 20 pp.

AUSTIN, TEXAS — AN EXAMPLE   8

General statement. Austin, Texas, the state capital, is a typical fast-growing American city. Since 1939 the population has grown as follows:

$$
\begin{array}{lr}
1939 & 97,012 \\
1949 & 132,459 \\
1959 & 186,500 \\
1969 & 257,507 \\
\end{array}
$$

Twenty years ago the hills in the north and west part of the city were covered with live oak and cedar and inhabited by white-tail deer; now they are covered with houses. To the east and south the city has grown over farm and pasture lands of the "black prairies" of central Texas. Another dam has created Town Lake on the Colorado River that separates south Austin from the rest of the city. Expressways and loops have been built. Increased power, water, and sewage requirements have resulted in construction of new power plants, reservoirs and pumping stations, and sewage treatment plants. Quarries and gravel pits in the path of the spreading urban development were abandoned and operators sought new deposits farther away.

The city occupies an area wherein the topography and geology are extremely variable. Thus the city's growth has presented very different engineering problems in different sections.

The geology of Austin, Texas.* A city is, among other things, a place; the place is there before the first settlers erect the first structures. The place is the land—the land that molds the people that come after, shapes their customs, and stamps their culture. The land gives a legacy which persists even as the people turn from the land to a manufactured urban complex where environment is machine-controlled. But even though paved with asphalt, concrete, and carpet grass, and planted with foreign trees and shrubs, the rocks, soil, and terrain of Austin are as much Austin now as in 1838 when the town was called Waterloo. Of course, on a small scale earth-moving equipment has cut here and filled there, but the basic contours of the land have only been nicked.

The really fundamental geological elements of Austin are two: the river with its valley and the Balcones fault system (Figure 27 and Color Map).

The river is a resource. It is the reason for the original selection of the site of the settlement and for many decades during the city's early history it was a major transportation artery. Now, in an increasingly water-short southwest, the water it brings to Austin makes the city one of the most fortunate in the state in terms of water supply. Outside the city, the alluvial deposits in the river valley are extensively farmed and fields are irrigated with water drawn from the river; pecan trees flourish along the terraces where soils are sandy. Dams have made the river a power resource and a recreation resource.

The river cut the valley and built the teraces on which Austin rests. A million years ago when the first of the great ice masses moved south over North America, the climate changed and the Colorado River, like other rivers, responded to the high volumes of waters entering its watershed and began vigorous erosion of the land, cutting down

* Modified from a chapter by the author in *A President's Country*, Alcalde Press, 1964, 80 pp., © 1964 by The University of Texas Ex-Students Association.

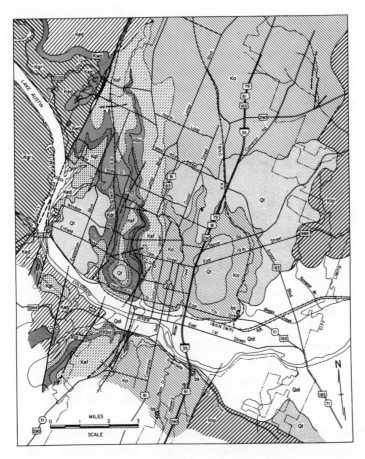

U/D: normal fault; D, downthrown side, U, upthrown side; Qal: lower terrace deposits and river valley alluvium; silt, sand, and gravel; Qt: higher terrace deposits; silt, sand, and gravel, local caliche layers; Kta: Taylor Formation; dark blue to gray calcareous clay, 600 ft thick; Ka: Austin Formation; white chalk with interbedded marl, 350 ft thick; Kef: Eagle Ford Formation; blue to gray–green clay and flaggy limestone, 40 ft thick; Kbu: Buda Limestone; massive, thick-bedded, tan limestone, 40 ft thick; Kdr: Del Rio Clay; dark green to gray clay, 70 ft thick; Kgt: Georgetown Formation; light-colored limestone with beds of marl, 40 ft thick; Ked: Edwards Formation; white to gray limestone, locally hard and massive, with beds of dolomite and nodules of chert, 300 ft thick; Kwa: Walnut Formation; yellowish clay, marl, and shell beds, 30 ft thick, and light-colored limestone, 30 ft thick; Kgr: Glen Rose Formation; interbedded light-colored limestone, locally flaggy, marl, and clay, 700 ft thick

FIGURE 27. Simplified geologic map of Austin, Texas. (Courtesy of S. P. Ellison and K. P. Young, Department of Geological Sciences, The University of Texas at Austin.)

through the rocks and leaving a record of its higher courses in a series of terraces. At Austin, the valley of the Colorado is 6 mi wide and includes a number of terraces—the higher, older terraces have been eroded so that only remnants are left.

The sequence of terrace units in the Austin area is as follows:

Terrace	Approximate elevation above present lake level
Asylum	200 ft
Capitol	120 ft
Sixth Street	60 ft
First Street ⎫	50 ft
River View ⎬	↕
Sand Beach ⎭	20 ft

The highest of the terraces was early named the Asylum Terrace for the state hospital, which is built on it. The airport also utilizes the flat, stable surface of this terrace. The elevation above sea level is slightly in excess of 600 ft, and it stands about 200 ft above the present level of the river. The next lower prominent terrace is the Capitol Terrace, about 120 ft above the river. It provides the foundation for the state capitol. Below the Capitol Terrace, about 60 ft above the river, is the Sixth Street Terrace; it is best preserved as a broad surface southeast of town around Montopolis. Lake Austin Boulevard follows this terrace. The next prominent lower terrace is the First Street Terrace. Most of downtown Austin below Sixth Street is built on it and the railroad tracks exploit this level ground. Eastward the surface widens to about 3.5 mi and is extensively cultivated. Elevation above sea level ranges from 520 ft at the west to 450 ft at the east. The lowest significant terrace is the River View Terrace, some 20 to 35 ft above the river. The Municipal Auditorium is built on this terrace. The lower terraces are farmed outside the city.

The Asylum and Capitol Terrace deposits are highly dissected and much bedrock is exposed around them. The Sixth Street Terrace deposit is slightly dissected and a narrow bedrock outcrop is present locally between the Sixth Street and First Street terrace deposits. Terrace units below the Sixth Street are relatively undissected and no bedrock is exposed between these terraces. Although the First Street, River View, and Sand Beach terrace deposits are in places readily distinguished, consistent and persistent delineation is difficult. Consequently the three lower units are treated as one—the Colorado River floodplain. The First Street Terrace is the level of the 50-yr flood cycle.

South of the river extensive high-level limestone gravels (St. Elmo terrace deposits) were deposited mainly by a tributary stream (probably the ancestral Barton Creek). This terrace deposit now occupies the divide between the Colorado River and Onion Creek at elevations of 600 to 660 ft. Still other higher gravels are present northeast and south of Austin, where most of the original deposit has been eroded, leaving a coarse gravel in the clay soils. These chert-rich gravels are the highest alluvial material in the region—slightly over 700 ft elevation south of Austin (Creedmor area) and slightly over 600 ft elevation northeast of Austin (Manor area). Both of these gravels contain crystalline rocks derived from the Llano region. Thus the river has made its mark on the land, cutting down, beveling the rock strata as it swung back and forth laterally, and depositing part of its load of silt, sand, and gravel in the valley.

Wherever deep cuts are made for new buildings in the business district of Austin, the contact between the reddish-brown sand and gravel of the terrace deposits and the white Austin chalk beneath is very conspicuous. The terrace gravels contain fragments of granite, quartz, and feldspar brought by the river from the old crystalline rocks of the Llano area. Builders cutting into terrace gravels in a new subdivision are sometimes troubled by local heavy and sustained flows of water. Maximum thickness of the terrace gravels is about 60 ft in the Asylum Terrace and in places in the lower terraces; most are 5 to 15 ft thick.

But the river in its work of erosion has merely modified the other fundamental geologic element of Austin, the Balcones fault zone and escarpment. The landscape changes abruptly at Austin. A traveler coming from the east and crossing the rolling prairies of the Texas Gulf coastal plain encounters at Austin a line of wooded hills rising as much as 300 ft above the undulating plain. This is the Balcones escarpment—it is not really a cliff but rather a line of hills indented by a number of valleys. It was recognized as early as 1880 that these hills are the surface expression of a major fault or fracture system, but the full geological, cultural, and economic significance of this great break in the earth's crust is seldom appreciated. The Balcones fault zone separates the Hill Country rancher fom the Blackland cotton and grain sorghum farmer. Cement, lime, and crushed rock industries are concentrated along it, and it is the site of numerous springs which nourished early Texas settlements. Wildlife and vegetation differ markedly on the two sides of the fault zone and, in fact, it separates the Old South from the West for the practical reason that cotton in large acreages never crossed the Balcones escarpment. Austin straddles the fault zone; the northwestern part of the city is in the hills on the northwest side of the zone. As the Colorado River emerges from its canyon in the Hill Country it follows the fault zone from Mount Bonnell to the Tom Miller dam.

Several hundreds of feet of movement have taken place along the fault zone; maximum movement occurred southwest of Austin where as much as 1300 ft of displacement has been calculated. In Austin total displacement was on the order of 1000 ft; about 700 ft of movement or "throw" occurred along one fault. In general, the crustal block to the northwest—the Hill Country or Edwards Plateau—has been raised in relation to the southeastern block, the inner part of the Gulf Coastal Plain. However, there is a series of fractures or faults rather than a single break, and in the adjustments that took place within the zone of fractures small blocks moved up and down erratically. A small slice of rock caught in the fault zone is well exposed in the park west of Highland Park School.

As a result of the elevation of the northwest side of the fault, the higher-standing rocks were vigorously eroded. The younger rocks were stripped away and the older rocks of the block were exposed. The hills in the western part of Austin are the remants of the dissected Edwards Plateau, capped by hard limestone called the Edwards Limestone. Some remnants of the once-extensive high surface remain. One such surface is the Jollyville Plateau. From a high point it can be seen that the summits of the hills are all about the same level, the remnants of a plain that was once contiguous.

The rocks of the hills are mostly limestone and cherty (flint-bearing) limestone of Lower Cretaceous Age (~100 million years old). Where they have been incised by streams their layered structure is plainly visible and it can be seen that the strata are more or less flat-lying. The hard limestone is interbedded with softer marly clay; the alternating hard and soft layers result in a "stair-step" topography. The Walnut Formation, made up of the hard Bull Creek Limestone Member (30 ft thick) overlain by about 30 ft of soft Bee Cave Marl Member, illustrates how the topography reflects the nature of the rock sequence. The soft marl has been stripped back to leave the harder Bull Creek Limestone as a prominent bench. Many of the layers are fossiliferous, containing well-preserved oysters, clams, snails, and sea urchins. These fossils, and the rocks that contain them, were deposited when this part of Texas was a warm, shallow sea similar to the modern Bahama Banks. Near Mount Bonnell the limestone contains beautiful sky-blue crystals of a mineral composed of strontium sulfate and known as celestite; it is much prized by collectors.

In the Hill Country soils are thin and rocky except in the valley bottoms. Range grasses, chiefly curly mesquite, thrive on flat surfaces, cedar (juniper) is abundant on rocky slopes, and live oaks flourish where soils are deeper. Where slopes are gentle, the marl and clay are cultivated in small upland fields.

South and east of the Balcones fault system younger rocks are preserved. These are Upper Cretactous rocks 80 to 100 million years old and include limestone, chalk, marl, and shale. The greater part of Austin is built on these rocks. The belts of different strata strike roughly northeast-southwest; each has a characteristic topography and vegetation so that the character of the city changes subtly. The chalk, named Austin Chalk, locally mantled by terrace gravels, supports the large structures of the city—the downtown area, the capitol, the university. The chalk forms a rolling hilly landscape, also known as the "white-rock country," with open grasslands interrupted by sporadic "mottes" of live oaks. It has been compared to the famous English downs. West of the white-rock belt, between the center of town and the hills, are belts of alternating limestone and shale. At the base of the hills, between the hills and the railroad, rocky outcrops of Edwards and Georgetown limestones were in the early days of Austin called the "hard scrabble" or Bear Creek country. Between the rocky area and the chalk is the Manchaca belt, shale and nodular limestone, typified by the terrain along Shoal Creek. The formations are the Del Rio Clay, Buda Limestone, and Eagle Ford Formation (mostly clay). This is the belt where most of the Austin foundation problems occur. The shales swell when wet and shrink when dry. Hackberry and mesquite grow well on the shales. Buda Limestone forms cliffs along the streams—it is prominent on the west side of Shoal Creek at 29th Street.

East of the chalk or white-rock belt is a broad prairie called the Taylor prairie. This is part of the famous black prairies or blackland belt of central Texas. Every farmer and bird hunter is familiar with the heavy black clay soils that crack deeply in hot, dry weather and become tenaciously adhesive when wet. The black prairies support rich farms. Cotton and grain sorghums are the principal crops. But, ironically, it is east of the fault system, where Austin's best farm lands are located, that the water-bearing formations are deep. Farms on the blacklands east of Austin that are not served by a water system must depend on cisterns or unreliable shallow wells because very deep and expensive wells are required to tap the Trinity Aquifer. On the northwest side of the fault system, where arable lands are scarce, the aquifer is much closer to the surface.

Unlike many of the great fault systems in California on the mobile and restless western margin of the continent, the Balcones fault system is not active. A minor earthquake attributed to movement along a fault occurred in northeast Texas and southeast Oklahoma in 1934, but there are no documented reports of major earth movements in central Texas in recorded history and no geologic evidence to indicate that the faults have moved in recent geologic time. The age of the series of fractures is not well fixed. Probably the movement continued over a considerable span of time in response to continued subsidence of the great mass of sediments that constitute the Gulf Coastal Plain. Movement probably occurred during Cretaceous time or even earlier (150 million years ago) and may have continued into the Late Tertiary (10 million years ago). At the time Austin Chalk was deposited, a volcano erupted within the fault zone. Basaltic lava and ash poured out on the shallow sea floor and built up a cone that projected upward to form an island. Reefs formed around the island and an abundant marine fauna flourished where today cattle graze. Reef-building fossils can be collected around the old volcano. The eroded core of the volcano rises south of Austin to form Pilot Knob, a well known land mark. Dense, hard, black basaltic rocks crop out on the knob and are very different from the other rocks exposed in and around Austin. At the time the volcano formed, Austin probably did not differ greatly from the Bahama banks of today—it was a warm, shallow, tropical sea where lime muds were being deposited. Roots of other such volcanoes occur along the Balcones fault zone from Kinney County to Williamson County and some small oil fields are developed where the broken fragmental rocks around the buried cones are porous. Probably the faults provided passageway for the molten rocks deep in the crust to ascend to the surface. This is evidence that the fault system formed before or at the same time as the volcanoes.

Some deep wells drilled in and around Austin, such as the Blunn Creek well, Insane Asylum well, St. Stephen's School well, and Perry water well, provide a glimpse of the deep basement rocks that constitute the floor under the stratified limestones and shales that crop out around the city. These wells penetrated the Austin Chalk, Eagle Ford, Buda, Del Rio, and older Cretaceous formations and passed through the basal water-bearing Trinity Sands. Below the aquifer they encountered a sequence of strongly deformed and altered quartzitic sandstones and slaty shales. These rocks are part of an ancient mountain range beveled by erosion 200 million years ago. They are part of the same mountain system exposed in southeast Oklahoma, the Ouachita Mountains. The distinctive rocks which make up the range can be traced in boreholes in the subsurface for over 1000 mi from northeastern Mexico to Oklahoma and beyond to the east.

RESOURCE, ENGINEERING, AND PLANNING SIGNIFICANCE OF THE GEOLOGIC MAP

General remarks. The Color Map which shows the Austin West Quadrangle (scale 1 in. = 2000 ft) is a detailed geologic map of the northwest part of Figure 27, the simplified geologic map of Austin, Texas. The Austin West Quadrangle includes the northwestern residential area of the city, the neighboring incorporated residential community of West Lake Hills, city recreational areas (Lake Austin, Town Lake, Barton Springs, City Park, Municipal Golf Course), quarries and quarry sites, and a large undeveloped area outside the city limits where urban development is intruding on primarily ranch land. The downtown area of Austin is not included, nor are the undulating prairies underlain by clay to the east of the city.

This map is a very useful model of a small part of the earth's crust. It shows topography with a contour interval of 20 ft. Interpolations of elevations between contours can be made with reasonable accuracy. Profiles or cross sections can be drawn to illustrate changes in slope and slope can easily be calculated in percentages. For planning purposes a slope map showing, for example, slopes greater than 15 percent, slopes 5 to 15 percent, slopes 2 to 5 percent, etc., can be very helpful.

Drainage and culture are prominently shown. However, in Austin and similar areas of fast-moving urban expansion, such cultural features as roads, buildings, power lines, and pipelines change in a very short span of years. Periodic aerial photography is a good supplement to the basic map, and map revision every 10 to 15 years is advisable.

The basic contribution of the geologic map to planning is that it shows the distribution of the various rock units or formations that constitute the foundation of all man's activities in the area. It gives the educated user knowledge about the composition and structure of the rocks. If the attitudes of the rocks are known and the sequence is known, the map user can make projections as to what rock units occur below the surface at a particular place. Thus the map is a three-dimensional model.

For example, in the Austin West Quadrangle the rocks are nearly everywhere flat-lying. Only in local collapsed areas, along steep slopes where there are slumped blocks, or in some small fault blocks, do the strata exhibit any pronounced dips. On maps of other areas where the strata have been faulted, folded, or otherwise deformed, the attitude of the rock layers is shown by an appropriate symbol. In the northeast corner of the Austin West Quadrangle sheet, the rocks at the surface are flat-lying Edwards Limestone. A look at the map explanation indicates that in stratigraphic sequence beneath the Edwards are the Walnut and Glen Rose formations. The Glen Rose is the oldest unit exposed in the area. For information on deeper strata in this area the geologist relys on water-well records and on work outside the Austin region. To the west and north it can be demonstrated that older sandstone and limestone units lie under the Glen Rose, and that they in turn rest on the truncated surface of older steeply dipping, strongly deformed sandstones and shales. All this information is in the geological literature so the geologist working in the Austin area does not need to visit and examine these other localities. However, it helps him if he does.

The geologic map of the Austin West Quadrangle does not show soils. This information is available in files and reports of the U. S. Soil Conservation Service. Over much of the Austin area rocks crop out at the surface and soils are very thin or lacking. The nature of the soils in the area is summarized in Table 11.

TABLE 11. **Relation of Soils to Geologic Formations in the Austin, Texas, Area**

Geologic units	Soil units	Soil character
A. HARD LIMESTONE UNITS Glen Rose, Walnut, Edwards, Georgetown, Buda formations	San Saba Clay, Tarrant Complex, Crawford Clay, Speck Clay and Stony Clay	Thin, (<20″) gray, brown, and red calcareous, commonly stony, clay soils, locally noncalcareous (parts of Buda and Edwards formations), locally cherty (Edwards Formation)
B. SOFT CLAYEY LIMESTONE AND MARL Glen Rose, Walnut, Georgetown formations	Brackett Gravelly Clay Loam, Denton Silty Clay, Purves Silty Clay	Dark gray to brown, locally stony, calcareous clay soils, thin (<20″) on harder units, thicker (> 20″) on softer units
C. CHALK AND MIXED UNITS Austin Group, Eagle Ford formation	Austin Silty Clay, Stephen Silty Clay, Eddy Gravelly Clay Loam, Brackett Clay Loam	Brown, mostly shallow calcareous soils
D. CLAY UNITS Del Rio and Taylor formations	Ferris Clay, Heiden Clay, Houston Black Clay	Gray, green, olive, yellow, calcareous clay soils
E. COLORADO RIVER AND TRIBUTARY ALLUVIAL UNITS Terrace deposits and river valley alluvium	23 formally named soil units	Mostly brown to red-brown, sandy to silty loam and clay loam, calcareous to noncalcareous, locally gravelly, minor amounts of clay soil and fine sandy soil

Resources. The geologic map is the basic earth resource document. It is fundamental for mineral resources investigations, including water. In a broader sense the perceptive user will find it useful in evaluating recreation resources such as sites for parks, golf courses, ponds and lakes, scenic drives, and green belts. In the Austin area, the different formations are characterized by distinctive vegetation (p. 233). During the preparation of the city's bid for the AEC (Atomic Energy Commission) accelerator (p. 249), the geologic map provided the basic data on the terrain and engineering site properties needed to answer the questions raised by the AEC.

The city's major water resource is Lake Austin, and the city water system takes its supply from the lake. There is also in the area a deep aquifer, the Trinity Sand that was in the past tapped by wells drilled by various public and private agencies. Although the Trinity does not crop out in the Austin West Quadrangle, the geologic map makes it possible to estimate depths to the Trinity Sands in various parts of the area. West of the Balcones fault, wells encounter the Trinity at depths of 800 to 1000 ft; east of the fault wells must pass through a succession of younger rocks to get the aquifer and, consequently, must be drilled to about 2000 ft. Small amounts of water are contained in the relatively porous terrace gravels. In the higher gravels this water has been both a nuisance to real estate developers who have had to make permanent provisions to drain it, and a blessing to landowners, who have drilled shallow wells for stock and small-scale irrigation or yard watering. Wells in lower terraces along the river are drilled to the water table and provide good, strong flows for irrigation; the source is river water that saturates the alluvial mass in the valley.

The course of Barton Creek in the southeast part of the map passes from the Glen Rose into a strongly faulted zone and flows over the Edwards Formation. The Edwards is a very porous, permeable unit and in the subsurface is a major aquifer, supplying water to San Antonio. Water flowing over the Edwards is absorbed by the porous limestone and dolomite until the formation is saturated. The ⋅underground flow emerges at Zilker Park, where it nourishes a strong spring known as Barton Springs, the site of a popular swimming pool and park. It has been proposed to build dams on Barton Creek to make a series of lakes and prevent the occasional flash floods that come down the creek and fill the Barton Springs pool with debris. The dams will prevent floods, but unless their sites are selected with geologic consultation to avoid the porous Edwards Formation, the catchment area upstream will not hold water.

The city treats the water it draws from Lake Austin by a softening process. Quicklime is added to the water to remove dissolved calcium carbonate. For every pound of quicklime added, 3.5 lb of very fine calcareous sludge is produced. This material is about 90 percent calcium carbonate and also contains silica, magnesium, and iron. It has a pinkish, off-white color, and individual particles are about 10μ in diameter. The city's water treatment plants produce an aggregate of about 40 tons of this material per day, which gives rise to a formidable waste disposal problem, for there appears to be no commercial use for the material. Up until about 4 years ago, it was mostly discharged into Lake Austin, where it formed a large lime mud bar. It was undesirable, clearly, to continue filling up the lake with this waste. At the present time it is dewatered in a centrifuge to cut down the bulk and then disposed of in pits close to the plants where suitable sites can be found.

The city continues to try to find some beneficial use for this calcium carbonate. Mixed with clay it would constitute an acceptable raw material for a portland cement plant feed. Since it is already very fine-grained, the crushing and grinding stage could be avoided. Unfortunately, however, there is not enough material to supply the entire raw material feed for a cement plant large enough to be economically competitive. It takes about 1.75 tons of raw material to make 1 ton of cement clinker. The smallest wet-process rotary kiln cement plants operating in the United States have capacities of 1 to 2 million barrels (376 lb per barrel) per year and the trend is toward larger facilities.

The map shows a gravel pit symbol (inactive) south of the Colorado River on a terrace of Barton Creek. The pit has been filled and the area is now covered by houses. The only large bodies of sand and gravel on the map are in these terraces or in the alluvium that fills the river valley. Since most of downtown Austin is built on top of these terraces, this resource is not economically exploitable within the map area. The value of improvements built on the gravel deposits, combined with the citizens proper objection to such mining operations within a highly developed area, means that for all practical purposes these deposits can no longer be considered as potential resources. Geologic investigations have shown that a very large deposit of sand

and gravel lies beneath the Municipal Airport. An old channel of the Colorado River has been mapped in this area. Information from drilling and seismograph profiles indicates that as much as 60 ft of sand and gravel fills this old channel.

Currently, sand and gravel is being produced by a dredge working the alluvial material in Town Lake. The operator is working on a lease from the city and pays a royalty of 10 cents per cubic yard on the material produced. The dredging operations are also designed to improve the shape and depth of the channel for flood-control purposes. Some sportsmen and conservationists have opposed the city's lease to the operator on the grounds that removal of the sand and gravel will destroy spawning grounds for fish and thereby reduce the sports-fishing-recreation value of the lake. Sand and gravel is also being produced from the low terrace along the Colorado River several miles below Montopolis Bridge. Exhaustion of the sand and gravel resources of Town Lake and depletion of the low terrace deposits close to Austin will require operators to move down the river toward Bastrop for new sources. New construction in Austin is currently at a very high level, and the forecast is for continued activity with high demand for aggregates. A large urban renewal project is in the planning stage.

A number of quarry symbols are shown in the outcrop of the Edwards Formation in the northeast corner of the map. The Edwards is the principal source of hard limestone that will meet specifications for an aggregate and base-course material. The quarries on the map are now abandoned. However, operations were not terminated because of any shortage of good stone. The quarries were completely surrounded by residential developments and the new residents were naturally opposed to a continuation of blasting, dust, and parades of heavy trucks. The abandoned quarries are now in the process of commercial development. A new junior high school occupies the center of the old excavation and at least part of the area has been landscaped to make the vertical quarry faces into more gentle slopes (Figure 28). An apartment complex is being constructed in another part of the quarry. Fortunately, there is no shortage of good quarry sites within the extensive outcrop of the Edwards Formation farther north and west of the city. New quarries have been located and are now operating there.

A visitor to Austin will note that many large structures in the city

FIGURE 28. Murchison Junior High School, built in an abandoned lime-stone quarry in Austin, Texas. Landscaping of the quarry was not complete when the photograph was taken in 1969. (Courtesy of Bureau of Economic Geology, The University of Texas at Austin.)

are faced with an attractive cream to buff stone. Some of the stone contains abundant imprints of fossil shells. This stone, under the trade name of Cordova Cream and Cordova Shell, is produced from quarries in the Cedar Park area north of Austin. It comes from the Whitestone Member if the Walnut Formation. This is the same geologic forma-tion that crops out in the Austin area, but the Whitestone Member is not present close to the city.

Many years ago, a small brick plant was located on the banks of the Colorado River near the intersection of West First Street and West Sixth Street. Bricks were made from sandy clays in the terrace deposit. About 1942, this plant was moved about 30 mi east of Austin between Elgin and McDade, where high-quality fire clays occur in the Wilcox Formation. Several other plants have also established in this area. Much of the pink to buff brick used in Austin is manu-factured here. Many of the new buildings on The University of Texas campus are faced with these bricks. Another common building stone on commercial and government buildings in Austin is a pink granite quarried in the so-called central mineral region of Texas about 100 mi northwest of the city.

Engineering properties. For engineering purposes the formations shown on the Color Map can be considered in three groups: (1) predominately limestone units, (2) clay units, and (3) sand and gravel (terrace deposits). The limestones occupy the western two-thirds of the map; they also occur in northeast–southwest trending blocks in the fault zone and in the southeast corner of the map. The clays form northeast–southeast trending belts in the fault zone and farther east. The most extensive clay terrain occurs east of the area covered by the Austin West Quadrange (see Figure 27). Terrace sands and gravels form a discontinuous blanket of irregular thickness under the heavily urbanized area in the southeast corner of the quadrangle.

The hard limestone units in general do not present any serious engineering problems. Excavation of these rocks is high-cost and any large project requires drilling and blasting. Most often, the softer chalks and marls can be ripped and removed with scrapers, shovels, and front-end loaders. These rocks have high load-bearing capacities. They are not subject to volume changes and, therefore, do not shrink and swell. They make excellent foundations for large and small structures. The Edwards Formation contains solution cavities of varying sizes ranging up to large caves. One such cavern is known in the map area. It is located in the Edwards Formation near the western edge of Lake Austin about where Windsor Road as projected intersects Scenic Drive. Small apartment units are built over the cavern. The entrance has been sealed to prevent access, but the developers of the area use the cavern as a drain for surface water. There has been a considerable effort in recent years to find ways to detect underground caverns in limestone terrains by geophysical methods such as seismic and resistivity surveys. However, the only certain method is by drilling. Several years ago, test borings at a bridge site for Interstate Highway 35 near Georgetown, Texas, a few miles north of Austin, encountered a large cavern after penetrating about 50 ft of limestone. The cavern extended under the highway right-of-way, but the cavern roof was judged strong enough to support the highway. The cavern itself has now been developed into a commercial attraction beneath the highway. The only surface clue to its presence was a sink-hole largely filled with earth and loose rock. These small closed basins, commonly called sinks or collapse-structures, can usually be detected by careful study of maps, aerial photographs, and inspection on the ground. Their presence should be a warning to engineers designing foundations for large and expensive structures (see Figure 8). There is a prominent sink or collapse structure east of Rocky River Road in West Lake Hills; it extends eastward about half a mile into a collapse area parallel to and north of the Bee Caves Road.

Another engineering problem, more of a nuisance than a serious problem, occurs in the areas where limestones are interbedded with clays and marls. The large exposure of the Glen Rose Formation is such a terrain. Surface waters percolating through porous limestones are trapped on the top of the impermeable clay layers and, in wet seasons, the water emerges at the surface in seeps and springs. In certain areas large flows of water persist for several weeks following a heavy rain. Homeowners in residential areas built on the Glen Rose Formation in the northeast corner of the map have had to contend with these surprising intermittent springs that suddenly burst forth in their back yards. For the most part, the problem can be handled by installation of drains. It should be noted, however, that the wet clay and marl layers are relatively weak and do not make adequate foundations for walls and other masonry structures. A concrete retaining wall improperly seated on marl collapsed in Austin in 1966 (Figure 29).

Although limestone units in general make excellent foundations, soils derived from these units are for the most part clay soils with poor load-bearing capacities. Since these soils are in most places very thin, foundations are seated on underlying bed rock. However, in some valleys and swales these soils are as much as 5 or 6 ft thick. Builders are well-advised to set piers or footings on the underlying limestone or chalk rather than to contend with the volume changes that occur in these clays.

The clay units, including the Del Rio and Eagle Ford formations in the map area, and the Taylor to the east, are subject to surficial volume changes that crack footings, sidewalks, driveways, and hearths, and result in windows that stick and doors that will not close. Slab foundations must be strongly reenforced to prevent failure under these powerful stresses (Figure 14). In some areas, architectural engineers have experimented with placement of impermeable barriers to try to insulate the clay immediately under and around the structure

FIGURE 29. Collapse of a reenforced concrete retaining wall designed to hold fill for a home site in Northwest Hills, Austin, Texas, in September 1966. The failure occurred after a period of heavy rains that saturated the marl on which the base of the structure rested. (Courtesy of Bureau of Economic Geology, The University of Texas at Austin.)

from moisture changes. However, this procedure is still in the experimental stage and is, of course, expensive. The problem is particularly acute in rolling terrain. Shrinking and swelling results in a downslope movement or creep (p. 37). Even large structures are endangered. Foundation failure of the University Baptist Church in Austin due to the lifting action of swelling clays has already been described (p. 49).

In a geologically composite slope where a clay underlies a limestone, as is beautifuly illustrated along Barton Springs Road in the southeast corner of the map where the Del Rio Clay underlies the Buda Limestone, improper engineering results in rapid retreat of the slope and jeopardizes structures built on the overlying limestone. The problem is schematically illustrated in Figure 30. The stable slope formed under natural processes consisted of a rather gentle slope of softer clay strewn with blocks of Buda Limestone slumped down from the harder limestone cap. In an attempt to widen Barton Springs Road and provide building sites on the southwest side of the road, the toe of the slope was excavated and the material was removed to leave a vertical face of clay capped by slumped limestone blocks. Under the influence

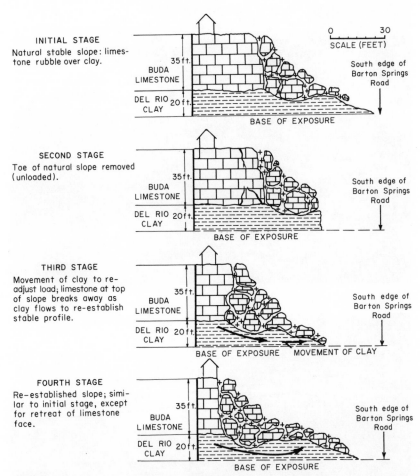

FIGURE 30. Diagrammatic sketch showing slope adjustment after removal of the toe of a natural stable slope; Buda Limestone overlying Del Rio Clay, Barton Springs Road, Austin, Texas.

of gravity, natural processes immediately began to restore a more gentle and stable profile. The clay flowed away from the face toward the unloaded toe, carrying limestone blocks with it and causing the limestone face to retreat. Owners of some property along Barton Springs Road had to construct retaining walls to prevent movement of the clay and maintain the more or less vertical face (Figure 31). Attempts to hold the clay in a vertical face have not been successful in all places.

FIGURE 31. Photographs of the slope shown diagrammatically in Figure 30. *Top*, natural slope with blocks of Buda Limestone over Del Rio Clay. *Bottom*, an attempt to hold back the advancing slope after removal of the toe. (Courtesy of Bureau of Economic Geology, The University of Texas at Austin.)

There is a continuing and expensive maintenance problem. Retreat of the slope through calving of the limestone off the face has brought some of the structures on the top of the hill close to the edge of the new cliff.

Excavation in the clay formations can be accomplished without blasting and it is relatively inexpensive, compared to limestone. The formations are impermeable and have little capability to absorb fluids. Septic tanks in these formations are generally not satisfactory. Long laterals are necessary to discharge even modest amounts of fluids. Planners of subdivisions in clay terrains beyond existing sewer facilities should recognize that they have a waste disposal problem.

Terrace sand and gravel, where it occurs in thicknesses in excess of several feet, provide an excellent foundation. These units are highly permeable and septic tank laterals operate efficiently. Excavation is cheap and easy. The only problem arises where there are local perched water tables due to impermeable clay or caliche layers within the sand and gravel body. Subdivision developers have on occasion encountered rather large flows of water that required changes of plans and installation of large permanent drains. As mentioned earlier, these local supplies of ground water can be utilized to water lawns and shrubs.

A peculiarly ironic situation occurs in some subdivisions in northeast Austin, where clays hills are capped by a few feet of terrace gravel. These gravel pads provide an adequate, stable base for small residential slab foundations. However, some contractors, in a misguided effort to prepare the site by removing the "weathered surface soil," excavated the gravel so that the slab was laid on a clay foundation much less satisfactory than the original gravel.

With regard to placement of iron pipes, the rate of corrosion is in general controlled by the number of free cations available in the host formation (p. 74). Corrosion problems are the greatest in clay formations and least in well-drained sands and gravels of the terraces. Problems are most acute where a pipe passes from one unit to another. Commonly, the abrupt change in composition between limestone and clay or sand and clay sets up a natural electrical system that, without cathodic protection, produces rapid corrosion. Thus, the geologic map can be very helpful to engineers routing pipelines. For example, a somewhat longer route that stays within terrace materials might in the long run prove less expensive than a direct route that crosses formation contacts.

The geologic map is also useful in regional landscaping projects or for planning greenbelts. Outside of the urban area, it is readily seen that each kind of formation has its own characteristic vegetation. It is not so evident in the city, where imported shrubs and trees are nourished by extra water and additions of chemical fertilizers to produce a favorable soil environment. In general, the limestones support a growth of cedar (juniper), Spanish oak, live oak, ash, laurel, and sumac. The clay units are characterized by mesquite and hackberry. The terrace deposits support large live oaks and post oak; pecans and cypress grow along the lower terraces and in the alluvium where their root systems can reach water.

Solid waste disposal. In 1968 the city of Austin disposed of 145,350 tons of solid wastes ($\sim$400 tons per day) of which about 30,000 tons were burned at the disposal site prior to emplacement in the sanitary landfill. Burning was terminated in 1969 to meet requirements of new state air pollution legislation. Travis County also operates landfills in the Austin area.

Plotting of landfills operated over the past two decades shows that the city has occupied a series of sites, mostly northeast and southeast of the city, using a site for two or three years and then moving farther out. Currently there are two active fills, one northeast of Austin on Walnut Creek near the old Sprinkle Community and the other southeast of Austin north of the Elroy Road near Onion Creek.

Apparently the city has been reluctant to do much excavation for its landfills, although a series of cuts are being made at the currently active northeast site. In the past, with a few exceptions, wastes have either filled existing pits from which construction materials have been removed (sand, gravel, caliche) or have been dumped in the heads of draws tributary to larger creeks and rivers. The city's landfills have not been completely successful in containing and isolating the wastes. The sand and gravel pits the city has filled are located in porous terrace deposits where leachates and gas from the decomposing fill are able to migrate through the porous terrace materials and enter surface drainages or mix with shallow ground water. Where the city has filled in the upper parts of small drainages, the liquified wastes and gases seep into the water of local creeks, eventually entering Town Lake or the Colorado River. Emissions from currently active fills will find their way into Walnut and Onion creeks.

Inspection in 1969 of old, abandoned fills revealed that three fills less than 5 years old were leaking foul-smelling gases and noxious brown sludge. Subsidence within the fills had resulted in closed surface depressions that held standing water. This water, percolating down into the porous mass of the fill, increased the production of leachate. In one old fill crossed by paved streets subsidence had buckled pavements and broken curbs. Gullies cutting headward into another abandoned fill had exposed the fill material.

The city of Austin has access to ideal disposal sites in the Taylor Formation east of the city. Placement of fills in the clay upland areas of the Taylor Formation away from creeks and draws would isolate the wastes above the water table and contain the gases and leachates; a compacted clay cover would prevent any significant amount of rainfall from reaching the wastes. Conversations with city engineers indicate that corrective measures are being taken and more attention will be paid to design of future fills.

As the volume of solid wastes increases with city growth it is increasingly important to contain the poisonous products of decomposition, at least until the organic material has been degraded. Over a much longer term, the environment should be protected against a flow of dissolved metals into ground and surface waters. Subsequent beneficial use of the surface of the "cured" fill is made difficult if either poor compaction or decomposition and dissolution of the fill materials present a potential for subsidence.

The Atomic Energy Commission accelerator competition of 1965. In 1965, the U. S. Atomic Energy Commission announced that it was seeking a site for construction of a new National Accelerator Laboratory that would include construction of a 200 Bev accelerator requiring a resident staff of approximately 2000 people, mostly scientists, engineers, and technicians. The estimated cost of construction of the accelerator housing and components, experimental facilities, original plant, and utilities was established at about $350 million. Annual operating costs were estimated at $60 million. Needless to say, such a facility was regarded as a great prize by communities in the United States. Some 126 communities in 46 states believed they could qualify under the site criteria established by the Atomic Energy Commission. The Commission reduced the original 126 proposals to 85 that seemed to meet specifications. The National Academy of Sciences was asked to screen the proposals; a number of site selection teams were sent to visit those communities with the best proposals. Austin, was among the five finalists. Weston, Illinois, west of Chicago, was finally selected for the new facility.

It is, nevertheless, interesting to review the proposal made by Austin because it was the first time that the city management and Chamber of Commerce were faced with the problem of developing a full spectrum of geological, engineering, economic, educational, industrial, and cultural information about their city.

The Austin Chamber of Commerce appointed a number of committees to develop and package the information requested by the Atomic Energy Commission. One group dealt with the electric power and water supply. The commission was particularly interested in (a) the quantity, quality, and cost of water, and (b) the cost and security of power, because of the anticipated large consumption. Other committees were concerned with the educational and cultural facilities of the city, transportation to and from Austin, and the variety of supporting research and development industries in the Austin area. The following discussion is concerned mainly with the activities of the Geology and Construction Committee.

The AEC originally specified that the site should contain at least 3000 acres, preferably with as much as 1500 additional acres available for expansion. It was required that the terrain be level with less than 100 ft of variation in topographic relief. The area had to be seismologically stable. Soils and bedrock had to have sufficient load-bearing capacity to insure a stable foundation. The AEC requested information on the depth to the water table and the character of the bedrock with respect to faults, joints, and fractures.

The AEC was also interested in costs of excavation and grading at the proposed site as well as general information on construction costs in the region. They asked for information on sources of heavy aggregate for shielding purposes.

The Geology and Construction Committee turned first to recent topographic maps of the Austin area to locate sites large enough and flat enough for consideration. The next step was to develop the geological information requested. Unfortunately, the only published geologic map of the Austin area is dated 1898. Although this map provided basic data, it was necessary to remap the geology of the potential sites from aerial photographs. Three of the six sites were immediately ruled out

—one was in the floodplain of the Colorado River and subject to possible flooding; two other sites were located on the Taylor Formation, which is composed of clay, and the engineering properties of this unit (p. 243) were considered undesirable for the kind of construction contemplated. Of the three sites finally offered to the AEC, one was located on the Austin Formation north of Austin in the Pflugerville area; another was on an outlier of the Edwards Plateau on Edwards Limestone northwest of Austin near Jollyville; and a third was on a block of Edwards Limestone southwest of Austin in the Slaughter Creek area. (None of the three sites are in the Austin West Quadrangle, shown in the Color Map.) Soils are thin or lacking on each of these sites. It was necessary to determine the character of the bedrock. Both the Austin Chalk and the Edwards Limestone have very high load-bearing capacities, ranging from 30 tons per square foot to more than 150 tons per square foot. The district office of the Texas Highway Department cooperated by furnishing cores and results of physical tests. The Bureau of Economic Geology of The University of Texas undertook the basic geological investigations. The Water Resources Division of the U. S. Geological Survey provided data on ground-water conditions. Local contractors provided information on construction costs. Soils engineers in private practice contributed information on soil mechanics. This information was presented to the AEC in written form and amplified to the members of the site visitation committee in a series of short oral presentations. The team then inspected the sites by helicopter.

The purpose of this review is to demonstrate the importance to a city of geological information. Austin was fortunate in having in residence federal, state, and university geological staffs willing to develop information that was not readily available. Other cities in the United States were not so fortunate. The point is, this kind of information should be available to any new industry or investor interested in a particular area. It should be in the files, or available at short notice from qualified people in city government.

APPENDIXES

APPENDIX I
International Conference of Building Officials
UNIFORM BUILDING CODE
OF 1964
CHAPTER 70
EXCAVATION
AND GRADING

PURPOSE

Sec. 7001. The purpose of this Chapter is to safeguard life, limb, property, and public welfare by establishing minimum requirements for regulating grading and procedures by which these requirements may be enforced.

SCOPE

Sec. 7002. This Chapter sets forth rules and regulations to control excavation, grading, and earthwork construction, including fills or embankments; establishes the administrative procedure for issuance of permits; and provides for approval of plans and inspection of grading construction.

PERMITS REQUIRED AND EXCEPTIONS

Sec. 7003. No person shall do any grading without first having obtained a grading permit from the Building Official, except for the following:

1. An excavation which (a) is less than two feet (2') in depth, or (b) which does not create a cut slope greater than five feet (5') in height and steeper than one and one-half horizontal to one vertical.
2. A fill less than one foot (1') in depth, and placed on natural terrain with a slope flatter than five horizontal to one vertical, or less than three feet (3') in depth, not intended to support structures, which does not exceed 50 cubic yards on any one lot and does not obstruct a drainage course.
3. An excavation below finished grade for basements and footings of a building, retaining wall, or other structure authorized by a valid building permit. This shall not exempt any fill made with the material from such excavation nor exempt any excavation having an unsupported height greater than five feet (5') after the completion of such structure.
4. Excavation or deposition of earth materials within a property which is dedicated or used, or to be used for cemetery purposes, except where such grading is within one hundred feet (100') of the property line or intended to support structures.
5. Mining, quarrying, excavating, processing, stockpiling of rock, sand, gravel, aggregate, or clay where established and provided for by law provided that such operations do not affect the lateral support or unduly increase the stresses in or pressure upon any adjacent or contiguous property.
6. Grading in an isolated, self-contained area if the Building Official finds that no danger to private or public property can now or thereafter result from the grading operations.

HAZARDOUS CONDITIONS

Sec. 7004. Whenever the Building Official determines that any existing excavation or embankment or fill has become a hazard to life and limb, or endangers property, or adversely affects the safety, use, or stability of a public way or drainage channel, the owner of the property upon

which the excavation or fill is located, or other person or agent in control of said property, upon receipt of notice in writing from the Building Official shall within the period specified therein repair or eliminate
such excavation or embankment so as to eliminate the hazard and be
in conformance with the requirements of this Code.

DEFINITIONS

Sec. 7005. *Bedrock* is the solid, undisturbed rock in place either at the
ground surface or beneath surficial deposits of gravel, sand, or soil.

Certify or certification shall mean the specific inspections and tests
where required have been performed and that such tests comply with
the applicable requirements of this Chapter.

Engineering geology is the application of geological data and principles to engineering problems dealing with naturally occurring rock
and soil for the purpose of assuring that geological factors are recognized and adequately interpreted in engineering practice.

Existing grade is the vertical location of the existing ground surface
prior to excavating or filling.

Fill is deposits of soil, rock, or other materials placed by man.

Finish grade is the final grade or elevation of the building site.

Grading is any excavating or filling or combination thereof.

Rough grade is an approximate elevation of the ground surface con-
forming to the proposed design.

Site is any lot or parcel of land or contiguous combination thereof,
under the same ownership, where grading is performed or permitted.

Soil is all earth material of whatever origin that overlies bedrock.

Soils engineering shall mean the application of the principles of soils
mechanics in the investigation and analysis of the engineering properties
of earth material.

GRADING PERMIT REQUIREMENTS

Sec. 7006. (a) *Permits Required.* Except as exempted in Section 7003
of this Code, no person shall do any grading without first obtaining a
grading permit from the Building Official. A separate permit shall be
required for each site, and may cover both excavations and fills.

(b) *Plans and Specifications.* With each application for a grading
permit and when required by the Building Official for enforcement of

any provisions of this Code, two sets of plans and specifications shall be submitted. Except as waived by the Building Official for small and unimportant work, the plans shall be prepared and signed by a civil engineer licensed by the state and shall show the following:

1. A vicinity sketch or other data adequately indicating the site location.
2. Property lines of the property on which the work is to be performed.
3. Location of any buildings or structures on the property where the work is to be performed, and the location of any building or structure on land of adjacent property owners which are within fifteen feet (15') of the property.
4. Accurate contours showing the topography of the existing ground.
5. Elevations, dimensions, location, extent, and the slopes of all proposed grading shown by contours and other means.
6. A certification of the quantity of excavation and fill involved and estimated starting and completion dates.
7. Detailed plans of all drainage devices, walls, cribbing, dams, or other protective devices to be constructed in connection with, or as a part of, the proposed work, together with a map showing the drainage area and estimated runoff of the area served by any drains.
8. Any additional plans, drawings, or calculations required by the Building Official.

(c) *Engineering Geological Reports.* Prior to issuance of a grading permit, the Building Official may require an engineering geological investigation, based on the most recent grading plan. The engineering geological report shall include an adequate description of the geology of the site, and conclusions and recommendations regarding the effect of geologic conditions on the proposed development.

All reports shall be subject to approval by the Building Official, and supplemental reports and data may be required as he may deem necessary. Recommendations included in the report and approved by the Building Official shall be incorporated in the grading plan.

(d) *Soils Engineering Reports.* The Building Official may require a soils engineering investigation, based on the most recent grading plan. Such reports shall include data regarding the nature, distribution, and strength of existing soils, conclusions and recommendations for grading procedures, and design criteria for corrective measures.

Recommendations included in the report and approved by the Building Official shall be incorporated in the grading plan or specifications.

PERMIT LIMITATIONS AND CONDITIONS

Sec. 7007. (a) *General.* The issuance of a grading permit shall constitute an authorization to do only that work which is described or illustrated on the application for the permit, or on the site plans and specifications approved by the Building Official.

(b) *Jurisdiction of Other Agencies.* Permits issued under the requirements of this Code shall not relieve the owner of responsibility for securing required permits for work to be done which is regulated by any other code, department, or division of the governing agency.

(c) *Time Limits.* The permittee shall fully perform and complete all of the work required to be done pursuant to the grading permit within the time limit specified. If no time limit is specified, the permittee shall complete the work within 180 days after the date of the issuance of the grading permit.

If the permittee is unable to complete the work within the specified time, he shall, prior to the expiration of the permit, present in writing to the Building Official a request for an extension of time, setting forth the reasons for the requested extension. If, in the opinion of the Building Official, such an extension is warranted, he may grant additional time for the completion of the work.

(d) *Storm Damage Precautions.* All persons performing any grading operations shall put into effect all safety precautions which are necessary in the opinion of the Building Official and shall remove all loose dirt from the grading site and provide adequate anti-erosion and/or drainage devices, debris basins, or other safety devices to protect the life, limb, health, and welfare of private and public property of others from damage of any kind.

(e) *Conditions of Approval.* In granting any permit under this Code, the Building Official may attach such conditions as may be reasonably necessary to prevent creation of a nuisance or hazard to public or private property. Such conditions may include, but shall not be limited to:

1. Improvement of any existing grading to bring it up to the standards of this Code.
2. Requirements for fencing of excavations or fills which would otherwise be hazardous.

(f) *Liability.* Neither the issuance of a permit under the provisions of this Code, nor the compliance with the provisions hereof or with any conditions imposed in the permit issued hereunder, shall relieve any person from responsibility for damage to other persons or property, nor impose any liability upon the city for damage to other persons or property.

DENIAL OF PERMIT

Sec. 7008. (a) *Hazardous Grading.* The Building Official shall not issue a permit in any case where he finds that the work as proposed by the applicant is liable to endanger any private property or result in the deposition of debris on any public way or interfere with any existing drainage course.

If it can be shown to the satisfaction of the Building Official that the hazard can be essentially eliminated by the construction of retaining structures, buttress fills, drainage devices, or by other means, the Building Official may issue the permit with the condition that such work be performed.

(b) *Geological or Flood Hazard.* If, in the opinion of the Building Official, the land area for which grading is proposed is subject to geological or flood hazard to the extent that no reasonable amount of corrective work can eliminate or sufficiently reduce the hazard to human life or property, the grading permit and building permits for habitable structures shall be denied.

FEES

Sec. 7009. (a) *Plan-Checking Fee.* For excavation and fill on the same site, the fee shall be based on the volume of the excavation or fill, whichever is greater. Before accepting a set of plans and specifications for checking, the Building Official shall collect a plan-checking fee.

Separate permits and fees shall apply to retaining walls or major drainage structures as indicated elsewhere in this Code. There shall be no separate charge for standard terrace drains and similar facilities. The amount of the plan-checking fee for grading plans shall be as set forth in Table No. 70-A.

Table No. 70-A—Plan-Checking Fees

50 cu yd or less——No fee
50 to 100 cu yd——$10.00
101 to 1000 cu yd——$15.00
1001 to 10,000 cu yd——$20.00
10,001 to 100,000 cu yd——$20.00 for the first 10,000 cu yd, plus $10.00 for each additional 10,000 cu yd or fraction thereof.
100,001 to 200,000 cu yd——$110.00 for the first 100,000 cu yd, plus $6.00 for each additional 10,000 cu yd or fraction thereof.
200,001 cu yd or more——$170.00 for the first 200,000 cu yd, plus $3.00 for each additional 10,000 cu yd or fraction thereof.

(b) *Grading Permit Fees.* A fee for each grading permit shall be paid to the Building Official as set forth in Table No. 70-B.

Table No. 70-B—Grading Permit Fees

50 cu yd or less——$10.00
50 to 100 cu yd——$15.00
101 to 1000 cu yd——$15.00 for the first 100 cu yd, plus $7.00 for each additional 100 cu yd or fraction thereof.
1001 to 10,000 cu yd——$78.00 for the first 1000 cu yd, plus $6.00 for each additional 1000 cu yd or fraction thereof.
10,001 to 100,000 cu yd——$132.00 for the first 10,000 cu yd, plus $27.00 for each additional 10,000 cu yd or fraction thereof.
100,001 cu yd or more——$375.00 for the first 100,000 cu yd, plus $15.00 for each additional 10,000 cu yd or fraction thereof.

The fee for a grading permit authorizing additional work to that under a valid permit shall be the difference between the fee paid for the original permit and the fee shown for the entire project.

BONDS

Sec. 7010. (a) *Bonds Required.* A permit shall not be issued for more than 1000 cu yd unless the permittee shall first post with the Building Official a bond executed by the owner and a corporate surety authorized to do business in this state as a surety in an amount sufficient to cover the cost of the project, including corrective work necessary to remove and eliminate geological hazards.

The bond shall include penalty provisions on a form approved by counsel for the governing agency, for failure to complete the work on schedule.

In lieu of a surety bond the applicant may file a cash bond with the Building Official in an amount equal to that which would be required in the surety bond.

(b) *Conditions.* Every bond shall include the conditions that the permittee shall:

1. Comply with all of the provisions of the Code, applicable laws, and ordinances;
2. Comply with all of the terms and conditions of the permit for excavation or fill to the satisfaction of the Building Official;
3. Complete all of the work contemplated under the permit within the time limit specified in the permit. (The Building Official may, for sufficient cause, extend the time specified in the permit, but no such extension shall release the surety upon the bond.)

(c) *Failure to Complete Work.* The term of each bond shall begin upon the date of filing and shall remain in effect until the completion of the work to the satisfaction of the Building Official. In the event of failure to complete the work and failure to comply with all of the conditions and terms of the permit, the Building Official may order the work required by the permit to be completed to his satisfaction. The surety executing such bond or deposit shall continue to be firmly bound under a continuing obligation for the payment of all necessary costs and expenses that may be incurred or expended by the governing agency in causing any and all such required work to be done. In the case of a cash deposit, said deposit or any unused portion thereof shall be refunded to the permittee.

DESIGN STANDARDS FOR CUTS

Sec. 7011. (a) *Maximum Slope.* Cuts shall not be steeper in slope than one and one-half horizontal to one vertical unless the owner furnishes a soils engineering or an engineering geology report certifying that the site has been investigated and indicating that the proposed deviation will not endanger any private property or result in the deposition of debris on any public way or interfere with any existing drainage course.

The Building Official may require the excavation to be made with a cut face flatter in slope than one and one-half horizontal to one vertical if he finds it necessary for stability and safety.

(b) *Drainage Terraces.* Cut slopes exceeding forty feet (40′) in vertical height shall be terraced at their approximate mid-height. Drainage terraces are to be a minimum of six feet (6′) wide, paved, and must carry water to a safe disposal area. Terraces shall be cut every thirty feet (30′) vertically, except that where only one terrace is required, it shall be at mid-height.

DESIGN STANDARDS FOR FILLS

Sec. 7012. (a) *Compaction.* All fills shall be compacted to a minimum of 90 per cent of maximum density as determined by U.B.C. Standard No. 70-1-64. Field Density shall be determined by U.B.C. Standard No. 70-2-64 or equivalent as approved by the Building Official. If the Building Official determines that the strict enforcement of this Section is unduly restrictive or imposes an undue hardship on the permittee, this requirement may be waived by the Building Official. This requirement shall not be waived when structures are to be supported by the fill or where the Building Official determines that compaction is necessary as a safety measure to aid in preventing the saturation, slipping, or erosion of the fill.

(b) *Preparation of Ground.* The natural ground surface shall be prepared to receive fill by removing vegetation, non-complying fill, top soil, and, where slopes are five horizontal to one vertical or steeper, by benching into sound bedrock or other competent material. Five feet (5′) of the lowermost bench shall be exposed beyond the toe of the fill. The bench shall be sloped for sheet overflow or a paved drain shall be provided.

(c) *Fill Slope.* No compacted fill shall be made which creates an exposed surface steeper in slope than one and one-half horizontal to one vertical. The Building Official may require that the fill be constructed with an exposed surface flatter than one and one-half horizontal to one vertical if he finds this necessary for stability and safety.

Slopes of fills which are not compacted in accordance with Section 7012 (a) may not exceed two horizontal to one vertical.

(d) *Fill Material.* No organic material shall be permitted in fills. Except as permitted by the Building Official, no rock or similar irreducible material with a maximum dimension greater than eight inches (8″) shall be buried or placed in fills.

(e) *Drainage Terraces.* All fill slopes in excess of thirty feet (30′) vertical height shall have paved drainage terraces at vertical intervals not exceeding twenty-five feet (25′) except that where only one terrace is required it shall be at mid-height. Such terraces shall drain into a paved gutter, pipe, or other watercourse adequate to convey the water to a safe disposal area. The terrace shall be at least six feet (6′) wide.

(f) *Slopes to Receive Fill.* Fills toeing out on natural slopes which are steeper than two horizontal to one vertical will not be permitted.

DESIGN STANDARDS FOR SETBACKS

Sec. 7013. Cuts and fills shall be set back from property lines and buildings shall be set back from cut or fill slopes in accordance with Figure No. 1 [Figure 32]. Retaining walls may be used to reduce the required setback when approved by the Building Official.

Fill placed on or above the top of an existing or proposed cut or natural slope steeper than three horizontal to one vertical shall be set back from the edge of the slope a minimum distance of six feet (6′).

Building foundations shall be set back from the top of slope a minimum distance of six feet (6′) for all cut slopes steeper than two horizontal to one vertical. No buildings shall be constructed on cut or fill slopes steeper than two horizontal to one vertical.

The setbacks given in this Section are minimum and may be increased by the Building Official if considered necessary for safety or stability or to prevent possible damage from water, soil, or debris.

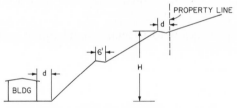

EXCAVATED SLOPE

REQUIRED SETBACKS			
H FEET	FILL SLOPES		CUT SLOPES
	a	b	a
0-15	1' 6"	3'	3'
15-50	H/10	H/5	H/5
Over 50	H/10	H/5	10'

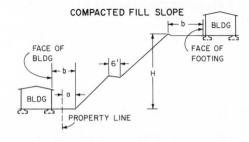

COMPACTED FILL SLOPE

FIGURE 32. **Required setbacks.** (After The Uniform Building Code of 1964, Sections 7013–7014, Fig. 1.)

DESIGN STANDARDS FOR DRAINAGE

Sec. 7014. (a) *Disposal*. All drainage facilities shall be designed to carry surface waters to the nearest practical street, storm drain, or natural watercourse approved by the Building Official and/or other appropriate governmental agency, as a safe place to deposit such waters. At least two percent grade toward the approved disposal area will be required for building pads, except as waived by the Building Official for non-hilly terrain.

(b) *Erosion Prevention*. Adequate provision shall be made to prevent any surface waters from damaging the face of an excavation or fill. All slopes shall be protected from surface water runoff from above by berms or swales.

(c) *Terrace Drains*. All swales or ditches on drainage terraces shall have a minimum grade of five percent and must be paved. Drainage devices shall be paved with concrete with a minimum thickness of three inches (3″) or approved equal. They shall have a minimum depth at the deepest point of one foot (1′).

If the drain discharges onto natural ground riprap may be required.

PLANTING

Sec. 7015. The face of all cut and fill slopes shall be planted and maintained with a ground cover approved by the Building Official to protect the slopes against erosion as soon as practical and prior to the final approval of the grading. Where cut slopes are not subject to erosion due to their rocky character, this requirement may be waived by the Building Official.

An irrigation system or watering facilities may be required by the Building Official.

GRADING INSPECTION AND SUPERVISION

Sec. 7016. (a) *Supervised Grading Required.* All grading in excess of 5000 cubic yards shall be performed under the supervision of a civil engineer and shall be designated "supervised grading." Grading not supervised in accordance with this Section shall be designated "regular grading." For grading involving less than 5000 cubic yards the permittee may elect to have the grading performed as either supervised grading or regular grading.

(b) *Regular Grading Requirements.* The Building Official shall inspect the work, and require adequate inspection and compaction control by a soils testing agency. The soils testing agency shall be approved by the Building Official.

Periodic reports certifying the compaction or acceptability of all fills shall be required except as exempted by Section 7012 (a). These shall include but need not be limited to inspection of cleared areas and benches prepared to receive fill and removal of all soil and unsuitable materials; the placement and compaction of fill materials; the bearing capacity of the fill to support structures; and the inspection or review of the construction of retaining walls, subdrains, drainage devices, buttress fills, and other similar measures.

The Building Official may require sufficient inspection to assure that all geologic conditions have been adequately considered. Where geologic conditions warrant, the Building. Official may require periodic geologic reports. These inspections may be required to include, but need not be limited to, inspection of cut slopes; canyons during clearing operations for ground water and earth material conditions; benches prior to placement of fill; and possible spring locations.

(c) *Supervised Grading Requirements.* For supervised grading it shall be the responsibility of the civil engineer to supervise and coordinate all site inspection and testing during grading operations. Soils and geology reports shall also be required as specified in Section 7006. All necessary reports, compaction data, and soils engineering and engineering geological recommendations shall be submitted to the Building Official by the supervising civil engineer.

(d) *Notification of Noncompliance.* If in the course of fulfilling his responsibility under this Chapter, the supervising civil engineer finds that the work is not being done in conformance with this Chapter or the plans approved by the Building Official, or in accordance with accepted practices, he shall immediately notify the person in charge of the grading work and the Building Official in writing of the nonconformity and of the corrective measures to be taken.

SAFETY PRECAUTIONS

Sec. 7017. If at any stage of the work the Building Official determines by inspection that further grading as authorized is likely to endanger any private property or result in the deposition of debris on any public way or interfere with any existing drainage course, the Building Official may require, as a condition to allowing the work to be completed, that such reasonable safety precautions be taken as he considers advisable to avoid such likelihood of danger.

Notice to comply shall be submitted to the permittee in writing. After a notice to comply is written, a period of 10 days shall be allowed for the contractor to begin to make the corrections, unless an imminent hazard exists, in which case the corrective work shall begin immediately.

If the Building Official finds any existing conditions not as stated in the grading permit or approved plans, he may refuse to approve further work until approval is obtained for a revised grading plan which will conform to the existing conditions.

RESPONSIBILITY OF PERMITTEE

Sec. 7018. (a) *Compliance with Plans and Requirements.* All permits issued hereunder shall be presumed to include the provision that the applicant, his agent, contractors, or employees, shall carry out the proposed work in accordance with the approved plans and specifications and in compliance with all the requirements of this Chapter.

(b) *Protection of Utilities.* During grading operations the permittee shall be responsible for the prevention of damage to any public utilities or services. This responsibility applies within the limits of grading and along any routes of travel of equipment.

(c) *Protection of Adjacent Property.* The permittee is responsible for the prevention of damage to adjacent property and no person shall excavate on land sufficiently close to the property line to endanger any adjoining public street, sidewalk, alley, or other public or private property without supporting and protecting such property from settling, cracking, or other damage which might result.

MODIFICATION OF APPROVED PLANS

Sec. 7019. All modifications of the approved grading plans must be approved by the Building Official. All necessary soils and geological reports shall be submitted with the plans.

No grading work in connection with the proposed modifications will be permitted without the approval of the Building Official. If, in the opinion of the Building Official, the strict enforcement of Section 7007 (d) will create an undue hardship on the permittee, or a hazard to the safety of operations, this requirement may be waived. Such a waiver shall not relieve the permittee of responsibility for compliance with the design standards of this Code.

Modifications which affect basic tract design or land use must have the approval of the appropriate control agency.

COMPLETION OF WORK

Sec. 7020. (a) *Final Reports.* Upon completion of the work, the Building Official may require the following reports:

1. The supervising civil engineer shall certify that all grading, lot

drainage, and drainage facilities have been completed in conformance with the approved plans and this Chapter, and shall furnish a final contour map of the completed work.

2. The soils engineering reports shall include certification of soil bearing capacity, summaries of field and laboratory tests, locations of tests, and shall show limits of compacted fill on an "as built" plan.

3. The engineering geology reports shall be based on the final contour map and shall include specific approval of the grading as affected by geological factors. Where necessary, a revised geologic map and cross sections and any recommendations regarding building restrictions or foundation setbacks shall be included.

(b) *Notification of Completion.* The permittee or his agent shall notify the Building Official when the grading operation is ready for final inspection. Final approval shall not be given until all work including installation of all drainage structures and their protective devices, has been completed and the final contour map and required reports have been submitted.

APPENDIX II
CLASSIFICATION
OF ROCKS

A rock is a coherent mineral aggregate. The point at which an unconsolidated sediment attains sufficient coherence to be called a rock is one of those fuzzy natural boundaries difficult to fix. Indeed, some geological theorists would call any mineral aggregate, even loose beach sand, a rock. However, practically, albeit arbitrarily, any mineral aggregate sufficiently durable to resist disaggregation when pressure is applied by the hand is a rock.

Rocks are commonly classified descriptively or genetically, or both—that is, by properties that can be observed or measured in the rock itself or by the process through which the rock was formed. Genetic classifications are at the same time more satisfactory because they give more information on the nature of the rock, and less satisfactory because they are based on inference and, therefore, are more subject to error. The process of origin is, of course, not observed directly.

It is inferred from the product of the process—e.g., the rock. Most genetic classifications of rocks are relatively secure because the properties of the product (chemical composition, mineralogy, and texture) permit accurate inference of the process of origin. However, for some kinds of rocks the process of origin cannot be unequivocally determined. The problem mostly concerns rocks formed deep in the earth's crust where igneous and metamorphic processes are difficult to separate. These problems are in the domain of the petrologist and of only casual interest to the environmental geologist. The following discussion covers basic facts of rock genesis.

Rock melts or magmas are generated deep in the earth's crust. The melts that crystallize slowly deep in the crust form coarsely crystalline mineral aggregates known as *plutonic rocks*. They range from granite to gabbro, depending on the chemical composition of the melt. Melts high in potassium, sodium, aluminum, and silicon form crystalline aggregates of alkali feldspars, quartz, micas, and other minor accessory minerals. These rocks are part of the *granitic suite*. Melts high in iron, magnesium, calcium, aluminum, and silicon form crystalline aggregates of calcic feldspar, olivine, pyroxenes, and amphiboles. These rocks are part of the *gabbroic suite*.

Where rock melts are cooled relatively rapidly at shallow depths in the crust, or where they are extruded on the surface as lavas, the product is fine-grained or glassy. *Lavas* or *volcanic rocks* range from rhyolite (the chemical equivalent of granite) to basalt (the chemical equivalent of gabbro), depending on the chemical composition of the melt.

Magma blown out of volcanic vents is cooled very rapidly or chilled in the air to form ash and cinders. This *pyroclastic ejecta* settles out of the air and forms a blanket of volcanic ash which, upon consolidation, is called *tuff*.

Igneous rocks (all rocks formed from rock melts or magma) exposed at the surface of the earth are subject to *weathering*. They are mechanically disaggregated, chemically altered, and more-or-less dissolved. The loose mineral grains and rock are *sediments*. Sediments are transported and mechanically deposited. Some minerals, of which quartz is an especially common example, are more durable than others, such as the amphiboles, and resist abrasion in natural transportation systems such as streams and rivers. Dissolved minerals are precipitated. The result is a layered or stratiform accumulation at the terminus of the transportation system, usually a lake or ocean basin. The sediments are consolidated and become *sedimentary rock*. Common sedimentary rocks are sandstone, shale, and limestone.

In some basins, sediments accumulated in great thicknesses in past geologic time. Some of these depositional basins were folded down deep into the crust and the sedimentary rocks were melted to form new magmas. These magmas crystallized to form a new generation of igneous rocks.

Both igneous and sedimentary rocks have in the past been metamorphosed. The mineralogy and texture have been changed in the solid state without melting because they were introduced into a new earth environment where, as a result of increased heat and pressure, new minerals were formed and new structures were imposed on the rock. Generally these changes occur deep in the earth, but they also occur at shallow depths adjacent to a hot igneous mass. Through *metamorphism*, limestone becomes marble, shale becomes schist, sandstone becomes quartzite, and granite becomes gneiss.

Sedimentary rocks, igneous rocks, and metamorphic rocks brought to the earth's surface through *tectonic movements* are subject to weathering and the product of weathering is sediments. The sediments are transported and redeposited to form a new generation of sedimentary rocks.

These *rock cycles* are repetitive. The cycles require long spans of time. At any particular time the chemical stuff of which a rock is made reflects through mineralogy and texture the most recent process (environment) which acted upon it. The environmental geologist and planner is concerned with the rocks now at the surface or near the surface. However, he needs to know how the rocks got there because their mode of origin controls their engineering properties. For example, some metamorphic rocks have a *schistosity*, a set of closely spaced planes of weakness, that cause the rock to *fail* in a predictable way under stress. The environmental geologist also needs to know what is happening to the rocks and what changes are taking place in them as they attempt to reach a chemical and physical equilibrium with the "new" environment.

The common rocks are classified in the following tables.

Igneous Rocks (Simplified Classification)

Coarse- or medium-granular (plutonic or deep-seated rocks)	Granite Diorite Gabbro	
	Silica and alkali elements decrease; iron, calcium, magnesium, increase	grain size decreases
Fine-granular or glassy (lavas and shallow intrusive rocks)	Rhyolite Andesite Basalt Obsidian	
Fine to coarse fragmental (surficial ash and cinder accumulations)	Tuff (fine-grained); Breccia (coarse-grained)	

Sedimentary Rocks (Simplified Classification)

Rocks formed by accumulation of rock and mineral fragments

Conglomerate and breccia	coarse grained
Sandstone (and fragmental limestone)	↓
Shale or mudstone	fine-grained

Rocks formed by accumulation of organic material

Peat, lignite, and coal
Coquinoid limestone
Diatomite

Rocks formed by chemical precipitation

Limestone and dolomite
Chert
Salt deposits

Metamorphic Rocks (Simplified Classification)

	Unmetamorphosed rock	Metamorphosed rock
Massive—without foliation	Sandstone Limestone Fine-grained igneous or sedimentary rocks	Metaquartzite Marble Hornfels
Foliated or schistose	Shale or tuff	Slate, phyllite, mica schist
	Basalt, gabbro, andesite	Chlorite schist, amphibole schist, amphibolite
	Granite, diorite, rhyolite	Gneiss

Note: Product of meatmorphism depends on (1) chemical composition of original rock, (2) quantity of hot aqueous solutions present, and (3) the relative strengths of stress and temperature—for example, a high shearing stress with low temperatures produces a fine-grained, crushed, foliated rock; a high temperature with low shearing stress produces a more coarsely crystalline aggregate with less pronounced foliation.

APPENDIX III
Glossary of Terms Common in Environmental Geology*

Ablation. "The term ablation is applied to the combined processes by which the glacier wastes." (Tarr, R. S., and Martin, L., *Textbook*, p. 205, 1914) "In summer, the phenomenon, which has been designated by the name of ablation—that is, the surface-melting of the ice—takes place rather rapidly." (Reclus, E., *Earth*, p. 197, 1873)

Acre-foot. The volume of liquid or solid required to cover 1 acre to a depth of 1 foot.

Aftershock. An earthquake which follows a larger earthquake and originated at or near the focus of the large earthquake. Generally, major earthquakes are followed by a large number of aftershocks, decreasing in frequency with increasing time. Such a series of aftershocks may last many days or even months.

* Extracted from *Glossary of geology and related sciences*: American Geological Institute, 1957, National Academy of Sciences-National Research Council publication 501, 325 pp. © 1957, 1960 American Geological Institute. See original source for explanation of reference abbreviations.

Aggrade. 1. "So long as deposition on the flood plain kept pace with the deposition in the channel, both would rise, but their relation to each other would not be altered. The valley bottom would be built up steadily; or, if we may coin a word to designate a process for which a name is needed, the valley bottom would be aggraded." (Salisbury, R. D., *Geol. Surv. of N. J.*, p. 103, 1893)   2. It is therefore suggested, in accordance with Davis' original proposal, that "graded" be used specifically for the stream in which equilibrium is maintained, and that "degrading" and "aggrading" be restricted to cases of the shifting equilibrium. "Degrading" is down-cutting approximately at grade, in contradistinction to such self-explanatory terms as trench or incise. "Aggrading" is upbuilding approximately at grade. "Regrading" refers to alteration in the form of the longitudinal profile by simultaneous aggrading and degrading in different parts. The term "degrade" is still available, of course, to describe the modeling of waste slopes in interstream areas. There is no justification or need for using either "aggrade" or "degrade" to describe short-period variations in stream activity; that is, as synonyms for "filling" or "scouring" (of a channel), or for the more general terms "erosion" and "deposition." (Mackin, J. Hoover, *GSA Bull.*, vol. 59, p. 478, 1948)   *See also* Graded Stream.

A-horizon, zone of eluviation. The uppermost zone in the soil profile, from which soluble salts and colloids have been leached, and in which organic matter has accumulated. (After Robinson, *Soils*, p. 56, 1936)   *See also* B-horizon; C-horizon; Soil horizon.

Alluvial fan. 1. "Deposit formed by a tributary of high declivity in the valley of a stream of less declivity." Fan first used in this sense by Haast in 1864 according to McGee. (McGee, W. J., *USGS 11th Ann. Rept.*, Pt. 1, p. 258, 1891)   2. "Alluvial fans are built by rivers issuing from mountains upon lowland. They are low, cone-shaped heaps, steepest near the mouth of the valley, and sloping gently outward with ever decreasing gradient." (Gregory, H. E., and others, *Mil. Geol. and Topog.*, p. 244, 1918)

Alluvial plain. 1. "If a stream be swift in one part of its course and slow in another, the swifter part may get a load which the slower cannot carry. Deposits will then be made in the valley where the current is sluggish. In this way flood plains are constructed. Flood plains produced by the filling of a valley bottom are alluvial plains. We commonly think of alluvial plains as made of fine mud, but alluvial plains may be made of sand or gravel, under the proper circumstances." (Salisbury, R. D., *Surf. Geol.*, p. 44, 1893)   2. "A plain resulting from the deposition of alluvium by water. In the southwestern United States most alluvial plains are formed by streams having a considerable grade, and hence they are generally referred to as alluvial slopes." (Bryan, Kirk, *U. S. G. S. Bull.*, 730–B, p. 86, 1922)

Alluvial terrace. "Alluvial terraces are those banks of loose material, generally unconsolidated, which skirt the sides of the valleys about rivers, ponds, and lakes, and rise above one another like the seats of an amphitheater." (Hitchcock, C. H., *Sixth Ann. Rept. of the Soc. of the Maine Board of Agri.*, p. 283, 1861)   "After filling its valley with waste for a time, a river may change its action and entrench its course in the built-up flood plain. The part of the plain then remaining above the new valley floor is commonly called an alluvial terrace, or simply a terrace." (Davis, W. M., 1898)

Alluvium. 1. "Earth, sand, gravel, and stones and other transported matter which has been washed away and thrown down by rivers, floods, and other causes, upon land not permanently submerged beneath the waters of lakes and seas." (Lyell, Charles)   2. A general term for all detrital deposits resulting from the operations of modern rivers, thus including the sediments laid down in river-beds, flood-plains, lakes, fans at the foot of mountain slopes, and estuaries. (Holmes, 1928)   3. The rather consistent usage of the term throughout its history makes it quite clear that alluvium is intended to apply to stream deposits of comparatively recent time, that the subaqueous deposits of seas and lakes are not intended to be included, and that permanent submergence is not a criterion. Alluvium may become lithified, as has happened frequently in the past, and then may be termed ancient alluvium. (Twenhofel, W. H., *Rept. Comm. Sed.*, p. 101, 1936-1937)

Anomaly. A deviation from uniformity; a local feature distinguishable in a geophysical, geochemical or geobotanical measurement over a larger area; a feature considered capable of being associated with commercially valuable petroleum or other mineral deposits; an area or restricted portion of a geophysical survey, such as magnetic or gravitational, which is different in appearance from the survey in general; specifically, an area within which it appears that successful drilling or other search for hydrocarbons or minerals may be conducted. In seismic usage anomaly is generally synonymous with structure, but it is also used for spurious or unexplainable seismic events or for local deviations of potential functions which can be conclusively attributed to no unique cause.

Aquiclude. A formation which, although porous and capable of absorbing water slowly, will not transmit it fast enough to furnish an appreciable supply for a well or spring. (Tolman, *Ground Water*, p. 557, 1937)

Aquifer. A formation, group of formations, or part of a formation that is water bearing. (Meinzer, *USGS WSP* 494, p. 30, 1923)

Areal geology. That branch of geology which pertains to the distribution, position, and form of the areas of the earth's surface occupied by different kinds of rock or different geologic units, and to the making of geologic maps. (La Forge)

Areal map. A geologic map showing the horizontal area or extent of rock units exposed at the surface.

Artesian water. Ground water that is under sufficient pressure to rise above the level at which it is encountered by a well, but which does not necessarily rise to or above the surface of the ground. (After Sayre, *USGS WSP* 678, p. 33, 1936)

Atterberg scale. A proposed grade scale for the classification of sediments based on a decimal system beginning with 2 mm. The limits of the subclass are found by taking the square root of the product of the larger grade limits. The subdivision thus made follows the logarithmic rule. This has become the accepted European standard for classification of particle size (Pettijohn, p. 18, 1949, after Atterberg, *Chem. Zeitung*, pp. 195-198, 1905.)

Azonal soils. Any group of soils without well-developed profile characteristics, owing to their youth, conditions of parent material, or relief that prevents development of normal soil-profile characteristics, (*U. S. Dept. Agr. Yearbook*, 1938)

Basalt. An extrusive rock composed primarily of calcic plagioclase, pyroxene, with or without olivine. The plagioclase is normally zoned and usually ranges in composition from bytownite to labradorite, but less calcic varieties are known. Augite, pigeonite, and hypersthene or bronzite are the common pyroxenes. Apatite and magnetite are almost always present as accessories. Basalts rich in olivine and calcicaugite are generally classified as olivine basalts; those poor in olivine and containing orthopyroxene and/or pigeonite are generally classified as tholeiites. The groundmass of tholeiitic basalts is commonly glassy, or, if crystallized, usually contains quartz or alkalic feldspar.

Basement rock. 1. A name commonly applied to metamorphic or igneous rocks underlying the sedimentary sequence.   2. Metamorphic and igneous Precambrian rocks.

Basin. 1. "A depressed area with the strata dipping inwards." (Emmons, E., *Man. of Geol.*, p. 284, 1863)   2. "Applied in geography to the whole extent of valley-shaped or basin-shaped country drained by any river and its tributaries." (Page, D., *Textbook*, p. 300, 1864)   3. "A tract of strata that dip towards a common center; also the drainage area of a large river and its tributaries; generally any hollow or depression of the surface, whether occupied by water or not; an area having no outlet is termed a closed basin." (Geikie, J., *Mountains*, etc., pp. 288-289, 1913)   4. An amphitheater, cirque, or corrie. Local in Rocky Mountains.   5. An extensive depressed area into which the adjacent land drains, and having no surface outlet. Use confined almost wholly to the arid West.   6. The drainage or catchment area of a stream or lake (Topog.)   7. In structural geology, a syncline that is circular or elliptical in plan; that is, the outcrop of each formation is essentially circular or elliptical, and the beds dip inward. (Billings, p. 50, 1954.)

Beach profile of equilibrium. A profile normal to the length of a beach and concave upward. The slope is steep above normal high water and more gentle seaward. Equilibrium is attained when the slope is so steep that the backwash aided by gravity can just return all the material which the larger swash can drive upward against the pull of gravity. (Johnson, D. W., *Shore Processes etc.*, p. 217, 1938)

Bedrock. The solid rock underlying auriferous gravel, sand, clay, etc., and upon which the alluvial gold rests (Roy. Com.).   Any solid rock underlying soil, sand, clay, etc.

Bentonite. Bentonite is a clay formed from the decomposition of volcanic ash and is largely composed of the clay minerals montmorillonite and beidellite. The rock must be produced by decomposition of volcanic ash and not from the decomposition of other substances. The color ranges from white to light-green and light-blue when fresh. On exposure the color frequently becomes a light-cream and gradually changes to yellow and in some cases to red or brown. (Twenhofel, W. H., *Rept. Comm. Sed.*, p. 99, 1936-1937)   The rock commonly has great ability to absorb or adsorb water and to swell accordingly.

B-horizon, Illuvial horizon. The lower soil zone which is enriched by the deposition or precipitation of material from the overlying zone or A-horizon. (After Robinson, *Soils*, p. 56, 1936)   *See also* A-horizon; C-horizon; Soil horizon.

Biosphere. The totality of living things on the earth's surface, as distinguished from the life in the atmosphere or in the lithosphere. (Hess)

Bolson. 1. A basin; a depression or valley having no outlet. Local in Southwest. (Wilson, H. M., *Bull. Am. Geog. Soc.* XXXII, p. 33, 1900) 2. The watershed of a centripetal drainage system, including all the area within the limits of the divides. (Tolman, *Jour. Geol.*, vol. 17, p. 141, 1909)   3. "A small intermontane desert basin does not merit description by a specific term. Where, however, the drainage is centripetal, with gentle gradients toward the low point of an extensive, mountain-girt, alluvium-floored basin, the term 'bolson' applies." (von Engeln, O. D., *Geomorphology*, p. 413, 1942)   4. (Sp., meaning "purse"). A large basin or depression; a wide valley drained by a stream flowing through canyons at each end. Local in Southwest. (Topog.)

Bottom load. 1. The material rolled and pushed along the bottom of a stream. (Russell, I. C., *Rivers of N. Amer.*, p. 67, 1898) (Obsolete) 2. "In the process by which running water transports detritus two factors are distinguished. The larger particles are rolled along the bottom, or else lifted momentarily, so as to make short leaps; they constitute the bottom load" (Gilbert, G K., *GSA Bull.*, vol. 18, *pp.* 657-658, 1906)

Braided stream. 1. "A braided stream is one flowing in several dividing and reuniting channels resembling the strands of a braid, the cause of division being the obstruction by sediment deposited by the stream." (USGS Physiographic Committee, 1918)   2. "Where more sediment is being brought to any part of a stream that it can remove, the building of bars becomes excessive, and the stream develops an intricate network of interlacing channels, and is said to be braided." (Dake, C. L., and Brown, J. S., p. 85, 1925)

Capacity. The ability of a water or wind current to transport detritus, as measured by the quantity it can carry past a given point in a unit of time.

Channel. 1. "The words 'bed' and 'channel' are frequently employed as synonymous terms when applied to rivers. There is, however, a difference, which will be rendered sensible by a little attention. By the word channel I understand generally the course, and more particularly the deepest part of the course, of a stream; that which by the French is termed *chenal*, and by the Germans *thalweg* . . . by this latter term (bed) I understand, as applied to a stream, that part of the channel over which the water generally flows, and that part of the basin of a sea or lake on which the water reposes." (Jackson, J. R., *Jour. Roy. Geog. Soc.*, vol. 4, pp. 80-81, 1834)   2. The deepest portion of a stream, bay, or strait through which the main volume or current of water flows.   3. The part of a body of water deep enough to be used for navigation through an area otherwise too shallow for navigation.   4. A large strait, as the English Channel.

C-horizon. 1. In soils, the substratum, or ". . . that portion of the underlying or parent material which has been penetrated by roots. The parent formation may be decomposed rock in place, or freshly deposited and nonindurated alluvium or other sedimentary material." (Tolman, C. F., *Ground Water*, p. 127, 1937)   2. "A layer of unconsolidated material, relatively little affected by the influence of organisms and presumed to be similar in chemical, physical, and mineralogical composition to the material from which at least a portion of the overlying solum has developed. Any slight alteration of the upper part of the C, such as reduction of calcium carbonate content in glacial till, unaccompanied by other changes, is designated as C_1." (*U.S. Dept. Agr. Soil Survey Man-*

ual, Handbook No. 18, p. 180, Aug. 1951)   *See also* A-horizon; B.-horizon; Soil horizon

Clastic. 1. In petrology, a textural term applied to rocks composed of fragmental material derived from preexisting rocks or from the dispersed consolidation products of magmas or lavas. (Holmes, A., p. 60, 1920) 2. A clastic rock is one composed principally of detritus transported mechanically into its place of deposition. It may consist of material that was originally chemically or biogenetically deposited within the same basin, provided it was moved as particles before its final deposition. The commonest clastics are sandstones and shales as distinct from limestones and anhydrites. However, limestones formed from particles derived from preexisting limes are clastic. (AAPG, 1949)

Clay. 1. The term clay as used today carries with it three implications: (1) a natural material with plastic properties, (2) an essential composition of particles of very fine grain size grades, and (3) an essential composition of crystalline fragments of minerals that are essentially hydrous aluminum silicates or occasionally hydrous magnesium silicates. The term implies nothing regarding origin but is based on properties, texture, and composition, which are of course, interrelated—for example, the plastic properties are the result of the constituent minerals and their small grain size. (Grim, 1942)   2. A natural substance or soft rock which, when finely ground and mixed with water, forms a pasty, moldable mass that preserves its shape when air dried; the particles soften and coalesce upon being highly heated and form a stony mass upon cooling. Clays differ greatly mineralogically and chemically and consequently in their physical properties. Most of them contain many impurities, but ordinarily their base is hydrous aluminum silicate. (USGS)   3. Soil consisting of inorganic material, the grains of which have diameters smaller than .005 millimeters. (U.S. Bur. Soils Classification)   4. Fine-grained soil that has a high plasticity index in relation to the liquid limit and consists mainly of particles less than 0.074 mm. (passing No. 200 sieve) in diameter. Compare silt. (Waterways Expt. Sta., Corps of Engrs., *Tech. Memo* 3-357, 1953)

Competence (of stream). The diameter of the largest particle a stream can move is a measure of its competence. (Jahns, R. H., USGS *Water Supply Paper* 996, p. 75, 1947)

Conglomerate, Puddingstone. Rounded water-worn fragments of rock or pebbles, cemented together by another mineral substance, which may be of a siliceous or argillaceous nature. This is locally termed "pudding stone." (Roberts, G., *Etymol, and Explan. Dict. Geol.,* p. 34, 1839) 2. A cemented clastic rock containing rounded fragments corresponding in their grade sizes to gravel or pebbles. Monogenetic and polygenetic types are recognized, according to the uniformity or variability of the composition and source of the pebbles. (Holmes, 1928)

Creep. 1. "The slow and imperceptible movement of finely broken up rock-matter from higher to lower levels. The material itself that has so moved." (Lowe, E. C., *Miss State Geol. Surv.*, Bull. 14, p. 326, 1919)   2. An imperceptibly slow, more-or-less continuous downward and outward movement of slope-forming soil or rock. The movement is essentially viscous, under shear stresses sufficient to produce permanent deformation but too small to produce shear failure, as in a landslide, q. v. (Stokes and Varnes, 1955)   3. Slow deformation that results from long application of a stress. By many it is limited to stresses below the elastic limit. Part of the creep is a permanent deformation. Part of the deformation is elastic; and from this part the specimen recovers. (After Billings, 1954)

Crust (of the earth). That part of the earth lying above the Mohorovičić disconformity. (Birch, F., *GSA, SP* 62, p. 102, 1955)

Debris avalanche. The sudden movement downslope of the soil mantle on steep slopes caused by its complete saturation through protracted heavy rains. (Sharpe, C. F. S., *Landslides and Related Phenomena*, p. 29, 1938)

Debris slide. The rapid downward movement of predominantly unconsoli-dated and incoherent earth and debris in which the mass does not show backward rotation but slides or rolls forward, forming an irregular hum-mocky deposit which may resemble morainal topography. (Sharpe, C. F. S., *Landslides and Related Phenomena*, p. 74, 1938)

Deflation. 1. "There is no need of travelling into the deserts in order to recognize the denuding activity of wind; and in the driest desert the traces of erosion may be observed . . . We say of the wind that it 'sweeps' over the ground; for this word means nothing else than that the wind cleans the ground of all loose particles that cover it. Translated into technical geologic language, it is called deflation." (Walther, J., *Nat. Geog. Mag.*, vol. 4, p. 176, 1893)   2. the removal of material from a beach or other land surface by wind action. (*BEB* 2)

Design flood. The flood against which a given area is to be protected. (Leopold, L. B., and Maddock, T., *The Flood Control Controversy*, p. 249, 1954)

Detritus. 1. "Matter worn from rocks by mechanical means." (Lee, C. E., *Elem. of Geol.*, p. 287, 1840)   2. Accumulations arising from the waste or disintegration of exposed rock surfaces. (Page, David, 1859)   3. "(Lat., a rubbing away) The materials that result from the breaking up, disintegration and wearing away of minerals and rocks; as, alluvial deposits generally." (Geike, J., *Mountains*, p. 291, Edinburgh, 1913)   4. A general name for incoherent sediments, produced by the wear and tear of rocks through the various geological agencies. The name is from the Latin for "worn." Rock waste (Kempe)   5. Fragmental material, such as sand, silt and mud, derived from older rocks by disintegration. The deposits produced by the accumulation of detritus constitute the detrital sediments. (Holmes, 1928)

Dike. 1. A tabular body of igneous rock that cuts across the structure of adjacent rocks or cuts massive rocks. Although most dikes result from the intrusion of magma, some are the result of metasomatic replacement. 2. A wall or mound built around a low-lying area to prevent flooding. (BEB 2)

Diorite. A plutonic rock composed essentially of sodic plagioclase (usually andesine) and hornblende, biotite, or pyroxene. Small amounts of quartz and orthoclase may be present. First used by Hauy.

Dip. The angle at which a stratum or any planar feature is inclined from the horizontal. (Billings, 1955) The dip is at a right angle to the strike.

Earth-flow. 1. ". . . landslides which are due to relatively large and sudden accessions of water to the unconsolidated materials of a slope . . . Such landslides may be discriminated from earth-slumps by reason of their greater mobility, under the designation of earth-flow." (Lawson, A. C., *Calif. Earthquake of April 18, 1906*, Vol. 1, p. 386, 1908)   2. A slow flow of earth lubricated with water, occurring as either a low-angle terrace flow or a somewhat steeper but slow hillside flow. (After Sharpe, C. F. S., *Landslides and Related Phenomena*, 1938)

Eolian, Aeolian (Obs.). 1. "A formation of recent origin, consisting of marine sand drifted and arranged by the wind." (Emmons, E., *Manual*, p. 288, 1863)   2. "A term applied to deposits arranged by the wind, as the sands and other loose materials along shores, etc. (From Eolus, the god of winds.) Sub-aerial is often used in much the same sense." (Oldham, R. D., *Glossary*, p. 18, London, 1879)   3. "A term applied to the erosive action of the wind, and to deposits which are due to the transporting action of the wind." (*Geol. Surv. of West. Australia, Memoir* 1, 1919)   4. (Formerly spelled aeolian.) Of, relating to, formed by, or deposited from the wind or currents of air. (La Forge)

Erosion. 1. "Wearing away by water." (St. John, Samuel, *Textbook*, 1851) "The sculpture and degradation of the lands are performed partly by shore-waves, partly by glaciers, partly by the wind; but chiefly by rain and running water."   2. "All indurated rocks and most earths are bound together by a force of cohesion which must be overcome before they can be divided and removed. The natural processes by which the division and removal are accomplished make up erosion. They are called disintegration and transportation." (Gilbert, G. K., *Rept. Geol. Henry Mtns.*, pp. 99-100, 1877)   3. "[It] may be considered as the general process whereby the earth matter is removed by running water from its original loci." (McGee, W. J., *GSA Bull.*, vol. 19, p. 199, 1908)   4. "A term which includes all processes by which earthy matter or rock is loosened and removed from place to place. In this country it is regarded as including weathering, corrasion, and transportation." (Bryan, Kirk, *USGS Bull.* 730-B, p. 88, 1922)   5. The group of processes whereby earthy or rock material is loosened or dissolved and removed from any part of the earth's surface. It includes the processes of weathering, solution, corrasion, and transportation. The mechanical wear and transportation are effected by running water, waves, moving ice, or winds, which use rock fragments to pound or grind other rocks to powder or sand. (Ransome, F. L., *USGS Prof. Paper* 115, p. 182, 1919)

Extrusive rocks. A term applied to those igneous rocks derived from magmas or magmatic materials poured out or ejected at the earth's surface, as distinct from the intrusive or plutonic igneous rocks which have solidified from magmas that have been injected into older rocks at depth without reaching the surface. Synonymous with effusive rocks; volcanic rocks.

Fall line. 1. A line characterized by numerous waterfalls, as the edge of a plateau in passing which the streams make a sudden descent. (Webster) 2. "A large river whose valley is extended across a coastal plain often has low falls or rapids near the inner margin of the plain, which determine the 'head of navigation' or uppermost point that can be reached by vessels from the river mouth. A line drawn through the falls on successive rivers is called the fall line. The falls occur where the river passes from a steeper slope on the resistant rocks of the older land to a nearly level channel excavated in the weak strata of the plain." (Davis, W. M., *Elem. Phys. Geog.*, pp. 157-158, 1904)

Fault. A fracture or fracture zone along which there has been displacement of the two sides relative to one another parallel to the fracture. The displacement may be a few inches or many miles. (Reid, 1913)

Flood plain. 1. "All great rivers annually flood portions of level land near their mouths, and cover them with sedimentary deposits. The whole area thus flooded is called the flood plain. The flood plain of a river may be divided into two parts, viz. the river swamp and the delta." (LeConte, Joseph, *Textbook*, p. 22, 1885)   2. Gilbert uses the term in a very different sense. He says in *Geology of the Henry Mountains*, p. 132: ". . . flood plains are usually produced by lateral corrasion." (Hicks, L. E., *GSA Bull.*, vol. 4, pp. 142-143, 1893)   3. A strip of relatively smooth land bordering a stream, built of sediment carried by the stream and dropped in the slack water beyond the influence of the swiftest current. Bryan, *USGS Bull.* 730-B, p. 88, 1922)   4. That portion of a river valley, adjacent to the river channel, which is built of sediments during the present regimen of the stream and which is covered with water when the river overflows its bank at flood stages. (Comm. Rec.)

Fold. A bend in strata or any planar structure. (Billings, 1954)

Formation. 1. "In geology, any assemblage of rocks which have some character in common, whether of origin, age, or composition." (Lyell, *Manual of Geol.*, 6th Ed., p. 2, 1858) 2. As defined and used by the U.S. Geological Survey, the ordinary unit of geologic mapping consisting of a large and persistent stratum of some one kind of rock. It is also loosely employed for any local and more or less related group of rocks. In Dana's *Geology* it is applied to the groups of related strata that were formed in a geological period. (Kemp) 3. In chronological geology formations constitute as it were the units, and several formations may go to make up a system. The word is often loosely used to indicate anything which has been formed or brought into its present shape. (Roy. Com.) 4. A genetic unit formed under essentially uniform conditions or under an alternation of conditions—and assumed to be limited in horizontal extent. (Ashley, *et al.*, *GSA Bull.*, vol. 44, p. 432, 1933) 5. "A sedimentary formation is a lithologically distinctive product of essentially continuous sedimentation selected from a local succession of strata as a convenient unit for purposes of mapping, description, and reference." (Stratigraphic Commission, *AAPG Bull.*, vol. 32, p. 366, 1948) The formation as defined above is one of the "rock units" whose "Differentiation [is] not based on time relations." (Stratigraphic Commission, *AAPG Bull.*, vol. 31, p. 520, 1947) 6. In speleology: a secondary mineral deposit formed by the accumulation, dripping, or flowing of water in a cave. In a more limited sense the term is confined to crystalline deposits formed from flowing, dripping, or standing water.

Gabbro. A plutonic rock consisting of calcic plagioclase (commonly labradorite) and clinopyroxene, with or without orthopyroxene and olivine. Apatite and magnetite or limonite are common accessories. First used by Leopold von Buch.

Geologic time scale. See p. 286.

Glacial drift. Sediment (a) in transport in glaciers, (b) deposited by glaciers, and (c) predominantly of glacial origin, made in the sea or in bodies of glacial meltwater. (Flint, *GGPE*, p. 102)

Gneiss. A coarse-grained rock in which bands rich in granular minerals alternate with bands in which schistose minerals predominate.

Graded stream. 1. "Mr. Gilbert has recently suggested to me that a stream in the condition of balance between degrading and aggrading might be called a graded stream; and its slope a graded slope." (Davis, W. M., *Jour. Geol.*, vol. 2, p. 77, 1894) (Original) 2. A graded

Geologic time scale

Era	Period	Epoch
Cenozoic	QUATERNARY (lasted 0-1 million years)	Recent Pleistocene
	TERTIARY (lasted 62 million years)	Pliocene Miocene Oligocene Eocene Paleocene
63 million years ago		
Mesozoic	CRETACEOUS (lasted 72 million years)	
	JURASSIC (lasted 46 million years)	
	TRIASSIC (lasted 49 million years)	
230 million years ago		
Paleozoic	PERMIAN (lasted 50 million years)	
	PENNSYLVANIAN (lasted 30 million years)	
	MISSISSIPPIAN (lasted 35 million years)	
	DEVONIAN (lasted 60 million years)	
	SILURIAN (lasted 20 million years)	
	ORDOVICIAN (lasted 75 million years)	
	CAMBRIAN (lasted 100? million years)	
600? million years ago		
Late Precambrian		
Early Precambrian		

stream is one in which, over a period of years, slope is delicately adjusted to provide, with available discharge and with prevailing channel characteristics, just the velocity required for the transportation of the load supplied from the drainage basin. The graded stream is a system in equilibrium; its diagnostic characteristic is that any change in any of the controlling factors will cause a displacement of the equilibrium in a direction that will tend to absorb the effect of the change. (Mackin, J. Hoover, *GSA Bull.*, vol. 59, p. 491, 1948)   *See also* Aggrade.

Granite. 1. A plutonic rock consisting essentially of alkalic feldspar and quartz. Sodic plagioclase, usually oligoclase, is commonly present in small amounts and muscovite, biotite, hornblende, or rarely pyroxene may be mafic constituents.   2. In seismology, a rock in which velocity of the compressional wave lies somewhat between 5.5 and 6.2 km/sec. (Burch, F., *Nuclear Geology*, p. 171)

Gravel. 1. "It may be of interest to observe here, that in some parts of England the inhabitants very improperly call any small, loose, rubble stones, though they are flat, pointed with angles, or of all shapes, provided they lie near the surface of the earth, by the name of gravel; but unless they are answerable to the above description, and apparently worn, or a great part of them worn and rounded, they ought not properly to be, neither indeed are they generally and commonly so called." (Catcott, A., *Treatise*, p. 293, London, 1768)   2. "Accumulations of rounded water-worn pebbles. The word gravel is generally applied when the size of the pebbles does not much exceed that of an ordinary hen's egg. The finer varieties are called sand while the coarser varieties are called shingle." (Oldham, R. D., *Geol. Gloss.*, p. 24, London, 1879)   3. An accumulation of rounded rock or mineral pieces larger than 2 mm in diameter. Divided into Granule, Pebble, Cobble, and Boulder gravel. (Wentworth, C. K., *Jour. Geol.*, vol. 30, pp. 377–392, 1922)   4. Small stones and pebbles or a mixture of sand and small stones; more specifically, fragments of rock worn by the action of air and water, larger and coarser than sand. (USGS)   5. Loose rounded fragments of rock, between 1 and 2 mm in diameter. (U. S. Bur. of Soils Classification)   6. "Consists of rock grains or fragments with a diameter range of from 76 mm (3 inc.) to 4.76 mm (retention on a No. 4 sieve). The individual grains are usually more or less rounded." (Tech. Man. 5–545, *Geol. and Its Mil. Applications*, Dept. of Army, p. 19, 1952)   Also soil consisting dominantly of such particles.

Hard rock. Rock which required drilling and blasting for its economical removal. (Technical Manual 5–545, *Geol. and Its Mil. Applications*, Dept. of Army, 1952, after Joint Comm. on Substructure Engineering, Am. Soc. of Civil Engineers)

Humus. Dark-colored, organic, well-decomposed soil material consisting of the residues of plant and animal materials together with synthesized cell substances of soil organisms and various inorganic elements. (Stokes and Varnes, p. 72, 1955)

Igneous (adj.). In petrology, formed by solidification from a molten or partially molten state: said of the rocks of one of the two great classes into which all rocks are divided, and contrasted with sedimentary. (La Forge)   Rocks formed in this matter have also been called plutonic rocks, and are often divided for convenience into plutonic and volcanic rocks but there is no clear line between the two. (Webster)

Impermeable, Impervious. (Hydrology) Having a texture that does not permit water to move through it perceptibly under the head differences ordinarily found in subsurface water. (After Meinzer, USGS WSP 494, p. 20, 1923)

Intensity (of an earthquake). A number describing the effects of an earthquake on man, on structures built by him, and on the earth's surface. The number is rated on the basis of an "earthquake intensity scale"; the scale in common use in the U. S. today is the Modified Mercalli Scale of 1931. (Wood, H. O., and Neumann, F., Bull., S.S.A., 21, pp. 277–283, 1931)

Intrusion. 1. A body of igneous rock that invades older rock. The invading rock may be a plastic solid or magma that pushes its way into the older rock. "Intrusion" should not be used for bodies of igneous-looking rock that are the result of metasomatic replacement.   2. The process of formation of an intrusion. (Billings, 1955)

Isostatic compensation, Isostatic adjustment. 1. An equilibrium condition in which elevated masses such as continents and mountains are compensated by a mass deficiency in the crust beneath them. The compensation for depressed areas is by a mass excess.   2. The process in which lateral transport at the earth's surface by processes such as erosion and deposition is compensated by lateral movements in a subcrustal layer.

Karst topography. "In Karst, on the eastern side of the Adriatic Sea, the limestone rocks are so honeycombed by tunnels and openings dissolved out by ground waters, that much of the drainage is underground. Large sinks abound, some of them five or six hundred feet deep. Streamless valleys are common, and valleys containing streams often end abruptly where the latter plunge into underground tunnels and caverns, sometimes to reappear as great springs elsewhere. Irregular topography of this kind, developed by the solution of surface and ground waters, is known as karst topography, after the type region in Austria-Hungary." (Blackwelder, E., and Barrows, H. H., p. 118, 1911)

Landslide. 1. The perceptible downward sliding or falling of a relatively dry mass of earth, rock, or mixture of the two. (Sharpe, C. F. S., Land-

slides and Related Phenomena, p. 64, 1938)   2. Earth and rock which becomes loosened from a hillside by moisture or snow, and slides or falls down the slope. (Topog.)

Laterite. 1. A name derived from the Latin word for brick earth, and applied many years ago to the red, residual soils, or surface products, that have originated *in situ* from the atmospheric weathering of rocks. They are especially characteristic of the tropics. Though first applied to altered, basaltic rocks in India, laterite has had in later years a general application without regard to the character of the original rock.(Kemp)   2. Applied to ores of aluminum, iron, manganese, nickel, and other metals developed by weathering.   3. Laterite is a mixture of hydroxides of iron and aluminum in any proportion with other substances which also have a wide range in quantity. It is commonly in the form of porous concretionary crusts and the color is some shade of red. Laterite forms as a residual product in tropical and subtropical latitudes under conditions of good drainage. (Twenhofel, W. H., *Rept. Comm. on Sed.,* p. 100, 1936–1937)   Name originally given by Buchanan Hamilton in 1807.

Lava. Fluid rock that issues from a volcano or a fissure in the earth's surface; also the same material solidified by cooling. (Topog.)

Lava flow. 1. A stream or river of fluid or viscous or solidified fragmented lava which issues from an individual volcanic cone or from a fissure in relatively quiet fashion, with little or no explosive activity.   2. The solidified, stationary mass of rock formed when the lava stream congeals. Lava flows are generally tabular igneous bodies, thin compared to their horizontal extent, and elongated in the main direction of flow. Their form and internal structure depend chiefly on the fluidity of the lava, which, in turn, is a function of composition. Thus basic lava flows, such as basalt, are usually highly mobile, and flow for great distances, whereas silicic lavas, such as rhyolite and trachyte, are ordinarily sluggish in their flow, commonly fragmented, and remain heaped up, often in steep-sided volcanic domes or in short, steep-sided flows known as coulees. (After Tyrrell, G. W., p. 14, 1950)

Law of superposition. The law that underlying strata must be older than overlying strata where there has been neither inversion nor overthrust. Upon this law all geological chronology is based. (Standard)

Limestone. 1. ". . . A bedded sedimentary deposit consisting chiefly of calcium carbonate ($CaCO_3$) which yields lime when burned. . . . Limestone is the most important and widely distributed of the carbonate rocks and is the consolidated equivalent of limy mud, calcareous sand, or shell fragments." (Stokes and Varnes, pp. 83–84, 1955)   2. ". . . A general term for that class of rocks which contain at least 80 percent of the carbonates of calcium or magnesium. . . . The suitability of the rock for the manufacture of lime is not an essential characteristic." (Pettijohn, p. 289, 1949)

Liquid limit. Moisture content at which the soil 'passes from a plastic to a liquid state. (Am. Assoc. of State Highway Officials, *Standard specifications for highway materials and methods of sampling and testing;* p. 228, 1950)

Lithology. The composition and texture of rock, e.g., "lithologic variations."

Littoral. 1. Belonging to, inhabiting or taking place on or near the shore. (Page, David, 1865)   2. The portion of the benthic which extends from the shore to approximately the 200 meter line. (Sverdrup, *et. al., The Oceans,* p. 276, 1924)   3. The benthonic environment between the limits of high and low tides. (After Moore, Lalicker, and Fischer, p. 20, 1952)

Littoral drift. 1. "This is the term applied to the movement along the coast of gravel, sand, and other material composing the bars and beaches." (Stead, Geoffrey, *Bull. Nat. Hist. Soc., New Brunswick,* vol. 5, p. 6, 1903)   2. The material moved in the littoral zone under the influence of waves and currents. (*BEB 2*)

Load. 1. "In erosion and corrasion the material which is transported may be called the 'load.' The load is transported by two methods, a portion floats with the water, and another portion is driven along the bottom." (Powell, J. S., *Science,* vol. 7, p. 229, 1888)   2. "The sediment moved by a stream, whether in suspension or at the bottom, is its load." (Salisbury, R. D., *Physiog.,* p. 122, 1909)   3. The quantity of material actually transported by a current. (After Twenhofel, *Prin. Sed.,* p. 194, 1939)

Loess. 1. A homogeneous, nonstratified, unindurated deposit consisting predominantly of silt, with subordinate amounts of very fine sand and/or clay; a rude vertical parting is common at many places. For a majority of workers, the term has genetic implications in terms of eolian deposition. According to A. Scheidig (*Del Löss,* Leipzig, p. 58, 1934), the term was first used in connection with deposits in the Rhine Valley, about 1821, and was introduced into English by Charles Lyell in 1834.   2. A sediment, commonly nonstratified and commonly unconsolidated, composed dominantly of silt-size particles, ordinarily with accessory clay and sand, deposited primarily by the wind. (Essentially NRC Comm. on *Eolian Map of N.A.* Map published by GSA in 1952) (Similar definition in Flint, *GGPE,* p. 175)   3. Thought by Russell to be colluvial rather than eolian in the Lower Mississippi Valley and to result from the reworking of older back-swamp deposits. (Russell, R. J., *GSA Bull.,* vol. 55, pp. 1–40, 1944)

Log. 1. A graphic presentation of the lithologic and/or stratigraphic units traversed by a bore hole.   2. The similar presentation of the variation of some physical property in a bore hole with depth, such as resistivity, self-potential, gamma-ray intensity or velocity.   3. The record of formations penetrated, drilling progress, record of depth of water, oil, gas, or other minerals, the record of size and length of pipe used, and other written or recorded facts having to do with drilling a well.

Magma. Naturally occurring mobile rock material, generated within the earth and capable of intrusion and extrusion, from which igneous rocks are considered to have been derived by solidification. It consists "in noteworthy part" of a liquid silicate-melt phase, which is liquid owing to the temperature attained, and a number of solid phases such as suspended crystals of olivine, pyroxene, plagioclase, etc. In certain instances a gas phase may also be present. Various authors differ in their interpretation of what constitutes "in noteworthy part." Some writers would specifically exclude from the definition those materials fitting the definition of migma. Magmatic (adj.)

Marl. 1. A calcareous clay, or intimate mixture of clay and particles of calcite or dolomite, usually fragments of shells. Marl in America is chiefly applied to incoherent sands, but abroad compact, impure limestones are called marls. (Kemp, 1940)   2. Marl is an old term of a considerable range of usage. In Coastal Plain geology of the United States it has been used as a name for little indurated sedimentary deposits of a wide range of composition among which are slightly to richly calcareous clays and silts; fine-grained calcareous sands; clays, silts, and sands containing glauconite; and unconsolidated shell deposits. In the interior of the United States the name is used for the calcareous deposits of lakes in which the percentage of calcium carbonate may range from 90 to less than 30 percent. The name does not connote any particular composition and it would seem that it should be abandoned, but it is useless to make a recommendation to that effect as the use is so extensive that the recommendation would be ignored. A writer should always define his meaning when the term is used. (Twenhofel. W. H., *Rept. Comm. Sed.*, p. 100, 1936–37)   Preferred: a calcareous clay.

Mass movement. Unit movement of a portion of the land surface as in creep, landslide, or slip. (SCS)

Mass-wasting. 1. The slow downslope movement of rock debris.   2. A general term for a variety of processes by which large masses of earth materials are moved by gravity either slowly or quickly from one place to another. (Stokes and Varnes)

Member. In the usage of the U. S. Geological Survey, a division of a formation generally of distinct lithologic character or of only local extent. (LaForge)   A specially developed part of a varied formation is called a member, if it has considerable geographic extent. Members are commonly, though not necessarily, named. (Ashley, *et al.*)

Mesh. One of the openings or spaces in a screen. The value of the mesh is usually given as the number of openings per linear inch. This gives no recognition to the diameter of the wire, so that the mesh number does not always have a definite relation to the size of the hole. (Richards)

Metamorphic rock. 1. First used by Lyell, *Princ. of Geology*, 1833. Applied to the group of gneisses and crystalline schists.   2. This term includes all those rocks which have formed in the solid state in response to pronounced changes of temperature, pressure, and chemical environment, which take place, in general, below the shells of weathering and cementation. (After G. W. Tyrrell)

Moraine. 1. Drift, deposited chiefly by direct glacial action, and having constructed topography independent of control by the surface on which the drift lies. (Flint, R. F., *USGS Prof. Paper* 262)   2. An accumulation of drift having initial constructional topography, built within a glaciated region chiefly by the direct action of glacier ice. (Flint, GGPE, p. 126)

Outwash. 1. ". . . stratified drift that is stream built—'washed out'—beyond the glacier itself." (Flint, GGPE, p. 133)   2. Stratified drift deposited by meltwater streams beyond active glacier ice.

Overburden. A term used by geologists and engineers in several different senses. By some it is used to designate material of any nature, consolidated or unconsolidated, that overlies a deposit of useful materials, ores, or coal, especially those deposits that are mined from the surface by open cuts. As employed by others overburden designates only loose soil, sand, gravel, etc., that lies above the bedrock. The term should not be used without specific definition. (Stokes and Varnes, 1955).

Peat. A dark-brown or black residuum produced by the partial decomposition and disintegration of mosses, sedges, trees, and other plants that grow in marshes and like wet places. (*Mineral Resources of the U. S.*, 1917, Pt. 2, p. 261)

Permafrost. Permanently frozen subsoil. (W)

Permeability. The permeability (or previousness) of rock is its capacity for transmitting a fluid. Degree of permeability depends upon the size and shape of the pores, the size and shape of their interconnections, and the extent of the latter. It is measured by the rate at which a fluid of standard viscosity can move a given distance through a given interval of time. The unit of permeability is the Darcy.

pH. The negative logarithm of the hydrogen ion activity (less correctly, concentration). For example, pH 7 indicates an H^+ concentration (activity) of 10^{-7} mole/liter.

Phi mean particle diameter. A logarithmic mean particle diameter obtained by using the negative logs of the class midpoints to the base 2. (Krumbein, *Jour. Sed. Petrol.*, vol. 4, pp. 65–77, 1934)

Porosity. The ratio of the aggregate volume of interstices in a rock or soil to its total volume. It is usually stated as a percentage. (After Meinzer, *USGS WSP* 494, p. 19, 1923)

Profile of equilibrium. 1. "There is a profile of equilibrium which the water would ultimately impart, if allowed to carry its work to completion. The continual change of shore line and the supply of new drift are ever-changing conditions with which no fixed form can be in equilibrium. There are, however, certain adjustments of current slope and load which when once attained, are maintained with some constancy. The form involved in these adjustments is commonly known as the profile of equilibrium." (Fenneman, N. M., *Jour. Geol.*, vol. 10, p. 1, 1902) (Original) 2. "A [shore] profile on which the incoming and outgoing of beach gravel and sand is balanced." (Goldthwait, J. W., *Ill. Geol. Surv. Bull.* 7, p. 32–33, 1908) 3. A marine platform consisting of a wave-cut platform which extends to shore and a built platform farther seaward whose slope has become smooth and nearly uniform. At all points on the slope there is a balance between erosion and deposition. This profile, termed a Graded profile or Profile of equilibrium, is slightly concave, being steepest near the shore. (Cotton, C. A., *Geomorphology of New Zealand*, p. 383, 1926) 4. "A profile of equilibrium, or graded profile, is a river profile in which the slope at every point is just sufficient to enable the stream to carry its load of sediment, neither depositing sediment nor eroding the river bed." (Rice, W. N., and Foye, W. G., *State Geol. and Nat. Hist. Surv., Conn., Bull.* 41, p. 40, 1927)

Reservoir. A natural underground container of liquids, such as oil or water, and gases. In general, such reservoirs were formed by local deformation of strata, by changes of porosity, and by intrusions. These, however, are classifications in the broadest sense.

Residual soil. Soil formed in place by the disintegration and decomposition of rocks and the consequent weathering of the mineral materials. Presumably developed from the same kind of rock as that on which it lies. (SCS)

Runoff. 1. "The water which flows on the surface is called the runoff though this term is used to include also the water which returns to the surface after a greater or less underground passage." (Veatch, A. C., *USGS Prof. Paper* 44, p. 53, 1906) 2. The discharge of water through surface streams. 3. The quantity of water discharged through surface streams, expressed usually in units of volume such as gallons, cubic feet, or acre-feet. (After Meinzer, *USGS WSP* 494, p. 116, 1923)

Sand. Detrital material of size range 2–1/16 mm diameter: very coarse, 1–2 mm; coarse, ½–1 mm; medium, ¼–½ mm; fine, ¼–⅛mm; very fine, ⅛–1/16 mm. (After Wentworth, *Jour. Geol.*, vol. 30, pp. 377–392, 1922)

Sandstone. A cemented or otherwise compacted detrital sediment composed predominantly of quartz grains, the grades of the latter being those of sand. Mineralogical varieties such as feldspathic and glauconitic sandstones are recognized, and also argillaceous, siliceous, calcareous, ferruginous, and other varieties according to the nature of the binding or cementing material. (Holmes, 1928)

Schist. 1. A synonym for slate. (Rogers, W. B., after Lyell, Va. Geol. Surv., 1840) This usage is now obsolete.   2. Rocks which have a foliated structure, split up in thin, irregular plates, not by regular cleavage as in clay slate, nor in large flat laminae, as in flagstones. (Page, 1859)   3. A medium- or coarse-grained metamorphic rock with subparallel orientation of micaceous minerals which dominate its composition.

Sedimentary. Descriptive term for rock formed of sediment, especially: (1) Clastic rocks, as conglomerate, sandstone, and shales, formed of fragments of other rock transported from their sources and deposited in water; (2) rocks formed by precipitation from solution, as rock salt and gypsum, or from secretions of organisms, as most limestone. (Webster)

Seismic velocity. The rate of propogation of seismic waves in earth materials (usually measured in feet per second).

Shale. 1. A laminated sediment, in which the constituent particles are predominantly of the clay grade. (Holmes, 1928)   2. Shale includes the indurated, laminated, or fissile claystones and siltstones. The cleavage is that of bedding and such other secondary cleavage or fissility that is approximately parallel to bedding. The secondary cleavage has been produced by the pressure of overlying sediments and plastic flow. (Twenhofel, W. H., *Rept. Comm. Sed.*, p. 98, 1936-1937)

Shingle. 1. "The loose and completely water-worn gravel on the seashore." (Lyell, C., *Prin. Geol.*, vol. 3, p. 338, 1834)   2. "The loose, water-worn gravel and pebbles on shores and coasts." (Lee, C. E., *Elem. Geol.*, p. 384, 1840)   3. "The loose rounded water-worn fragments of stone or gravel found on the seashore, or where the sea has once been." (Ansted, D. T., *Elem. Course Geol.*, p. 581, London, 1856-1869)   4. "It might seem at first that we ought to have the same shapes in the river-pebbles, but we notice that these are usually a little larger one way than they are the other; they are often so flattened that they are called 'shingle.'" (Shaler, N. S., p. 3, 1891)   5. Strictly and properly, beach gravel composed of smooth, well-rounded pebbles and cobbles roughly the same size. The spaces between pebbles and cobbles are not filled with finer materials.   6. Loosely and commonly, any beach gravel which is coarser than ordinary gravel, especially if consisting of flat or flattish pebbles and cobbles. (Wiegel, R. L., *Glossary*, p. 66, 1953)

Silt. 1. An unconsolidated clastic sediment, most of the particles of which are between 1/16 and 1/256 mm in diameter. (After Wentworth, C. K., *Jour. Geol.*, vol. 30, pp. 377–392, 1922)   2. A clastic deposit (one that has been transported mechanically and deposited) of an inorganic granular material with median diameter between 0.005 mm and 0.05 mm. It is thus between sands and clays in size. (U. S. Bur. of Soils size classification)   3. Fine-grained soil that has a low plasticity index in relation to the liquid limit, or is entirely nonplastic, and consists mainly of particles less than 0.074 mm (passing No. 200 sieve) in diameter. The individual grains are largely angular in shape. In the Army's Unified Soil Classification System, silt and clay are considered fines and are differentiated wholly on a physical basis, not by the dimensions of the particles. Compare Clay. (After *Waterways Experiment Station, Corps of Engineers, Tech. Memo.* 3-357, 1953)

Slate. A fine-grained metamorphic rock possessing a well-developed fissility (slaty cleavage).

Soil. 1. In pedology, that earth material which has been so modified and acted upon by physical, chemical, and biological agents that it will support rooted plants.   2. In engineering geology the term soil is equivalent to Regolith.   3. The term is also loosely applied to all unconsolidated material above the bedrock that has been in any way altered or weathered. (After Stokes and Varnes, p. 139, 1955)   4. In military geology, "soil" is used in the sense of regolith or mantle rock in discussion of engineering problems, and in the standard pedologic sense in discussion of cross-country movement problems.

Soil horizon. A layer of soil approximately parallel to the land surface with observable characteristics that have been produced through the operation of soil-building processes. The letters A, B, and C are used to designate soil horizons. A. The A-horizon is the upper part. It consists of mineral layers of maximum organic accumulation; or layers from which clay materials, iron and aluminum have been lost; or both. (The loose surface organic matter in unplowed areas is not strictly part of the A horizon). B. The B-horizon lies under the A. It consists of weathered material with an accumulation of clay, iron, or aluminum; or with more or less blocky or prismatic structure; or both. Usually it is more strongly colored than the horizon above or below. C. The C-horizon, under the B, is the layer of unconsolidated, weathered parent material. In addition the letter D is used to designate any such stratum under the soil as hard rock, sand, or clay that is not parent material, but which may have some significance to the overlying soil. Note: Not all these horizons are present in all soils. (SCA)   *See also* A-horizon; B-horizon; C-horizon.

Tailings. 1. Those portions of washed ore that are regarded as too poor to be treated further: used especially of the debris from stamp mills or other ore-dressing machinery, as distinguished from material (concentrates) that is to be smelted. (Standard)   2. The sand, gravel, and cobbles which pass through the sluices in hydraulic mining were formerly generally designated as tailings, but of late years, especially in state and United States legislative documents, they have been called "mining debris" or simple "debris." (Century)   3. The lighter or refuse ore accumulated at the lower end of a buddle, or washing apparatus, or carried away by the water. (Webster)   4. The material from which one of more concentrated or partly concentrated products have been removed, and which is available for further treatment. (*Eng. and Min. Jour.*, vol. 107, p. 317)   5. The decomposed outcrop of a coal vein or bed. (Murray's Dict.)

Talus, Scree. 1. "When fragments are broken off by the action of the weather from the face of a steep rock, as they accumulate at its foot, they form a sloping heap, called a talus." (Lyell, C., *Prin. of Geol.*, vol. 3, p. 340, London, 1834)   2. "A sloping heap. When, from disintegration, the fragments of a face of a rock accumulate at its base and form a sloping heap, the heap is called a talus." (Humble, W., London, 1840)   3. "The fragments of rocks or debris at the base of a cliff; they form a sloping declivity of loose materials." (Emmons, E., *Manual*, p. 296, 1863)   4. "The natural slope produced by the falling away of the upper part of the steep face of a hill or escarpment." (Ansted, D. T., p. 156, 1868)   5. "A heap of coarse waste at the foot of a cliff, or a sheet of waste covering a slope below a cliff; same as Scree, which is more commonly used in Great Britain, whereas Talus is more commonly used in the United States, but is often incorrectly used for the material composing the talus." (La Forge, L., 1919)   6. A collection of fallen disintegrated material which has formed a slope at the foot of a steeper declivity. (Topog.)

Tectonic. Of, pertaining to, or designating the rock structure and external forms resulting from the deformation of the earth's crust. As applied to earthquakes, it is used to describe shocks not due to volcanic action or to collapse of caverns or landslides.

Terrace. 1. "It is hardly necessary to say that, though the term terrace applies to any level-topped surface, with a steep escarpment, whether it be solid rock or loose materials, it is only the latter kind which are treated in this paper. . . ." (Hitchcock, E., 1860)   2. "The terrace is a plain of greater or less extent and of absolute or approximate horizontality of surface, overlooked on one side by more elevated land perhaps belonging to a similar but higher plain, and bounded on the other side by an escarpment; and commonly it is an implied term in the definition that the plain was originally at or below but is now above, the water level." (McGee, W. J., *USGS 11th Ann. Rept.*, Pt. 1, p. 256, 1891)   3. "Benches and terraces are relatively flat, horizontal or gently inclined surfaces, sometimes long and narrow, which are bounded by a steeper ascending slope on one side and by a steeper descending slope on the opposite side. Both forms, when typically developed, are step-like in character. By increase in breadth they grade into plains. In this book the term bench will be used to denote form in solid rock, and terrace, form in unconsolidated materials." (Lehee, F. H., p. 271, 1916)   4. A flaw in marble, commonly cored out and filled up. Also spelled Terras. (Webster)

Till. 1. ". . . a stiff clay full of stones varying in size up to boulders. To this deposit the name of boulder clay or till has been given. . . . [It is the product of] abrasion carried on by the ice sheet as it moved over the land." (Geikie, A., Geol. Soc., *Glasgow Trans.*, vol. 1. Pt. 2, 1. 185, 1863)   2. The term "till" was first applied in Scotland to the stiff, unstratified clays containing angular, subangular and rounded blocks of rock, mostly polished and striated, and is now generally used as synonymous with Boulder clay." (Woodward, H. B., *Geol. of Engl. and Wales*, p. 483, 1887)   3. Nonsorted, nonstratified sediment carried or deposited by a glacier. (Comm.)   4. Equivalent to Moraine of some European geologists and to Boulder clay of some British geologists. (Comm.)

Time. *See* Geologic time scale.

Trace elements. Elements present in minor amount in the earth's crust; all elements except the eight abundant rock-forming elements, O, Si, Al, Fe, Ca, Na, K, and Mg. Synonymous with Minor elements and with Accessory elements. (Rankama and Sahama, p. 34)

Tuff. A rock formed of compacted volcanic fragments, generally smaller than 4 mm. in diameter. (After Holmes, 1928)

Udden scale. A logarithmic scale for size classification of sediments, starting from 1 mm. and progressing by the ½ in one direction and 2 in the other. This was the scale adopted by Wentworth, and by the Committee on Sedimentation. (After Udden, *Augustana Library Publications*, No. 1, 1898)   *See also* Wentworth scale.

Water table. The upper surface of a zone of saturation except where that surface is formed by an impermeable body. (Meinzer, *USGS WSP* 494, p. 22, 1923)

Weathering. The group processes, such as the chemical action of air and rain water and of plants and bacteria and the mechanical action of changes of temperature, whereby rocks on exposure to the weather change in character, decay, and finally crumble into soil. (Ransome)

Wentworth scale. A logarithmic grade scale for size classification of sediment particles, starting at 1 mm and using the ratio ½ in one direction (and 2 in the other), providing diameter limits to the size classes of 1, ½, ¼, etc., and 1, 2, 4, etc. This was adopted by Wentworth from Udden's scale, q.v., with slight modification of grade terms and limits. (After Wentworth, *Jour. Geol.*, Vol. 30, pp. 377–392, 1922)

INDEX

Abelson, P. H., 131, 173
Acid mine waters, 163
    See also Mines and mining
Acidity, soil, 73
Aerosols, 128, 136, 162
    See also Wastes, gaseous
Aggregates, 122, 123
  aggregates industry, 113
    See also Crushed stone; Sand and
    gravel
Agricultural culture, 85
Agriculture, 178
Ahearn, V. P., 113, 114
Air
  industrial atmosphere, 128, 129
  pollution, 129
    See also Wastes, gaseous
Air Conservation Commission, 130, 131,
    135, 137, 139, 159
Air Quality Act of 1967, 132

Alaska earthquake, effects, 26
    See also Earthquakes
Albee, A. C., 26
Albuquerque, New Mexico, 39
Aldehydes, 134, 135
Alexander, Tom, 148
Alkalinity, soil, 73
Allen, D. R., 46, 47
Allen, M. W., 26
Alluvium, 3
Aluminum ore processing, 156
American Association of Petroleum
    Geologists, 145, 161
American Association of State Highway
    Officials (AASHO), 69
  soil classification, 67
American River, California, 211
American Society for Testing and
    Materials (ASTM), 69, 70
  soil classification, 69

301

Amphibolite, 274
Anaconda, Montana, 131
Anchorage, Alaska, 220
Andesite, 273
Animal wastes, 126, 156
    See also Wastes
Antimony, halide salts of, 143
Appalachian coal mining region, 89, 165
Appalachian Regional Commission, 189
Aqueducts, 7
    First Los Angeles, 107
    Mono Basin Extension, 107
    Owens River, 107
    Roman, 106
    Second Los Angeles, 107
        See also Water
Aransas Wildlife Refuge, 197
Ardrey, Robert, 194
Asbestos, 136, 138
    asbestos-related cancer, 138
    asbestosis, 138
Atomic Energy Commission, 145, 160,
        189, 238, 249
    National Accelerator Laboratory, 249
        See also United States
Atterberg limits, 15, 67, 72
Austin, Texas, 122, 227
Austin Chalk, 233
    strength of, 14
Austin West Quadrangle, 235, 236
Autúnez Echagaray, Francisco, 166

Bacterial action, 76
Bailly, Paul A., 163, 164
Balcones escarpment, 231
Balcones fault zone, 11, 228, 234
Baldwin, H. L., 105
Barton Creek, Texas, 238
Barton Springs, Texas, 238
Bartow, Florida, 40
Basement, 7·
Basalt, 7, 271, 273
Bates, R. L., 94
Batteries
    lead-acid, 140
    lithium, 140
    nickel-cadmium, 140
    silver-zinc, 140
    sodium-sulfur, 140
    zinc-air, 140

Bauer, A. M., 122
Beaches
    erosion
        effect of dams, 58
        San Buenaventura State Park, 57
        Yorkshire coast, 56
    groins, 56
    profile of equilibrium, 56
Bearing capacities, 75
Beaumont, Texas, 11
Beautification, 92
Beazley, Ronald, 186
Bedrock, 257
Bellevue, Ohio, 40
Beneficial land use, 92
        See also Conservation; Multiple
        land use
Benefit-cost analysis, 206, 208, 210
Bentonite, 49
        See also Clays
Bergstrom, R. E., 150
Beryllium, 136
Bibliography of North American Geol-
        ogy, 17
Birmingham, Alabama, 41
Boca Ciega Bay, Florida, 199
Bootlegger Cove Clay, 221
Brace, W. F., 22
Branson, E. R., 41
Breccia, 273
Breeder reactors, 140
        See also Nuclear energy
Brooks, D. B., 165, 210, 211
Brown, Harrison, 84
Brownian movement, 68
Bry, T. S., 170, 171
Buda Limestone, 233
Buenos Aires, Argentina, 54
Building codes, 29, 221
Bureau
    of Mines, 16, 122, 123, 153, 188
    of Reclamation, 16, 188
    of the Budget, 189
        See also United States
Butte, Montana, 11
Burton, Ian, 84

Cadmium, 136
California Bearing Ratio, 73
        See also Soil

California Water Plan, 108
    See also Water
California Water Project, 174
    See also Water
Campbell, Ian, 218
Carbon 14, 159
Carbon dioxide, 3, 129, 130, 136, 139, 150
Carbon monoxide, 131
Carbon tetrachloride, 143
Carter, L. J., 144
Casagrande, A., 71
Castleberry, Florida, 40
Cathodic protection, 76
Caveat emptor, 90
Cesium 137, 159, 160
Chamberlin, T. C., 201, 202
Chert, 273
Chicago, Illinois, 7, 113, 153
    Chicagoland Deep Tunnel Project, 142
Chiefland, Florida, 40
Chlorinated hydrocarbons, 143, 179
Chlorite schist, 274
Chromates, 136
Cigarette smoking, 130
Citizens' Advisory Council on Environmental Quality, 189
Cities, location of, 11
Civil engineering, 63, 191
Classification
    descriptive, 270
    genetic, 270
Clay
    sensitive, 72
    swelling
        Austin, Texas, 49
        bentonite, 49
        Eagle Ford Formation, 49
        Taylor Formation, 49, 51
Cleveland, Ohio, 11
Coal, 89, 90, 132, 164, 273
    Appalachian coal mining region, 87, 165
    deposits, 139
    Freeport coal seam, 48
    mining, 119
    Pennsylvania Bituminus Mine Subsidence and Land Conservation Act of 1966, 48
    Pittsburg coal seam, 48

Coast and Geodetic Survey, 23, 188
    See also United States
Coastal engineering, 53
Coastal processes, 52
    England, 55
        Yorkshire coast, 55
Cobalt 60, 160
Cole, LaMont, 139
Colorado River, 172, 174
    Aqueduct, 107
    of Texas, 228
Columbia River, 174
Combustion, 3, 121, 130, 138, 139, 140, 165
    See also Air
Committee on Pollution, National Academy of Sciences-National Research Council, 141, 142
Common law, English, 88
"Common varieties," of earth materials, 89
Compaction, 42, 263
Conglomerate, 273
Connecticut River, 110, 145, 176
Conservation, 186
    Conservation Foundation, 130
    laws, 88
Consolidation Coal Company, 48
Construction materials, 90, 93, 104, 111, 114, 122, 164
    See also Aggregates; Crushed stone; Sand and gravel
"Contrails," 136
Cooper, H. H., Jr., 40
Copper, 136
Corps of Engineers, 16
    See also United States
Corpus Christi, Texas, 96
Corrosivity, soil, 74, 75, 76
    cathodic protection, 76
Coulter, H. W., 28
Council of Economic Advisers, 189
Council for Urban Affairs, 189
Creep, see Soil creep
Crushed stone, 113
    See also Aggregates; Construction materials
Crust, continental, 7, 10
Crustal processes, 20
Cultural, failure, 84
Curry, K. K., 39

Cyanides, 143
Cypress Creek, Texas, 109

Dallas, Texas, 100, 123
Dalton, A. E., 142
Daly, R. A., 31
Davidoff Plan, 174
    See also Water
Davis, R. K., 213
DDT, 179, 180
Del Rio Clay, 233
Del Rio Formation, 243
Department
    of Agriculture, 67, 69
    of Commerce, 188
    of Health, Education and Welfare,
        132, 189
    of Housing and Urban Development,
        212
    of Interior, 188
    See also United States
Denver, Colorado, 39
    earthquakes, 22
    Rocky Mountain Arsenal disposal
        well, 22, 146
Desalting, 106, 177
    See also Water
Design standards, in cuts and fills, 263
Desulfurization, 132, 133
    See also Wastes, gaseous
Detroit, Michigan, 130
Dewatering, of clays, 42
Diatomite, 273
Diorite, 273
Dobrovolny, Earnest, 28, 220
Dolomite, 273
Drainage terraces, 263, 264
Dredging, 176
Drift, glacial, 112
Ducktown, Tennessee, 131
Duisberg, Germany, 176
Dust storms, 58
    volcanic, 128
Dykes, D. R., 170, 171

Eagle Ford Formation, 233, 243
Earth flows, 34
Earthquakes, 19, 20, 21
    Alaska earthquake, (Good Friday
        earthquake), 25

effects of, 26
    epicenter, 28
    building codes, 29
    "design earthquakes," 29
    epicenters, 25
    Field Act, 29
    focal depths, 25
    intensities, 24
    Lisbon, Portugal, 25
    Long Beach, California, 26
    man-made, 147
    measurements, 23
    Mercalli scale, 23
    New Madrid, Missouri, 25
    Owens Valley, California, 26
    prediction, 22, 28
    prevention, 28
    Richter scale, 23
    San Francisco, California, 25
Earth resources, 104, 119
    high-value, 93
    low-value, 93, 104
    place value, 93
    See also Mineral resources
Ecology, 189, 190
Economic analysis, 214
    See also Benefit-cost analysis
Edwards Formation, 232, 233, 238, 242
Edwards Plateau, 232
El Paso, Texas, 39, 110
Electrochemical reactions, in soil, 76
Eminent domain, 113
Energy, 81
    geothermal, 82
    solar, 82
    tidal, 82
English common law, 88
Engineering geologic maps, 15
Engineering geological reports, 258, 269
England, coastal erosion, 54
Environmental geological reports, 219
Environmental legislation, 189
Environmental Pollution Board, Presi-
        dent's Science Advisory Commit-
        tee, 130
Environmental Quality Council, 189
Environmental Sciences Services Admin-
        istration, 188
    See also United States
Ephesus, Port of, 53

Erlich, P. R., 180
Ethylene, 135
Eutrophication, 142
Evans, D. M., 22, 146
Evaporation, 170, 171
Excavation, underground, 6
Exhausts, vehicle, 136

Fall line, 11
"Fallout," radioactive, 159
Fault zones, 10
Faults, 10
  active, 21
    Houston, Texas, 43, 45
  dead, 21
Feather River, California, 174
Federal Aviation Agency, Soil Classification, 67
  See also United States
Federal Water Pollution Control Administration, 143, 188
  See also United States
Feibusch, Hans A., 178
Fertilizers, 178
Field Act, 29
Fill material, 264
Fill slope, 264
Finland, 86
Fish and Wildlife Service, 186
  See also United States
Flawn, P. T., 83, 215
Fluorosis, 135
Fly ash, 122, 158
Forest Service, 189
  See also United States
Formations, geologic, 13
Fossil fuels, 82, 139, 165
  See also Coal; Petroleum
Foundation engineering, 65
  See also Soil mechanics
Ft. Worth, Texas, 110
Fremlin, J. H., 180
Fuel cells, 140
Fungicides, 179

Gabbro, 271, 273
Galley, J. E., 145, 147, 161
Gasbuggy, project, 159
Gaseous wastes, 126, 127

Gases
  industrial, 129
  volcanic, 128
Geologic formations, groups, members, 13
Geologic maps, engineering, 13, 15, 111
Geologic processes, 18
Geologic standards, 119
Geological Hazards Committee, Los Angeles, 223
Geological Survey, 16, 188
  See also United States
Geomorphology, 12
Georgetown Limestone, 233
Geothermal energy, 82
Gerard, R. D., 110, 176
Gilluly, James, 30, 32, 59
Glacial drift, 3
Glaciers, 59
Glendale, California, 223
Gneiss, 274
Goldsmith, John R., 130
Good Friday earthquake, Alaska, 220
Goodwin, J. T., 209
Grade, 257
  existing, 257
  finish, 257
  grading, 257
    Los Angeles ordinance, 222
    permit requirements, 257
  rough, 257
Granite, 271, 273
Great Lakes, 141
Groins, 56
  See also Beaches
Gross National Product, 83
Ground water, 152
  contamination, 152
  withdrawal, 164
Groups, geologic, 13
Grouting, 41
Grubb, H. W., 209
Guanajuato, Mexico, 166
Gulf Coast Aquifer, 42
  See also Water

Hackett, J. E., 15
Hammond, R. J., 206
Hanford, Washington, 160
Hansen, W. R., 221

Harlow, E. H., 42
Harris, F. R., 42
Hartsook, E. A., 96
Hayward fault, 28
Heat, 141
  earth's heat budget, 139
Henderson, B. C., 215
Herbicides, 136, 179
Hibbard, W. R., Jr., 6, 155
Hickman, K., 174
Highway Research Board, Landslide
  Committee, 35, 49
Historical landmarks, preservation of,
  212
Hornfels, 274
Houston, Texas, 42, 43, 175
Houston ship channel, 149
Housatonic River, 110, 176
Hubbert, M. King, 164
Hughes, G. M., 150
Hunter, W. H., 53
Huntington Beach, California, 96
Hutchinson, C. A., 96
Hydrodynamics, 147
Hydrogen fluoride, 135
Hydrogen sulfide, 128, 133
Hydropower, 82

Iceland, 86
Idaho National Reactor Testing Station,
  160
Igneous rocks, 271, 273
Illinois Geological Survey, 219
Incineration, 127, 148, 158
Indiana Geological Survey, 112
Indianapolis, Indiana, 112
Industrial atmosphere, 128, 129
Industrial culture, 85, 86
Industrial minerals and rocks, 94
Industrial vibrations, 20
Industrialization, 118
Infectious agents, 141
Insecticides, 136, 180
Internal combustion engine, 121, 129,
  130, 134
International Boundary Commission, 16
  See also United States
International Conference of Building
  Officials, Uniform Building Code,
  29, 224

International Society of Soil Science
  (ISSS), 69
Interstate Oil Compact Commission,
  146
Iodine, 131, 159
Iron ore, 93
Iron sulfate, 143
Irrigation, 167, 176
  See also Water
Isostasy, 32
Isostatic movements, 19, 20, 30

Jahns, R. H., 37
Johns-Manville Corporation, 138
Johnson, Craig, 114, 122, 131
Jollyville Plateau, Texas, 232
Joslyn, M. A., 86

Kame, 112
Kanats, 106
  See also Water
Kane, J. W., 171
Kansas City, Missouri, 7
Kaolin, 66
Kaplan, S. R., 17
Karst regions, 40
Kates, R. W., 84
Kimball, R. L., 165
Kline, C. H., 170, 171
Kneese, A. V., 211
Koelzer, B. A., 142
Kollmorgen, W. M., 208
Krumbein, U. C., 69

La Plata Estuary, 54
Lake Cayuga, 144
Lake Michigan, 142
Lake Tahoe, 212
Landaw, Stephen, 130
Landsberg, H. H., 84
Landslides, 20, 33
  bedrock slides, 34
  man-made, 37
  parts of, 35
  Portuguese Bend, 36
  rate of movement, 34
Leachates, 150
  See also Wastes, sanitary land-
  fills

Lead, 135, 136, 137
"halo," 121
lead-acid battery, 140
lead arsenate, 137
lead salts, 134
poisoning, 121
tetraethyl, 121, 136, 137
Lee Creek, North Carolina, 95
Leeds, Alabama, 41
Legget, R. F., 40, 42, 50, 53, 58, 69, 71, 168, 170, 176
Leith, C. K., 215
Lexington, Kentucky, 40
Lignite, 273
Limestone, 273
Limestone terranes
ground-water pollution, 40
karst regions, 40
solution and collapse, 40
Bartow, Florida, 40
Birmingham, Alabama, 41
Castleberry, Florida, 40
Chiefland, Florida, 40
Leeds, Alabama, 41
Lincoln Lakes, Illinois, 114
Linear shrinkage, 72
See also Soil
Lisbon, Portugal, 25
Lithium battery, 140
Littoral drift, 53, 56
See also Beaches
Load-bearing capacity, 73, 78
See also Soil, strength
Loess, 3
Lofgren, B. E., 42
London, England, 85, 131, 154
Long Beach, California, 26, 29, 44, 47
See also Earthquakes
Long Island Sound, 110, 176
Longshore currents, 53
Los Angeles, California, 13, 22, 28, 85, 95, 96, 97, 107, 108, 114, 122, 123, 130, 135, 148, 222
Geologic Qualifications Board, 223
Grading Ordinance of 1952, 222
Los Angeles County, 36, 38, 42, 223
Lovering, T. S., 200
Lubbock, Texas, 110

McClelland Engineers, 45
McGauhey, P. H., 126, 131, 156
McHenry County, Illinois, 78
Magma, 271
Magnuson, M. O., 165
Mahoning River, 144
Major, R. L., 123, 124, 125
Malthus, Thos. R., 84
Malthusian theory, 84
Manganese, 136
Mantle, 7
Marble, 274
Marine biology, 193
Mass movement, 19, 33, 38
See also Landslides
Maxwell, J. C., 105
Mayeda, H. S., 107
Mayuga, M. N., 46
Members, 13
See also Geologic formations
Mercalli scale, 23
See also Earthquakes
Mercaptans, 133, 135, 143
Mercury, 136
Mero, John C., 177
Merriman, Richard, 36
Metal-using cultures, 154
Metalliferous wastes, 155
See also Wastes
Metamorphic rocks, 272, 274
Metaquartzite, 274
Meteorology, 191
Methane, 150
Methanol, 143
Mica schist, 274
Migliaccio, R. R., 28
Miller, R. D., 28, 43, 220
Mineral resources, 86, 91
mineral demand explosion, 83
mineral estate, 88
mineral industry, 94, 111
mineral interest, 88
mineral rights, 88, 89
Mines and mining
deepest mines, 6
metal mines, 84, 164
open-pit mining, 164
reclamation, 210
tailings, 157

Mines and mining (*Continued*)
  wastes, 157, 163
  waters, acid, 163
Mississippi River, 172
Missouri Geological Survey, 168
Mono Basin Extension, 107
    See also Aqueducts; Water
Monogahela River, 165
Montana, 131
Montgomery, R. H., 195
Montmorillonite Clay, 49, 66
    See also Clay, swelling
Moore, R. F., 64, 67
Moraine, glacial, 112
  Cape Cod, 59
  Long Island, 59
Mudflows, 20, 33, 38
  rate of movement, 39
Mudstone, 273
Muir, John, 215
Multiple land use, 91
  sequential, 90, 91
  simultaneous, 88, 89, 91
Multiple working hypotheses, 208
Muskeg, 50

Nace, R. L., 170, 173, 174
National Academy of Sciences-National
    Research Council, 108, 189
National Aeronautics and Space Admin-
    istration, 189
National Board of Fire Underwriters,
    building code, 75
National Center for Air Pollution Con-
    trol, 132
National Sand and Gravel Association,
    114
    See also Sand and gravel
Natural gas, 164
New Madrid, Missouri, 25
    See also Earthquakes
New York City, 113, 131, 132, 133,
    137, 143, 148
  water supply, 176
New Zealand, 86
Nickel-cadmium battery, 140
Nickel carbonyl, 136
Nitric acid, 135
Nitric oxide, 134
Nitrogen dioxide, 134

North American Water and Power
    Alliance, 108, 110, 173, 174
    See also Water
Nonmetallic industrial rocks and min-
    erals, 164
Nonrenewable resources, 82
    See also Earth resources; Mineral
    resources
North Carolina Board of Water and
    Air Resources, 95
Nuclear-electric society, 141
Nuclear energy, 159
Nuclear-fuel cycle, 159, 160
Nuclear fuels, 82
Nuclear power plants, 140, 144
Nutrient wastes, 142

Oak Ridge National Laboratory, 160
Obsidian, 273
Occidental Petroleum Corporation, 96
Ocean, waste disposal in, 143
Oceanic engineering, 192
Ohio River, 165
Office
  of Saline Water, 188
  of Science and Technology, 190
  of Water Resources Research, 188
    See also United States
Oil, 158
    See also Petroleum
Olcott, H. S., 86
Olefins, 135
Open-pit mining, 164
    See also Mines and mining
Orange County, California, 223
Organic chemicals, 141
Organic gases, 135
Organic phosphate pesticides, 143
Orlando, Florida, 40
Ostia, Port of, 53
Outland, Charles, 107
Owens River Aqueduct, 107
    See also Aqueducts; Water
Owens Valley, California, 107
  earthquake, 26
Oxidation, 76
Oxygen
  carbon-dioxide balance, 139

Oxygen (*Continued*)
  producing plants, 139
  supply, 139
Ozone, 134

Palm Springs, California, 39
Palos Verdes Hills, California, 36, 38
Particulate matter, 135, 136
Patton, John B., 112
Peace River, 173
Pearl, R. M., 17
Peat, 273
Penetration tests, 73
    See also Soil, strength
Pennsylvania Bituminus Mine Sudsid-
    ence and Land Conservation Act
    of 1966, 48
    See also Coal; Subsidence
Perched water tables, 247
Permafrost, 50, 174
Peroxybenzoyl nitrate, 135, 139
Pesticides, 179
Petroleum, 93, 95, 164
  deposits, 139
Pflaker, George, 26
Phenol, 158
  derivatives, 143
Phi scale, 69
Phosphate, 142
  compounds, 143
  detergents, 142
  slimes, 156
Photochemical smog, 134
Photosynthesis, 139
Phyllite, 274
Physiography, 12
Pittsburgh, Pennsylvania, 11
Placer gold mining, 178
Planning, 86, 92, 219
Plant nutrients, 141
Plutonic rocks, 271
Pollution, 126, 127, 129, 141
  air, 129
  water, 127, 141
Population growth, 84, 86, 108, 113
  policy, 92
Portland, Oregon, 8
Portland Cement Association, 68
Portola Valley, California, 224

Portuguese Bend Landslide, 36
Potomac Estuary, 142
Potomac River Project, 211
Powell, John Wesley, 215
President's Science Advisory Committee,
    131, 138, 179, 189
Press, Frank, 22
Proctor, R. J., 107
Public domain, 88, 89
Public Land Law Review Commission,
    189
    See also United States

Qualitative analysis, 200
Quick Clay, 72
    See also Clay, sensitive
Quicksand, 72
Quinn, Frank, 174

Radioactive materials 136, 141
  wastes, 145, 159, 161
    See also Wastes
Red River, 109
Reclamation, land, 90, 92, 163
  costs, 165
Reining, Don, 122, 123
Renewable resources, 82
Resistivity measurements, 76
Rhine River, 176
Rhyolite, 271, 273
Rich, T. A., 128, 138
Richter, C. F., 23
Richter scale, 23, 25
    See also Earthquakes
Rio Grande, 109
Rippibility, 14
Risser, H. E., 123, 124, 125
River and Harbor Act of 1902, 206
Rock, definition of, 3
Rock cycles, 272
Rockfalls, 20, 33
Rocky Mountain Arsenal disposal well,
    22, 146
    See also Denver, earthquakes
Rogier, D. A., 114, 122
Romney, M. P., 83
Rough grade, 257
Rulison, project, 159
Ruthenium 106, 160

Sacramento River, 178
Salt deposits, 273
Salt-water disposal plants, 146
San Andreas fault, 28
San Antonio, Texas, 77, 123
San Fernando Valley, 30
San Francisco, 6, 9, 22, 25, 28, 153
  Bay, 177
  Bay Conservation and Development
      Commission, 178
San Gabriel Mountains, 30
San Joaquin Valley, 42, 44, 178
San Jose Hills, 30
Sand and gravel, 93, 94, 111, 112, 113,
      122, 164, 176, 240
      See also Aggregates
Sand dunes, 58
Sandstone, 273
Sanitary landfills, 148, 149, 153
      See also Wastes
Sansabar Estates, Indiana, 114
Savannah River, 160
Schellie, K. L., 114, 122
Schist, 274
Scranton, Pennsylvania, 48
Scrap, automobiles, 155
Scullin, C. M., 222, 223, 225
Sea waves, 21
      See also Tsunamis
Sediment transport, 52
Sedimentary basins, 7
Sedimentary rocks, 272, 273
Seed, H. B., 71
Seismic movements, 22
      See also Tectonic movements
Seismic velocity, 14
Seismology, 23
Sequential multiple land use, 90, 91
Sewage
  domestic, 141
  industrial, 156
Shale, 273
Shale oil, 164
Sheets, M. M., 43, 44
Sheppard, Thomas, 56
Sherlock, R. L., 11, 154
Silver-zinc battery, 140
Simultaneous, multiple land use, 88,
      89, 91

Sinkholes, 20, 40
  waste disposal in, 40
      See also Limestone terranes
Slags, 157, 158
Slate, 274
Slides, 19
      See also Landslides
Slopes, 12
  equilibrium, 33
Slosson, J. E., 56, 57, 224
Slumps, 34
Smelters, 163
  pollution, 131
Smith, J. L., 26
Smith, W. C., 78
Smog, 131, 134
Snake River, 174
Snowy Mountain-Tumut Project, 174
      See also Water
Sodium salts, 143
Sodium-sulfur battery, 140
Soil
  A-horizon, 4
  absorption, 72
  activity index, 71
  alkalinity, 73
  Atterberg limits, 15, 67, 70, 72
  B-horizon, 4
  C-horizon, 4
  California Bearing Ratio, 73
  classification of, 65, 66, 67
  corrosivity, 73
  creep, 20, 33
  definition, 3, 4, 5, 64
  density, 73
  electrochemical reactions in, 76
  eluviation, 5
  engineering, 63
  freezing and thawing, 20, 190
  leaching, 5
  liquid limit, 70
  liquidity index, 71
  parent material, 5
  mechanics, 63
  mineralology, 71
  moisture content, 66
  permeability, 73
  plastic limit, 70
  plasticity index, 70
  potential vertical rise, 73

Soil (*Continued*)
  profiles, 4
  reports, 258, 269
  resistivity, 73
  shrink-swell potential, 72
  shrinkage, linear, 72
  shrinkage limit, 70
  strength, 73, 78
  surveys, 5
  swell-pressure curves, 73
  triaxial compression test, 73
  volumetric shrinkage, 72
Soil Conservation Service, 16, 66, 189
    See also United States
Soil Science Society of America (SSSA),
    69
Solar energy, 82
Solid Waste Disposal Act of 1965, 153,
    155
    See also Wastes
Solid wastes, 126, 148, 153, 166, 248
Spaulding, A. O., 95, 97
Spoil banks, 165
Steam power plants, 141
  cars, 141
Steers, J. A., 54
Stone, Robert, 30
Strip mining, 88, 89, 92
    See also, Coal
Strontium 89, 159
Strontium 90, 159, 160
Subsidence, 20
  Appalachian coal mining region, 46
  Coaldale, Pennsylvania, 46
  ground-water withdrawal 43, 46
  Houston, Texas, 42, 44, 45
  liability insurance, 48
  Long Beach, California, 44
  man-made, 39
  Mexico City, 42
    Palacio de Bellas Artes, 42
  mine workings, 46
  Primrose coal seam, 46
  San Joaquin Valley, California, 42,
    44
  Scranton, Pennsylvania, 48
  Terminal Island, California, 42
  Wilkes Barre, Pennnsylvania, 48
  Wilmington oil field, 44
Subsurface fires, 49

Subsurface reservoirs, 141
Subsurface waste disposal, 145, 160
    See also Wastes
Sudbury, Ontario, 131
Sulfur, 132
  compounds, 131, 143
  pollutants, 131
  sulfur-bearing fuels, 131
Sulfur River, 109
Supersonic jet transports, 136
Surface estate, 88
Surficial processes, 20
Swenson, H. A., 105

Tar sands, 164
Taylor Formation, 243, 249
Tectonic movements, 19, 20, 21
  creep, 30
  uplift, 30
  warping, 32
Tennessee Valley Authority, 189
"Territorial imperative," 195
Technological change, 195
Temblors, 19
    See also Earthquakes
Ten Eyck, H. S., 179
Tetraethyl lead, 121, 136, 137
    See also Lead
Texas bays and estuaries, 109
Texas Gulf Sulfur Company, 95
Texas Railroad Commission, 146
Texas Water Plan, 108, 109, 110, 172,
    209
    See also Water
Thermal pollution, 144
Three Lakes Community (Denver,
    Colorado), 114
Tidal energy, 82
Tipps, C. W., 77
Titanium, 136
  oxide, 143
Tocher, Don, 23, 25
Tolman, C. F., 106
Tom's River, New Jersey, 143
Tom's River Chemical Corporation, 143
Toronto, Canada, 7
Townley, S. D., 26
Trace elements, in nutrition, 179
Transpiration, 170, 171

Trefethen, J. M., 51
Truax, C. N., Jr., 166
Tsunamis, 21, 26
    See also Earthquakes
Tuff, 271, 273

Udden classification, 67
    See also Soil
Udden scale, 68
    See also Soil
Unified Soil Classification
    (Casagrande classification), 67
    See also Soil
Uniform Building Code of 1964, Inter-
    national Conference of Building
    Officials, 224, 255
United States
    Army Chemical Corps, 146
    Army Corps of Engineers, 16, 189
    Bureau of Mines, 16, 122, 123, 153,
        188
    Bureau of Reclamation, 16, 188
    Bureau of the Budget, 189
    Coast and Geodetic Survey, 23, 188
    Committee on Large Dams, 168
    Department of Agriculture, 69
    Department of Commerce, 188
        Environmental Sciences Services
        Administration, 188
    Department of Health, Education and
        Welfare, 132, 189
    Department of Housing and Urban
        Development, 212
    Department of Interior, 188
    Federal Aviation Agency, 67
    Federal Water Pollution Control
        Administration 143, 188
    Fish and Wildlife Service, 186
    Forest Service, 189
    Geological Survey, 16, 83, 220
    International Boundary Commission,
        16
    Office of Saline Water, 188
    Office of Science and Technology, 190
    Office of Water Resources Research,
        188
    Public Health Service, 138
    Public Land Law Review Commis-
        sion, 189

    Soil Conservation Service, 16
    Weather Bureau, 186
Unklesby, A. G., 40
Urban mineral development, 96
Urbanization, 118

Vaiont Reservoir disaster, 34
Valdez, Alaska, 28
Van Hise, C. R., 215
Van Siclen, D. C., 43, 45
Vanadium, 136
Vandale, A. E., 48
Vehicle, number in United States, 140
Vernon, R. O., 40
Volcanic rocks, 271
Volcanoes, 32, 139
    volcanic activity, 12, 20, 32

Wallace, A. Russell, 85
Walnut Formation, 232, 241
Warner, D. L., 146
Wastes
    animal wastes, 126, 156
    disposal problems, 2
        in oceans, 143
    gaseous, 126, 127
    liquid, 127, 141
    metalliferous, 155
    mining, 157, 163
    organic, 156
    radioactive, 160
    sanitary landfills, 148, 149, 153
    solid, 126, 148, 153, 155, 166, 248
    subsurface disposal, 145, 160
Water, 104
    aqueducts, 107
    aquifers, 42
    desalting, 106, 177
    ground water, 152, 164
    irrigation, 167, 176
    kanats, 106
    quality, 104, 119
    supply, 104, 106
    vapor, 130
Water-resource projects, 167
    California Water Plan, 108
    Davidoff Plan, 174
    North American Water and Power
        Alliance, 108, 110, 173, 174
    Snowy Mountain-Tumut Project, 174

Water resource projects (*Continued*)
  Texas Water Plan, 108, 109, 110, 172, 209
Waters, A. C., 30, 32, 59
Weather Bureau, 186
  See also United States
Weathering, 10
Weaver, Paul, 43, 44
Wells, deepest, 6
Wentworth classification, 67
  See also Soil
Wentworth scale, 68
  See also Soil
White, G. F., 87
Whooping cranes, 196

Wilderness areas, 87
Wilkes Barre, Pennsylvania, 48
Wilmington Oil Field, 44
  See also Subsidence
Wilson, R. R., 107
Woodford, A. O., 30, 32, 59
Woods Hole Oceanographic Institute, 143

Yukon River, 173

Zinc, 136, 142
Zinc-air battery, 140
Zoning laws, 95, 113